Second Edition

Problem Solving Strategies

CROSSING THE RIVER WITH DOGS
and Other Mathematical Adventures

Ken Johnson

Ted Herr

Illustrations by Dan Piraro

Key Curriculum Press
Innovators in Mathematics Education

Project Editor: Greer Lleuad
Editorial Assistants: James A. Browne, Heather Dever
Accuracy Checkers: Lars Rohrbach, Jim Stenson
Copy Editors: Barbara King, Kristin Ferraioli
Production and Manufacturing Manager: Diana Jean Parks
Production Coordinator: Ann Rothenbuhler
Text Designer: Suzanne Montazer
Art Editor and Photo Researcher: Jason Luz
Photo Enhancement: Laurel Roth Patton
Illustrator: Dan Piraro
Technical Art: Monotype Composition Company and
  Ann Rothenbuhler
Student Illustrations: Lisa DaValle, Kerry Harrigan
Art and Design Coordinator and Cover Photo Stylist:
  Caroline Ayres
Cover Designer: Design Deluxe
Cover Photographer: Jim Hildreth
Composition and Prepress: Monotype Composition Company
Printer: R R Donnelley & Sons Company

Executive Editor: Casey FitzSimons
Publisher: Steven Rasmussen

Key Curriculum Press
1150 65th Street
Emeryville, CA 94608
editorial@keypress.com
http://www.keypress.com

Printed in the United States of America
10 9   11
ISBN: 978-1-55953-370-6

Instructor Reviewers, Second Edition

Kathryn Anderson, Aptos High School, Aptos, California

Eduardo A. Chamorro, Los Banos Junior High School,
Los Banos, California

Beth Fox-McManus, Pope High School, Marietta, Georgia

Marty Larkin, Southern Utah University, Cedar City, Utah

Brian R. Lawler, California Academy of Mathematics and Science,
Carson, California

Jonathan Merzel, Holy Names College, Oakland, California

Lisa Stueve, South Gwinnett High School, Lawrenceville, Georgia

Sherry Swearngin, Highland Park High School, Highland Park, Illinois

Debi Willis, North Layton Junior High School, West Point, Utah

Multicultural and Equity Reviewer, Second Edition

Marilyn Strutchens, University of Maryland, College Park, Maryland

Field Testers, First Edition

Christine Arum, Jefferson High School, Portland, Oregon

Keith Calandri, Luther Burbank High School, Sacramento, California

Barry Chapelle, Jefferson High School, Portland, Oregon

Bob Daniel, Centaurus High School, Lafayette, Colorado

Steve Ganong, Tandem School, Charlottesville, Virginia

Gary Haas, Tokay High School, Lodi, California

Brad Kincaid, Luther Burbank High School, Sacramento, California

Bob Licht, Portland Lutheran School, Portland, Oregon

Sue Loube, Grant's Pass High School, Grant's Pass, Oregon

Don McGinnis, Thompson School District, Loveland, Colorado

John McMillen, St. Andrew's School, Bethesda, Maryland

Barbara Olmstead, Long Trail School, Dorset, Vermont

Barb Saxe, Bear River High School, Grass Valley, California

Susan Smith, Suffield High School, Suffield, Connecticut

Jay Swartz, Norwell High School, Norwell, Massachusetts

Reanee Wall, Eads High School, Eads, Colorado

LaVeda Ward, Magnolia Senior High School, Magnolia, Arkansas

Acknowledgments

The support for this book has come in many forms, from computer equipment to inspiration to trust in us. We wish to publicly thank the people who supported us in some of those ways: Allyson Angus Stewart, Alan Barson, Dan Bennett, Randall Charles, Corey Craig, Lisa DaValle, Carolyn Donohoe, Ed Gieszelmann, Gary Haas, Kerry Harrigan, Holly Herr, Joe Herr, Jennifer Johnson, Lucille Johnson, Rick Johnson, Steve Legé, Jonathan Merzel, Ed Patriquin, Steve Rasmussen, Tom Sallee, Dave Seymour, Joanne Weatherly, Steve Weatherly, the Northern California Mathematics Project, and the students enrolled in the problem-solving courses at Luther Burbank High School, Sacramento, California, and Sierra College, Rocklin, California.

We also owe thanks to our colleagues who were the sources for some of these problem ideas. You'll recognize in this book some classic problems (many with new twists) and familiar themes from the lore of the problem-solving community at large. It would be impossible to even guess at, much less acknowledge, a source for each of those problems—but we're grateful to be in a profession that values sharing ideas.

Special acknowledgment is reserved for Judy Kysh, director of the Northern California Mathematics Project. Her insight and leadership are part and parcel of her ability years ago to foresee what many of us are struggling to understand today. She brought together the people and ideas that opened our eyes to a different way of teaching.

And finally, thanks to our children, Daniel, Gary, and Will Johnson, and Alyse, Jeremy, and Kevin Mason-Herr.

This book is dedicated to our wives, Janie Johnson and Allyson Mason-Herr.

Foreword to the Second Edition

During my fifteen years as a hospital administrator, it was my sense that problem solving is one of the most vital skills one can have in almost any profession. Problem solving is not simply about figuring out a solution when things go wrong, although it certainly is useful in those situations. Problem solving is also a means of finding ways to improve systems and to better serve people. In this way problem solving is not only *reactive* but also *proactive*.

Recently I returned to school as an aspiring secondary school teacher, and one of the courses I've taken is based on *Problem Solving Strategies: Crossing the River with Dogs and Other Mathematical Adventures.* In this exceptional course, I developed a new appreciation for my problem-solving abilities. I'd always learned that mathematics is a subject you master as an individual. Yet, as we get older and leave school, we do very little of our work in isolation. Because the authors of this book have acknowledged this fact, my class used *Problem Solving Strategies* in small groups. This experience was so powerful! By working in groups, presenting my solutions to the class, and watching other students present their solutions, I learned that there are many valid ways to solve a problem, not just one "best" way. This book and my classmates astounded me with the different avenues you can take to arrive at a solution. I learned that it's fine to be stellar at one particular problem-solving method, but the best problem solvers are able to use them all.

One of my challenges as a teacher will be to figure out which methods of instruction will most benefit those students who struggle with mathematics. In my mind, *Problem Solving Strategies* goes a long way in recognizing that some students have had frustrating experiences with mathematics and feel that most math books don't "speak" to them. This book is unique in that it often models how and what students think as they solve problems. Student dialogues and solutions reveal how students interpret the information in a problem. Sometimes they misinterpret the information and reach the wrong conclusion, or their logic isn't completely sound. However, when they read this book and watch how other students solve the problem, they recognize their mistakes and move through them to solve the problem themselves. In the process, they become more confident problem solvers—they realize that it's all right to make mistakes, work with others to arrive at a solution, and start over if necessary.

Students also learn that being able to solve a problem is only one part of the challenge, especially in the working world—your also being able to provide a clear explanation of your solution and communicate it effectively to others is often what determines whether or not your solution will be implemented.

Here are a couple of final thoughts I would like to share with the students who are about to use this book: I feel that *Problem Solving Strategies* teaches many worthy lessons in addition to those I've just described, but even if I had gained nothing else from this book, I learned that the key to problem solving is truly understanding a problem. This understanding isn't hard to attain: All you need to do is clarify what the problem is asking of you, organize the information given in the problem, ask questions, and don't give up.

And have fun! Be creative. Throw math parties for solving the problems you're assigned. And if you want to have some real fun, share the problems with your friends and family. Don't hold it against them if they tell you, "Hey, this is your work!" or "It's been twenty-five years since I've done this stuff." It just may be that they have never had the opportunity to learn problem-solving skills as directly and with as much fun as you're about to do now. Enjoy!

DAVE SEYMOUR

Teacher, Mathematics and Computer Applications
San Juan High School
Citrus Heights, California

Foreword to the First Edition

Since 1980, when the yearbook of the National Council of Teachers of Mathematics sparked a general resurgence of interest in teaching problem solving, a great many attempts have been made to incorporate this elusive set of skills into the curriculum. Many early responses to this goal involved simply adding a chapter at the end of existing texts, calling it "Problem Solving," and adding a few nonroutine problems throughout. The cynical view is that the authors added something to make their books pass for the new look; a more charitable view is that the authors simply did not understand how difficult a task it is to teach problem solving.

In contrast, the authors of this text treat problem solving very seriously indeed. They understand that teaching problem solving to a student is not just an add-on skill, like teaching the long-division algorithm, or even displaying a collection of techniques, but rather involves getting in and tinkering with the very way that the student structures reality. Seen in this light, it is clear that teaching problem solving is a difficult business which needs lots of time to do well.

In this useful book, Herr and Johnson have managed to present a broad set of strategies in an accessible way. The chapter that covers each strategy starts with an interesting problem followed by a dialogue which examines different ways of solving the problem with this one strategy. An appealing set of problems provided at the end of the chapter provides excellent practice for internalizing the strategy and gives a good sense as to its range of utility. It will be a rare student—or teacher—who does not gain much use from the book.

There are three features of the book which I found particularly appealing. First is the variety and interest of the examples. There are problems which arise in real life—such as deciding when you should leave for the airport—and problems which are useful in other courses—such as converting from one system of units to another—and some simply fun problems. Each set of problems illustrates the strategy under discussion and gives a good indication of its power.

Second, the authors provide examples which validate different approaches. One of my more vivid memories when I taught problem solving was the student who came up at the end of one class when four different solutions had been displayed by participants and confessed, "I never knew there was more than one way to solve a problem." Too many students can get all the way through high school without ever coming to realize that mathematics is not just a collection of methods to be memorized, but a structure which allows many paths to success. Herr and Johnson should help remedy this outdated and dangerous view that there can be only one way to solve a problem.

Finally, I enjoyed the dialogues which suggest various approaches to the problems in a nonthreatening way. This technique offers a good intermediate ground between no direction whatsoever and the voice of authority with which most books of mathematics are invested. Real students do have different ideas and different approaches, and the wise teacher will both cherish and exploit this diversity. The wiser teacher will cherish even wrong approaches and let the class find out why they are wrong.

As the twentieth century comes to an end, it is clear that we need more mathematically competent people, a description which requires more than people who can recite familiar formulas or solve standard problems. We need people who can intuitively reach for the strategies in this book and apply them in a broad range of situations. In short, we need people who know what to do when they don't know exactly what to do.

TOM SALLEE

Professor of Mathematics
University of California, Davis

Contents

Problem Solving Strategies

CROSSING THE RIVER WITH DOGS

and Other Mathematical Adventures

You'll meet greater challenges and have more fun solving problems when you work together with others.

Introduction

Letter to the Student

This book is intended for a mathematics class that may differ from other math classes you've encountered. In this class you'll be asked to solve some equations, but mostly you'll be asked to think about *problems,* solve them, then write about your solutions. You may know some students who have gotten through a math class without really understanding the material, but that won't happen in this class. Our goal for you is that when you finish this class, you are able to understand the mathematics you are doing and explain your reasoning in writing or to other students.

This class is based on the idea that you'll learn the strategies people in the real world use to solve problems. You will develop specific problem-solving strategies, communication skills, and attitudes. Learning problem-solving strategies will help you on the Scholastic Aptitude Test (SAT) and other standardized tests, which often test problem-solving skills more than the ability to solve equations. In this class you will also learn to have fun doing mathematics. For centuries many people have considered challenging problems, often called puzzles or brain teasers, to be a source of entertainment.

In this class you will be asked to solve some tough problems. You will be able to solve most of them by being persistent and by talking with other students. When you come across an especially difficult problem, don't give up. Remember the techniques you've already learned in the class, such as drawing diagrams, asking other people for help, looking at your notes, trying other approaches, and so on.

You will be expected to talk to your classmates! Your teacher will ask you to get help from one another. Thus, not all of the learning you'll do in this class will be "book learning." You'll also learn how to work with one another. Working with other people helps even students considered "the smartest" by many of their peers. The communication skills you learn in this class will help you throughout your lifetime.

This letter implies that you will learn, but of course you realize that learning doesn't just happen on its own. What you get out of this class will depend on how much you are willing to invest. You have a chance here to take an active role in your education. Our wish for you, besides good luck, is that you will apply yourself to the point of excelling.

Enjoy the journey!

Answers to Questions That Students Usually Ask

Some people have said that America is not ready for a math book with the word *dogs* in the title, but we think the country can handle it. This book is different from many other mathematics books, from its title page to its last page. For one thing, this book is meant to be enjoyable to read. It is also meant to teach problem-solving strategies, and it incorporates research on how students best learn mathematics.

This book was written to take advantage of the strength of cooperative learning and the benefits of communicating your math work to others. You've probably attended classes in which your teacher encouraged you to work with others. Your teacher used this approach because research shows that students learn more when they work together. Roughly one-third of the learning in this course will come from teacher explanations, one-third from this textbook, and one-third from your classmates. In addition to working with your classmates, reading the book, and learning from your teacher, you will also be expected to communicate about your work and your mathematical thinking. You will do this by presenting your solutions to the entire class and by writing up complete solutions to problems. You will do presentations and write-ups, because talking and writing allow you to show your thinking. These communication processes will further develop your thinking skills.

Now here are our answers to questions students usually ask about this course.

What is problem solving?

Problem solving has been defined as what to do when you don't know what to do. In some of your math classes, you probably learned about mathematical ideas by first working on an example and then practicing with exercises. An **exercise** asks you to repeat a method you learned from a similar example. A **problem** is usually more complex than an exercise, so it is harder to solve because you don't have a preconceived notion about how to solve it. In this class you will learn general, wide-ranging strategies for solving problems. These strategies, many of them popularized by George (György) Pólya's classic book *How to Solve It* (Princeton University Press, 1988), apply to many different types of problems. (First published in 1945, *How to Solve It* was evidence that Pólya was far ahead of his time in his approach to mathematical problem solving.)

Many of the problems you do in this class will be unique to you. That is, you won't have seen a similar example in class or have a "recipe" to follow. To solve the problems, you will use the broad **heuristic**, or discovery-based, strategies you'll learn in this book. You may find that sometimes your first approach to a problem doesn't work. When this happens, don't be afraid to abandon the approach and try something else. Be persistent. If you get frustrated with a problem, put it aside and come back to it later. Let your subconscious work on it—you may find yourself solving problems in your sleep! But don't give up on the problem.

Why should we work together? Can't we learn just as well on our own?

You will have many opportunities to work with other students in this class. Also try to get together with other students outside of class. When you work with other students, you are free to make conjectures, ask questions, make mistakes, and express your ideas and opinions. You don't have to worry about being criticized for your thoughts or your wrong answers. You and other members of your in-class groups won't always proceed down the correct path, but support one another. Question one another, ask another person to explain what you don't understand, and make sure the other members of your group understand too. If others in your group make mistakes, don't get angry or make fun of them. Instead, help them to see why they are wrong.

How should we study? How should we read the book?

The book is organized into chapters. Each chapter introduces a new problem-solving strategy and presents several problems within the text, which are identified by an icon of a dog. You are asked to first solve each problem, then read its sample solution. To get the maximum benefit from this book, work the problems before reading the solutions. Even if you successfully solved a problem, read the solution anyway because it may differ from your own or bring up some points you hadn't thought about. If you don't have time to solve all the text problems, just read the problems and solutions you don't have time for. You'll learn the most by trying the problems yourself, but you'll get something out of simply reading the solutions. As you read, follow along with the solutions by working the problems out on a piece of paper, mirroring the solutions as they are presented in the book. You'll learn the least if you don't read the book at all. Be willing to read the text slowly and carefully. It does not read like a novel. Rather, you must read each sentence and understand it before you go on.

Sometimes you will see a problem that you saw earlier in another chapter. You'll solve this same problem again, but you'll use a different strategy. Solving the same problem in many different ways will help you become a better problem solver. You'll also often see sample solutions that actual students came up with as they worked through the problems in this book. Their work shows that there are many valid ways to tackle a problem, even if one particular approach doesn't result in a correct answer.

What other problems will we do besides those within the text?

Each chapter ends with a Problem Set A. The problems in these sets can always be solved with the strategy presented in that particular chapter. Some of the problems could also be solved by using a strategy you learned in an earlier chapter. But, because you're learning a new strategy with each new chapter, solve the Set A problems with their chapter-specific strategy. (To get more benefit from this class, you may also want to try solving many of the problems in other ways.)

Beginning in Chapter 3, a Problem Set B follows each Problem Set A. Set B problems can be solved with any strategy you've already learned, and it's up to you to pick an appropriate strategy. The Set B problems are harder than the Set A problems. In fact, toward the end of the book many of the Set B problems are very difficult. Each Problem Set B is meant to be a weeklong assignment that you turn in. The sets act as tests, although they probably differ from tests you're used to. You may work on the sets with other students, but each person will turn in his or her own work. You will be asked to provide answers *and* to explain how you arrived at your solutions. There are only five problems in each Problem Set B because you will usually write between one-half of a page and two pages for each problem. Each set will probably require between five and seven hours of work.

In other math classes, your grade for the course may have depended on how well you did on tests. Many people have test anxiety and do not perform as well as they could on exams. A common complaint is "I study so hard, do all my homework, and spend hours and hours on this class, but then I fail the test and get a poor grade." In this course, if you spend those hours and hours working through the book, you should get a very good grade.

What is the role of the teacher in this class?

In many classes, the teacher is the final authority who determines whether the student is right or wrong. In this class your teacher will play that role at times, such as when she or he grades your weekly problem sets. But there will also be many times when the teacher will not play that role. For example, during student presentations several people may have different answers to the same problem. When this happens, it's natural to ask your teacher who is right. But in this class your teacher will let you make up your own minds. Your in-class groups can discuss which answer they think is correct and why. Explaining why is a very important part of this class. Not relying on the teacher to verify your work will help you become a better problem solver. Learn to carefully evaluate your own work and the work of others.

Some Comments on Answers

When you turn in written work, please express your answer to each problem in the form of a sentence. Don't expect the teacher to dig through your work to find your answer.

Think carefully about what your answer means, and make sure that the form of the answer makes sense and is reasonable given the circumstances of the problem. For example, if the answer to a question is a certain number of people and your answer is a fraction or a decimal, think carefully about what the question's answer should be. Does it make sense to round your answer up or down, or to leave it the way it is? To see what we mean, try the following problem.

The Vans

There are 25 people going on a trip. They are traveling by van, and each van has a capacity of 7 people.

Some people might think the answer to this problem is $3^4/_7$ vans. But the answer depends on what question is posed about the problem. Here are some possible questions:

a. How many vans will be needed to transport all 25 people?

b. How many vans can be filled to capacity?

c. How many vans will have to be filled to capacity?

d. What is the average number of people in a van?

e. Must any van have seven people in it?

f. How many more people could fit into the vans that will be required?

The answer to each of these questions is different, even though the problem is the same. The difference is in the question asked. For example, the van problem looks like it could be solved by dividing 25 by 7, but only one of the questions above looks like a division problem. In the van problem, we're working with units that are generally considered indivisible (vans or people) as opposed to units that are clearly divisible (pizzas). Thus, the answer to our division problem is reasonable only if our answer's units are also reasonable. That is, no matter what arithmetic is done to the numbers in this problem, the answer must still apply to human beings going somewhere in vans. Keep these issues in mind when working problems.

This book is meant to be enjoyed. Have fun!

Some Introductory Problems

During this course you will learn many problem-solving strategies and use them to solve many different problems. Solve the problems in this chapter with whatever strategy you wish. You will have an opportunity to share your solutions to some or all of these problems with a small group or the whole class. You can solve these problems with a variety of different strategies. In fact, you may wish to solve each problem several times, using a different strategy each time. (The solutions to the example problems in this book are shown following those problems, but the solutions to these introductory problems are not shown.)

1. SOCCER GAME

At the conclusion of a soccer game whose two teams each included 11 players, each player on the winning team "gave five" to (slapped hands with) each player on the losing team. Each player on the winning team also gave five to each *other* player on the winning team. How many fives were given?

2. ELEVATOR

The capacity of an elevator is either 20 children or 15 adults. If 12 children are currently in the elevator, how many adults can still get in?

3. MATH CLUB

There are eight more girls than boys in the high school math club. The club has a total of 44 members. How many boys and how many girls are there?

4. DUCKS AND COWS

Farmer Brown had ducks and cows. One day she noticed that the animals had a total of 12 heads and 32 feet. How many of the animals were ducks and how many were cows?

5. STRANGE NUMBER

If you take a particular two-digit number, reverse its digits to make a second two-digit number, and add these two numbers together, their sum will be 121. What is the original number?

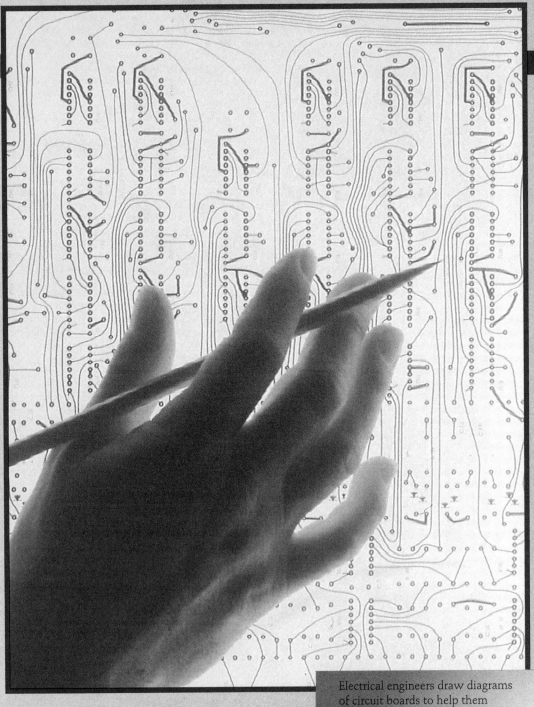

Electrical engineers draw diagrams of circuit boards to help them visualize the relationships among a computer's electrical components.

Draw a Diagram

You've probably heard the old saying "One picture is worth a thousand words." Most people nod in agreement when this statement is made, without realizing just how powerful a picture, or a **diagram**, can be. (**Note** that words in **bold** type are terms that are defined in this book's glossary.) A diagram has many advantages over verbal communication. For example, a diagram can show positional relationships far more easily and clearly than a verbal description can. To attempt to clarify ideas in their own minds, some people talk to themselves or to others about those ideas. Similarly, a diagram can help clarify ideas and solve problems that lend themselves to visual representations.

One of the best examples of a diagram in the professional world is a blueprint. An architect's blueprint expresses ideas concisely in a visual form that leaves little to interpretation. Words are added only to indicate details that are not visually evident. A blueprint illustrates one of the strengths of diagrams: the ability to present the "whole picture" immediately.

Problem solving often revolves around information and how it is organized. When you draw a diagram, you organize information spatially, which then allows the visual part of your brain to become more involved in the problem-solving process. In this chapter you will learn how diagrams can be used to clarify ideas and solve a variety of problems. You'll improve your diagramming abilities, and you'll discover that a diagram can help you understand and correctly interpret the information contained in a problem. You'll also see the value of using diagrams as a problem-solving strategy.

Solve this problem by drawing a diagram.

MODERN BASKETBALL ASSOCIATION

A new basketball league was formed in which each of the teams will play three games against each of the other teams. There are seven teams: the Antelopes, the Bears, the Cubs, the Dusters, the Eagles, the Foxes, and the Goats. How many games will be played in all? Do this problem carefully before reading on.

As you read in Chapter 0, you'll see many different problems as you work through this book. The problems are indicated by an icon of a dog. To get the maximum benefit from the book, solve each of the problems before reading on. You gain a lot by solving problems, even if your answers are incorrect. The *process* you use to solve each problem is what you should concentrate on.

You could use many different diagrams to solve the Modern Basketball Association problem. But you could also solve this problem

in ways that do not involve diagrams. As you read in Chapter 0, throughout this book you will see some of the same problems in different chapters and solve them with different strategies. This will help you become a better problem solver in two ways: by solving many different problems and by solving the same problem in many different ways. In this chapter, the solutions involve diagrams. If you solved the Modern Basketball Association problem without a diagram, try solving it again with a diagram before reading on.

What comes next is a solution process that is attributed to a student. The people mentioned in this book are real students who took a problem-solving class at either Luther Burbank High School in Sacramento, California, or at Sierra College in Rocklin, California. In those classes, the students presented their solutions on the board to their classmates. Ted Herr and Ken Johnson, the authors of this book, taught these classes. Our students presented their solutions because we felt that the other students would benefit greatly from seeing many different approaches to the same problem. We didn't judge each student's solution in any way. Rather, we asked each member of the class to examine each solution that was presented and decide which approach or approaches were valid or, perhaps, better.

We have tried to re-create the same learning atmosphere in this book. Sometimes you'll see several different approaches to a problem in this book, but for the most part those approaches and the resulting solutions won't be judged. You are encouraged to make up your own mind about the quality of the approaches. You may have been led to believe that there is always one right way and many wrong ways to solve problems. This notion couldn't be further from the truth. There are many right ways to solve problems, and you are encouraged to solve the problems in this book more than once, using different methods.

Here's how Rita solved the Modern Basketball Association problem:

She used a letter to represent each team. A stood for Antelopes, B stood for Bears, and so on, through G. She drew a diagram that showed the letters arranged in a circle. Next to each letter she drew a dot.

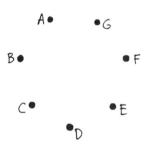

She then drew a line from A to B to represent the games played between the Antelopes and the Bears. Then she drew a line from A to C to represent the games played between the Antelopes and the Cubs.

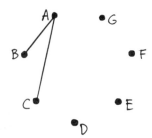

She finished representing the Antelopes' games by drawing lines from A to D, E, F, and G.

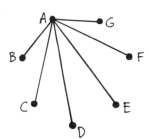

Next she drew the lines for the Bears. She'd already drawn a line from A to B to represent the games the Bears played against the Antelopes, so the first line she drew for the Bears was from B to C.

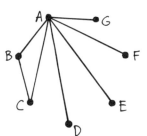

She continued drawing lines to represent the games that the Bears played against each other team.

From C she drew lines only to D, E, F, and G because the lines from C to A and from C to B had already been drawn. She continued in this way, completing her diagram by drawing the lines needed to represent the games played by the rest of the teams in the league. (**Note** that when she finally got to the Goats, she did not need to draw any more lines because the games the Goats played against each other team had already been represented with a line.)

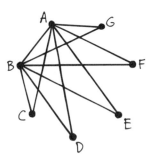

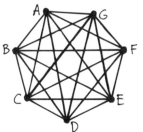

She then counted the lines she'd drawn. There were 21. She multiplied 21 by 3 (remember that each line represented three games), and she came up with an answer of 63 games. Finally, Rita made sure that she'd answered the question asked. The question was "How many games will be played in all?" Her answer, "Sixty-three games will be played," accurately answers the question.

Mirka solved this problem with the diagram shown below. She also used the letters A, B, C, D, E, F, and G to represent the teams. She arranged the letters in a row and, as Rita did, she drew lines from team to team to represent games played. She started by drawing lines from A to the other letters, then from B to the other letters, and so on. She drew 21 lines, multiplied 21 by 3, and counted 63 games.

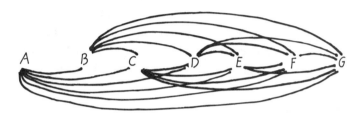

MODEL TRAIN

Jenny's model train is set up on a circular track. Six telephone poles are spaced evenly around the track. The engine of Jenny's train takes 10 seconds to go from the first pole to the third pole. How long would it take the engine to go all the way around the track? Solve the problem carefully before reading on.

If you read the problem quickly and solved it in your head, you might think the answer is 20 seconds. After all, the problem states that the engine can go from the first pole to the third pole in 10 seconds, which is three poles out of six and apparently halfway around the track. So it would take the engine 2 times 10, or 20 seconds, to go all the way around the track. But this answer is wrong. The correct answer becomes apparent when we look at a diagram.

Dustin's diagram is shown at right. Dustin explained that the train goes one-third of the way around the track in 10 seconds, not halfway around the track. So the train goes around the entire track in 3 times 10 seconds, or 30 seconds.

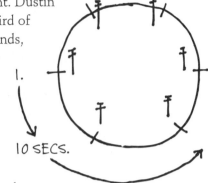

Phong drew the same diagram, but he interpreted it differently. He explained that if it takes 10 seconds to go from the first pole to the third pole, then it takes 5 seconds to go from the first pole to the second pole. So, it takes 5 seconds to go from pole to pole. There are six poles, so it takes the train 30 seconds to go all the way around the track.

Pete interpreted the problem as Phong did, but he didn't draw a diagram. Thus, he neglected the fact that the train must return from the sixth pole to the first pole in order to travel all the way around the track. Therefore, he got the incorrect answer of 25 seconds.

The diagram helped Dustin and Phong solve the Model Train problem. If you used a diagram to solve the problem, you probably got the correct solution. If you were able to get the correct solution without drawing a diagram, think back on your process. You probably visualized the train track in your mind, so even though you didn't actually draw a diagram, you could "see" a picture.

Do you get the picture? Do you see why diagrams are important? Research shows that most good problem solvers draw diagrams for almost every problem they solve. Do not resist drawing a diagram because you think you can't draw, or that smart people use only equations to solve problems, or whatever. Just draw it!

ALIEN INVADERS

Sam, Mamie, Ralph, and Gail are all skilled at the video game Alien Invaders. Gail consistently scores higher than Ralph. Sam is better than all of them, and Mamie is better than Ralph. Who is the better player, Gail or Mamie? Before reading on, use the clues in the problem to solve it.

Jamie drew the diagram shown below. Each figure's height represents that player's skill level: the tall figures are more skilled than the short figures. (Jamie is very tall, and she thinks that tall people are good at video games.) As the diagram shows, Sam is the best player, followed by Mamie, Gail, and Ralph. Thus, Mamie is better than Gail.

Kurt drew the diagram shown below. The larger heads represent the players with more video game prowess, and the smaller heads represent the players with less skill. (Kurt has a very large head, so he thinks that large-headed people are good at video games.) As the diagram shows, Sam is the best, followed by Gail, Mamie, and Ralph. So Kurt's answer is that Gail is better than Mamie.

Rena drew the diagram shown at right. Her diagram shows arrows that represent each relationship described in the problem. The arrows point from one person to another, and they show that the person the arrow *starts from* is better at playing Alien Invaders than the person the arrow *points to*. When no arrow is shown, then the problem did not describe a relationship between them. Rena's diagram makes it clear that the question can't be answered because there is no way of establishing a comparison between Mamie and Gail.

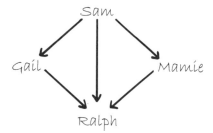

Curly used a shovel to dig his own swimming pool. He figured he needed a pool because digging it was hard work and he could use it to cool off after working on it all day. He also planned to build a rectangular concrete deck around the pool that would be 6 feet wide at all points. The pool is rectangular and measures 14 feet by 40 feet. What is the area of the deck? As usual, solve this problem before continuing.

Simon drew the following diagram to show the correct dimensions of the deck and pool, which together are 12 feet longer and 12 feet wider than the pool alone.

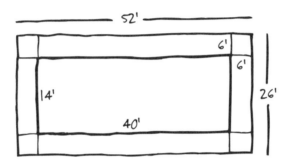

The diagram helps show the difficult parts of the problem. However, Simon solved the problem incorrectly by finding the outside perimeter of the pool and deck together, then multiplying the perimeter by the width of the deck.

52 feet + 26 feet + 52 feet + 26 feet = 156 feet
156 feet x 6 feet = 936 square feet

His approach overcounts the corners.

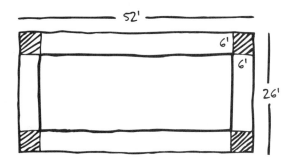

Rajesh used the same diagram, but he solved the problem by first computing the area of the deck along the sides of the pool, then adding in the corners of the deck.

Two lengths: 40 ft X 6 ft X 2 = 480 sq ft
Two widths: 14 ft X 6 ft X 2 = 168 sq ft
Four corners: 6 ft X 6 ft X 4 = 144 sq ft
                                  Total 792 sq ft

May's diagram shows the corners attached to the length of the deck.

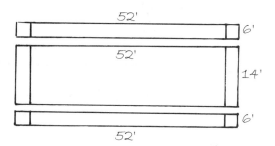

She calculated the area as follows:

52 ft X 6 ft = 312 sq ft
312 sq ft X 2 = 624 sq ft for extended lengths
14 ft X 6 ft = 84 sq ft
84 sq ft X 2 = 168 sq ft for widths
Total = 624 sq ft + 168 sq ft = 792 sq ft

Hung solved this by first computing the area of the pool and the deck together, then subtracting the area of the pool, leaving the area of the deck.

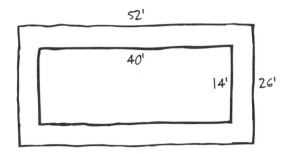

Area of entire figure = 52 ft × 26 ft = 1352 sq ft
Area of pool alone = 40 ft × 14 ft = 560 sq ft
Area of deck = 1352 ft − 560 ft = 792 sq ft

FARMER BEN

Farmer Ben has only ducks and cows. He can't remember how many of each he has, but he doesn't need to remember because he knows he has 22 animals and that 22 is also his age. He also knows that the animals have a total of 56 legs, because 56 is also his father's age. Assuming that each animal has all legs intact and no more, how many of each animal does Farmer Ben have? Do this problem, then read on.

Bill drew the following diagram:

"These 22 circles represent the 22 animals. First, I made all of the animals into ducks." (Bill is not much of an artist, so you just have to believe that these are ducks.) "I gave each animal two legs because ducks have two legs."

"Then I converted the ducks into cows by drawing extra legs. The ducks alone had 44 of the 56 legs initially, so I drew 12 more legs (six pairs) on 6 ducks to turn them into cows. So there are 6 cows and 16 ducks."

Of course, Ben might have a problem when his father turns 57 next year.

Any idea that can be represented with a picture can be communicated more effectively with that picture. By showing what a person is thinking, a diagram becomes a problem-solving strategy. A diagram clarifies ideas and communicates those ideas to anyone who looks at it. Many people use diagrams as a part of their jobs, especially those that require a planning stage to complete a project. Occupational diagrams include blueprints, project flow charts, and visual representations of concepts. And diagrams are often used to show position and direction because these concepts can be communicated more easily and clearly with a diagram than with words.

One final word about diagrams: Had the person who coined the phrase "One picture is worth a thousand words" lived in modern times, he undoubtedly would have said, "One TV is worth a thousand radios." Today we recognize that a television image gives clearer and far more information than a radio's verbal description. For these reasons, a diagram works to solve problems better and to communicate more effectively.

Problem Set A

You must draw a diagram to solve each problem.

1. **WORM JOURNEY**

   A worm is at the bottom of a 12-foot wall. Every day the worm crawls up 3 feet, but at night it slips down 2 feet. How many days does it take the worm to get to the top of the wall?

2. **UPS AND DOWNS OF SHOPPING**

   Roberto is shopping in a large department store with many floors. He enters the store on the middle floor from a skyway, and he immediately goes to the credit department. After making sure his credit is good, he goes up three floors to the housewares department. Then he goes down five floors to the children's department. Then he goes up six floors to the TV department. Finally, he goes down ten floors to the main entrance of the store, which is on the first floor, and leaves to go to another store down the street. How many floors does the department store have?

3. FOLLOW THE BOUNCING BALL

A ball rebounds one-half the height from which it is dropped. The ball is dropped from a height of 160 feet and keeps on bouncing. What is the total vertical distance the ball will travel from the moment it is dropped to the moment it hits the floor for the fifth time?

4. FLOOR TILES

How many 9-inch-square floor tiles are needed to cover a rectangular floor that measures 12 feet by 15 feet?

5. COUNTING ON NINJA TURTLES

Joanne sets up her Teenage Mutant Ninja Turtles in a big circle, spacing each turtle at an equal distance from its neighbors. She then begins counting them in order around the circle, but she loses track of where she started before she finishes counting. Then she notices that the sixth turtle is directly opposite the seventeenth turtle, and she realizes that she can still figure out how many turtles are in the circle. How many turtles are in the circle?

6. DANGEROUS MANEUVERS

Somewhere in the Mojave Desert, the army set up training camps named Arachnid, Feline, Canine, Lupine, Bovine, and Thirty-Nine. Arachnid is 15 miles from Canine. Bovine is 12 miles from Lupine. Feline is 6 miles from Thirty-Nine. Lupine is 3 miles from Canine. Bovine is 9 miles from Thirty-Nine. Bovine is 7 miles from Canine. Thirty-Nine is 1 mile from Arachnid. Feline is 11 miles from Lupine. No other pairs of training camps are connected by roads.

Answer each of the following questions (in each answer, indicate both the mileage and the route): What is the shortest route from

Feline to Bovine?

Canine to Thirty-Nine?

Lupine to Thirty-Nine?

Lupine to Bovine?

Canine to Feline?

Arachnid to Feline?

Arachnid to Lupine?

7. RACE

Betty, Cathy, Isabel, Lani, Alma, and Ursula ran an 800-meter race. Alma beat Isabel by 7 meters. Ursula beat Betty by 12 meters. Alma finished 5 meters ahead of Lani but 3 meters behind Ursula. Cathy finished halfway between the first and last girls. In what order did the girls finish? What were the distances between each girl?

8. A WHOLE LOTTA SHAKIN' GOIN' ON!

If six people met at a party and all shook hands with one another, how many handshakes would be exchanged?

9. HAYWIRE

A telephone system in a major manufacturing company has gone haywire. The system will complete certain calls only over certain sets of wires. So, to get a message to someone, an employee of the company first has to call another employee to start a message on a route to the person the call is for. As far as the company can determine, these are the connections:

Cherlondia can call Al and Shirley (this means that Cherlondia can call them, but neither Al nor Shirley can call Cherlondia). Al can call Max. Wolfgang can call Darlene, and Darlene can call Wolfgang back. Sylvia can call Dalamatia and Henry. Max can get calls only from Al. Carla can call Sylvia and Cherlondia. Shirley can call Darlene. Max can call Henry. Darlene can call Sylvia. Henry can call Carla. Cherlondia can call Dalamatia.

How would you route a message from

Cherlondia to Darlene?	Shirley to Henry?
Carla to Max?	Max to Dalamatia?
Sylvia to Wolfgang?	Cherlondia to Sylvia?
Henry to Wolfgang?	Dalamatia to Henry?

10. **CONNECTIONS**

How have you used diagrams in other classes?

11. **WRITE YOUR OWN PROBLEM**

In each chapter you'll be given the opportunity to write your own problem that can be solved by using the strategy you studied in that chapter. The book will give you suggestions for how to go about writing these problems. Each time you write your own problem, solve it yourself to be sure that it's solvable. Then give it to another student to solve and, as needed, also to help you with the problem's wording.

Create your own Draw a Diagram problem. Model it after either this chapter's Worm Journey problem or the Ups and Downs of Shopping problem.

Train schedules are systematic lists that help travelers find information easily and quickly.

Systematic Lists

Leslie has 25¢ in her pocket but does not have a quarter. If you can tell her all possible combinations of coins she could have that add up to 25¢, she will give you the 25¢. Solve this problem before continuing.

Many people start solving this problem as follows: "Let's see, we could have 5 nickels, or 2 dimes and 1 nickel. We might have 25 pennies. Oh yeah, we could have 10 pennies, 1 dime, and 1 nickel. Perhaps we could have . . ." Solving the problem this way is extremely inefficient. It could take a long time to figure out all the ways to make 25¢, and you still might not be sure that you'd thought of all the ways.

A better way to solve the problem is to make a **systematic list**. A systematic list is just what its name says it is: a list generated through some kind of system. A **system** is any procedure that allows you to do something (like organize information) in a methodical way. The system used in a systematic list should be understandable and clear so that the person making the list can verify its accuracy quickly. Additionally, another person should be able to understand the system and verify the solution without too much effort.

Many systematic lists are in the form of a table whose columns are labeled with the information given in a problem. The rows of the table are used to indicate possible combinations. As you read the following solutions for the Loose Change problem, make your own systematic list. Label the columns of the list "Dimes," "Nickels," and "Pennies," then fill in the rows with combinations of coins that add up to 25¢.

Brooke started her list in the first row of the Dimes column by showing the maximum number of dimes Leslie could have: two. In the Nickels column, she showed the maximum number of nickels possible with two dimes: one. In the second row, she decreased the number of nickels by one because it's possible to make 25¢ without using nickels.

Dimes	Nickels	Pennies
2	1	0
2	0	5
1	3	0
1	2	5
1	1	10
1	0	15

and so on

She then filled in the Pennies column by showing how many pennies she had to add to her dimes and nickels to make 25¢. After finding all the ways to make 25¢ with two dimes, Brooke continued filling in her list with combinations that include only one dime. In the third row, she showed the maximum number of nickels possible in one-dime combinations: three. As she did for the two-dime combinations, she decreased the number of nickels by one in each row until she ran out of nickels.

Brooke's completed list is shown at right, and it includes all the possible zero-dime combinations. Finish your own list before reading on.

Brooke's systematic list is not the only one that will solve this problem. Heather used the system that follows. Before you look at her entire solution, cover all but the first three rows of the table with a piece of paper. Look at the uncovered rows to figure out her system, then complete the list yourself.

Dimes	Nickels	Pennies
2	1	0
2	0	5
1	3	0
1	2	5
1	1	10
1	0	15
0	5	0
0	4	5
0	3	10
0	2	15
0	1	20
0	0	25

Pennies	Nickels	Dimes
25	0	0
20	1	0
15	2	0
15	0	1
10	3	0
10	1	1
5	4	0
5	2	1
5	0	2
0	5	0
0	3	1
0	1	2

Heather explained her system like this: "I started with the most number of pennies, which was 25. Then I let the pennies go down by fives and filled in the nickels and dimes to make up the difference."

Making systematic lists is a way to solve problems by organizing information. In this chapter you'll make systematic lists to organize information in tables and charts. You will also learn a little about using a special type of diagram called a *tree diagram,* which is used to organize information in a spatial way. Many of the strategies you'll explore later in this book involve organizing information in some sort of a table or chart, and you'll learn other strategies that involve organizing information spatially.

Remember that there is often more than one correct approach to solving a problem. This is often true with systematic lists. Many different systems can produce a solution to a given problem. When you solved the Loose Change problem, you may have used a different list than those that Brooke and Heather used. Any list is fine as long as you have a system that you understand and can use effectively. If you ever find that your original system is too confusing, try a different system.

Just as you can use the *same* strategy to solve a problem in different ways, you will also often find that you can use *more than one strategy* to solve a given problem. In Chapter 1 you solved the Modern Basketball Association problem with a diagram. Solve the problem again, but this time use a systematic list. Please don't refer back to the diagram solution!

Each team in a new basketball league will play three games against each of the other teams. There are seven teams: the Antelopes, the Bears, the Cubs, the Dusters, the Eagles, the Foxes, and the Goats. How many games will be played in all? Do this problem before continuing. This time solve it by using a systematic list.

John is a basketball player and he's always interested in the matchups. In this problem there are seven teams, which John quickly assembled into pairs of teams for games.

ANTELOPES vs CUBS	CUBS vs DUSTERS
BEARS vs GOATS	GOATS vs ANTELOPES
FOXES vs ANTELOPES	CUBS vs GOATS
DUSTERS vs EAGLES	BEARS vs ANTELOPES
CUBS vs GOATS	FOXES vs EAGLES
EAGLES vs BEARS	DUSTERS vs GOATS
CUBS vs GOATS	CUBS vs ANTELOPES
EAGLES vs DUSTERS	DUSTERS vs BEARS
BEARS vs EAGLES	GOATS vs EAGLES

Is John's list systematic? Are all possible matchups represented? Does the list contain omissions or duplications?

Instead of trying to verify the accuracy of John's nonsystematic list, look at the first two columns of Monica's systematic list, shown at right.

AB	BC
AC	BD
AD	BE
AE	BF
AF	BG
AG	

Monica represented each of the teams by the first letter of its name. For example, AB represents a matchup between the Antelopes and the Bears. She started her list by showing the matchups between the Antelopes and the other six teams. In the second column of her list, she showed the matchups between the Bears and the other teams. **Note** that she didn't include the matchup between the Antelopes and the Bears because she'd already shown it in the first column.

She continued by listing, in order, the opposing teams for each remaining matchup.

CD	DE	EF	FG
CE	DF	EG	
CF	DG		
CG			

The whole list is shown below.

AB	BC	CD	DE	EF	FG
AC	BD	CE	DF	EG	
AD	BE	CF	DG		
AE	BF	CG			
AF	BG				
AG					

There are 21 different pairs of teams, and each pair played 3 games against each other. So to answer the question "How many games will be played in all?" multiply 21 and 3: The answer is 63 games. The system Monica used is easy to understand, and the solution is easy to verify. She used a pattern to develop the list, and the pattern should be evident to anyone checking the list.

Compare Monica's solution to this problem's diagram solutions in Chapter 1. You can see that the diagram lines, which represent games, were drawn systematically so that they'd be easy to understand and follow. Diagrams are often very systematic. Did you also **notice** that the diagram lines correspond exactly to the pairs in Monica's list?

PENNY'S DIMES, PART I

Penny has 25 dimes. She likes to arrange them into three piles, putting an odd number of dimes into each pile. In how many ways could she do this? Solve this problem before continuing.

Randy solved this problem by making a systematic list of the possible combinations. He made three columns for his list and called them Pile 1, Pile 2, and Pile 3. In the first row of the list, he indicated the first combination of dimes. He put 1 dime in the first pile and 1 dime in the second pile. This left 23 dimes for the third pile. In the second row he started again with 1 dime in the first pile, then increased the second pile by 2 and decreased the third pile by 2. (**Remember** that each pile contains an *odd* number of dimes.) He continued in this way for a while, as shown at right.

Pile 1	Pile 2	Pile 3
1	1	23
1	3	21
1	5	19
1	7	17
1	9	15
1	11	13
1	13	11

At this point in his list, Randy needed to decide whether or not 1, 13, 11 is a repeat of 1, 11, 13. In other words, is 13 in one pile and 11 in the other the same as 11 in one pile and 13 in the other? Randy decided that the piles were indistinguishable and therefore that, yes, these two combinations were the same. He realized that crossing out repeats would save him a lot of work and make his list a lot shorter. So he crossed out 1, 13, 11. (**Notice** that 1, 13, 11 is crossed out in the list below.) He noticed that his next combination would be 1, 15, 9, which is a repeat of 1, 9, 15. So, he concluded that he'd exhausted the combinations for 1 dime in the first pile.

Next he began finding combinations that began with 3 dimes in the first pile. The first combination he wrote down was 3, 1, 21. But he quickly crossed this combination out because he realized that 3, 1, 21 was a repeat of the second combination in the list, 1, 3, 21. So he started with 3, 3, 19. He continued listing combinations with 3 dimes in the first pile until he reached 3, 11, 11. He stopped at this combination because he knew the next combination would be 3, 13, 9, which again would be a repeat.

Pile 1	Pile 2	Pile 3
1	1	23
1	3	21
1	5	19
1	7	17
1	9	15
1	11	13
1	13	11
3	1	21
3	3	19

He then moved on to listing combinations with 5 dimes in the first pile. To avoid repeating 5, 1, 19 and 5, 3, 17, he started his combinations with 5, 5, 15. He immediately discovered a pattern in the list: every time he increased the number in the first pile, he needed to start the second pile at the lowest possible number that would let him avoid repeating himself. This lowest possible number happened to be no less than the number in the first pile. In other words, when he began with a new increment in the first pile, he needed to repeat that number in the second pile: 3, 3, . . . ; 5, 5, . . . ; and so on.

Randy also noticed that he began to get repetitious combinations after the number in the second pile became as high as the number in the third pile. For example, when he reached 1, 13, 11, he had a repeat of 1, 11, 13. So, here is the primary pattern present in this list: When moving from the first pile to the second pile to the third pile, the numbers cannot decrease. The second pile must be equal to or greater than the first pile, and the third pile must be equal to or greater than the second pile. This is a type of system that can appear in many systematic lists.

Randy continued with his list, using the pattern he'd discovered. When he began listing combinations with 9 dimes in the first pile, his first combination was 9, 9, 7. But at that point his list was complete because 9, 9, 7 is a repeat of 7, 9, 9.

Randy's complete list is shown at right. There are 16 ways to form three piles of dimes.

You can solve this problem differently by experimenting with other systems—we encourage you to do so. One possible system would begin with 23 dimes in the first pile. You might also decide to solve the problem again, but this time assume that the three piles are distinguishable, which leads to a much longer list of 78 possible combinations. You should make this list, too. You'll have to modify the system that Randy used, because it will no longer be true that 1, 3, 21 is the same as 3, 1, 21.

Pile 1	Pile 2	Pile 3
1	1	23
1	3	21
1	5	19
1	7	17
1	9	15
1	11	13
3	3	19
3	5	17
3	7	15
3	9	13
3	11	11
5	5	15
5	7	13
5	9	11
7	7	11
7	9	9

On a famous episode of *Star Trek,* Captain Kirk and the gang played a card game called Phisbin. This problem is about another game, called Frisbin. The object of Frisbin is to throw three Frisbees at three different-sized bins that are set up on the ground about 20 feet away from the player. If a Frisbee lands in the largest bin, the player scores 1 point. If a Frisbee lands in the medium-sized bin, the player scores 5 points. If a Frisbee lands in the smallest bin, the player scores 10 points. Kirk McCoy is playing the game. If all three of his Frisbees land in bins, how many different total scores can he make? Make a systematic list for this problem before reading on.

You can make two different types of systematic lists for this problem. Here is an example of each.

Derrick set up a list with columns titled 10 Points, 5 Points, 1 Point, and Total. He began by indicating the maximum number of 10-point throws: 3. He continued by indicating the other possible 10-point throws: 2, 1, and 0. In each row he adjusted the 5-point and 1-point throws so that three throws were always accounted for. After calculating all the point totals, Derrick concluded that Kirk McCoy can make ten different total scores.

Notice the system in the list. The 10 Points column starts with the highest possible number of throws, then decreases by 1. The column

10 POINTS	5 POINTS	1 POINT	TOTAL
3	0	0	30
2	1	0	25
2	0	1	21
1	2	0	20
1	1	1	16
1	0	2	12
0	3	0	15
0	2	1	11
0	1	2	7
0	0	3	3

stays on each particular possible number of throws (3, then 2, then 1, and 0) as long as it can. The 5 Points column follows a similar process: It starts with the highest possible number of 5-point throws for each particular score and decreases by 1 each time. The 1 Point column makes up the difference in the scores.

Derrick made this list very quickly, and anyone seeing the list for the first time should immediately be able to follow the system. To help ensure that the system is evident, we have provided an explanation of the system. In this course, when you write solutions to problems that you'll turn in to your teacher, you'll be asked to also provide a written explanation of your work. By explaining your work, you'll not only become a better problem solver, but you'll also become proficient at explaining your reasoning, which is a very valuable skill.

Julian used a different method, shown next. He titled each column with the number of the three possible throws. Then he wrote down the points for each throw. What system did Julian use?

THROW 1	THROW 2	THROW 3	TOTAL
10	10	10	30
10	10	5	25
10	10	1	21
10	5	5	20
10	5	1	16
10	1	1	12
5	5	5	15
5	5	1	11
5	1	1	7
1	1	1	3

Julian started by letting the first throw earn 10 points. He then adjusted the other two throws to include all possible point combinations. When he ran out of combinations for which the first throw earned 10 points, he began listing combinations for which the first throw earned 5 points, then 1 point. (**Note** that he didn't repeat score possibilities by rearranging the points earned. In other words, 10, 10, 5 is the same as 10, 5, 10 or 5, 10, 10.) The point totals came out exactly the same as those in Derrick's list. But Julian's approach made it easier to add up the total scores.

What system did Emily use in the list shown below? Before reading on, study her list to figure out her system.

Throw 1	Throw 2	Throw 3	Total
10	10	10	30
5	5	5	15
1	1	1	3
10	10	5	25
10	10	1	21
5	5	10	20
5	5	1	11
1	1	10	12
1	1	5	7
1	5	10	16

Emily started by listing the situations where all three throws landed in the same bin. Then she listed the situations where two throws landed in the same bin. Finally she listed the one possibility where all three landed in different bins.

AREA AND PERIMETER

A rectangle has an area measuring 120 square centimeters. Its length and width are whole numbers of centimeters. What are the possible combinations of length and width? Which possibility gives the smallest perimeter? Work this problem before continuing.

Tuan explained his solution for this problem: "I read that the area of the rectangle was 120 sq cm. The first thing I did was to draw a picture of a rectangle.

"I had no idea whether this rectangle was long and skinny, or shaped like a square. But I did know that the area was supposed to be 120 sq cm. So I made a list of whole-number pairs that could be multiplied to get 120.

"I knew I was done at this point because the next pair of factors of 120 is 12 and 10, which I'd already used. A 12 cm by 10 cm rectangle is the same as a

WIDTH	LENGTH	AREA
1 cm	120 cm	120 cm²
2 cm	60 cm	120 cm²
3 cm	40 cm	120 cm²
4 cm	30 cm	120 cm²
5 cm	24 cm	120 cm²
6 cm	20 cm	120 cm²
8 cm	15 cm	120 cm²
10 cm	12 cm	120 cm²

10 cm by 12 cm rectangle turned on its side, and I saw no need to list it twice. I also realized that neither 7 nor 9 would work for the width, because they don't divide evenly into 120.

"Now I had to find which possibility gives the smallest perimeter. I knew that the perimeter of a rectangle is the distance around the rectangle so I needed to add up the length and width. But this would only give me half of the perimeter, so I would have to double the sum of the length and width. I added the perimeter column to my chart."

WIDTH	LENGTH	AREA	PERIMETER
1 cm	120 cm	120 cm²	242 cm
2 cm	60 cm	120 cm²	124 cm
3 cm	40 cm	120 cm²	86 cm
4 cm	30 cm	120 cm²	68 cm
5 cm	24 cm	120 cm²	58 cm
6 cm	20 cm	120 cm²	52 cm
8 cm	15 cm	120 cm²	46 cm
10 cm	12 cm	120 cm²	44 cm

"Now I can see from my chart that the 10 cm by 12 cm rectangle (which does have an area of 120 cm²) gives the smallest perimeter of 44 cm."

WHICH BOOKS SHOULD YOU READ?

For an English assignment, you are to choose three of the following books to read: *To Kill a Mockingbird*, *All Quiet on the Western Front*, *The Stranger*, *The Adventures of Huckleberry Finn*, and *A Midsummer Night's Dream*. How many different sets of three books can you choose? Do this problem before continuing.

Li explained her systematic list, shown at right: "I decided to abbreviate the names of the books so I wouldn't have to write out the whole names each time. I used TKM, AQWF, TS, HF, and MND. Then I just made a list. I made my list by letting TKM stay in front as long as it could, and rearranged the other four books into the remaining two spots. Once I had all the combinations that include TKM, I dropped it from the list. Then I used AQWF in the first spot

TKM	AQWF	TS
TKM	AQWF	HF
TKM	AQWF	MND
TKM	TS	HF
TKM	TS	MND
TKM	HF	MND
AQWF	TS	HF
AQWF	TS	MND
AQWF	HF	MND
TS	HF	MND

and listed all the combinations that included it. Then I dropped AQWF, and finally I used TS in the first spot. I listed the combination that included TS, but by that time there was only one more way to do it. There are ten ways altogether."

Jim used a different systematic list to solve the problem. "I made columns for the different books, then I checked off three in each row. There are ten ways."

	TKM	AQWF	TS	HF	MND
1	X	X	X		
2	X	X		X	
3	X	X			X
4	X		X	X	
5	X		X		X
6	X			X	X
7		X	X	X	
8		X	X		X
9		X		X	X
10			X	X	X

A **tree diagram** is another type of systematic list and is used to organize information spatially. A tree diagram's name reflects the fact that it looks like the branches of a tree. (**Note** that tree diagrams will be discussed again in Chapter 17: Spatial Organization.)

After David solved the Which Books Should You Read? problem, he was then interested in knowing the number of different orders in which he could read a particular group of three books. He solved the problem with a tree diagram.

"I learned how to do tree diagrams in eighth grade, and I really like them. It's sort of a combination of a diagram and systematic list. The first branch of the tree shows the book I read first. The second branch shows the book I read next. In the second branch I didn't repeat the book that I read in the first branch. Finally, the third branch shows the book that I have yet to read."

David's tree diagram of the different orders in which he could read the three books TKM, AQWF, and TS is shown on the next page.

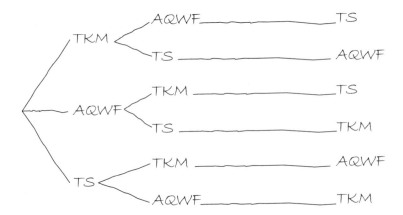

"I then realized that there would be six different reading orders for each set of three books in the original list. So I multiplied 6 by 10 to get 60 orders if the order in which I read the books made a difference."

You can solve some systematic list problems with tree diagrams. However, sometimes a tree diagram would be too confusing or cumbersome. You will need to decide when using a tree diagram would be appropriate or easier than using a standard systematic list.

As you work through this book, one major challenge you'll face will be choosing an appropriate strategy to solve a problem. Often you will find that the best strategy is the first one you chose, but sometimes you'll have to experiment with different strategies to see which one is most effective. And sometimes you'll need to use two or more strategies together to solve a difficult problem. Being persistent when you try different strategies will pay off. The most important thing to know about problem solving is that most problems can be solved. As you solve more and more difficult problems, your confidence in your abilities will increase.

Real-World Problem Solving

Joe uses systematic lists to solve problems in his job as a computer programmer for a large bank. His job responsibilities include dealing with the occasional failures of one particular computer system and network of terminals.

Failures occur in any computer system because of problems with the hardware, the software, the power supply, or user actions. When a system fails, Joe begins solving the problem by printing out a computer memory dump, which is a list of what was in the computer's memory when its system failed. He checks to see what program was being used, the time of the failure, and the data stored in the computer's memory registers. He must check each of these things systematically to make sure that he covers all possibilities for the failure. He also compares different system failures to see if there is a pattern to them. To make these comparisons, he prepares diagrams called **histograms** to show the frequency of certain data present at the time of system errors.

By comparing system failures, Joe was able to detect that a computer's hardware was not correctly processing negative numbers. He noticed that in numerous system failures, negative numbers were stored in certain memory cells. He knew that there can be many different causes for a system failure, and it appeared that negative numbers were causing some of the failures in this case. He tested the system by using negative numbers to force system failures. His tests worked, causing the system to fail. Using the results of his tests to guide him, he rewrote some of the computer's software so that he could detect and prevent other potential system failures.

Jennifer, an accountant, also uses systematic lists. For example, she receives piles of deposit slips and of checks that were posted in random order. Before she can properly account for funds received and paid out, she must separate the checks from the deposit slips, then organize the checks by check number and the deposits by date. She also uses systematic lists when she works on clients' tax returns, which can be quite complex. Some clients have many investments, and Jennifer must separate them by category: stocks, mutual funds, and savings accounts. Then for each category she must subcategorize: dividends, interest, and long-term capital gains or losses from stock sales. And some of the subcategories may have further subcategories: regular dividends and short-term capital gains are subcategories of dividends, for example. Using systematic lists helps Jennifer easily keep track of what could otherwise be confusing or overwhelming financial information.

In conclusion, making a systematic list is a great way to organize information. Before you start a list, take some time to think carefully about your system. When you make your list, be sure you have a system that you thoroughly understand. Continue to monitor the system as you work through the list. When you reach a logical break in your list, think carefully about what your next entry should be. And finally, don't be afraid to change systems if you don't think your system is working for you. Enjoy this strategy. Making systematic lists can be a lot of fun.

Problem Set A

Solve each problem by making a systematic list.

1. CARDS AND COMICS

Charmaign has $6.00 she wants to spend on comic books and superhero cards. Comic books cost 60¢ each, and deluxe packages of superhero cards cost $1.20 each. List all of the ways Charmaign can spend all of her money on comic books, superhero cards, or both.

2. FREE CONCERT TICKETS

Alexis, Bart, Chuck, and Dariah all called in to a radio show to get free tickets to a concert. List all the possible orders in which their calls could have been received.

3. **APARTMENT HUNTING**

A management company offers two payment plans for leasing an apartment for one year. Plan A is designed so that a tenant's entry cost is low, and Plan B is designed so that there are more gradual price increases:

PLAN A	PLAN B
12-month lease	12-month lease
$400 first month	$500 first month
$30 per month increase each month	$15 per month increase each month

Which plan costs more for only the ninth month of tenancy? Which plan costs more for the entire year?

4. **TENNIS TOURNAMENT**

Justin, Julie, Jamie, Matt, Ryan, and Roland are the six players in a round-robin tennis tournament. Each player will play a set against each of the other players. List all the sets that need to be played.

5. **STORAGE SHEDS**

Andre's company manufactures rectangular storage sheds. The sheds are made with aluminum side panels that measure 8 feet, 10 feet, 12 feet, and 15 feet along the bottom edge. For example, one possible shed measures 10 feet by 10 feet. Another possible shed measures 12 feet by 15 feet. List the measurements of all the possible sheds.

6. **MAKING CHANGE**

Ms. Rathman has lots of nickels, dimes, and quarters. In how many ways can she make change for 50¢?

7. **FINISHED PRODUCT**

The product of two whole numbers is 360, and their sum is less than 100. What are the possibilities for the two numbers?

8. BASKETBALL

Holley scored 10 points in a basketball game. She could have scored with one-point free throws, two-point field goals, or three-point field goals. In how many different ways could she have scored her 10 points?

9. TWENTY-FOUR

How many ways are there to add four positive even numbers to get a sum of 24?

10. TARGET PRACTICE

In a target shooting game, Scott had four arrows. He hit the target with all four shots. With each shot he could have scored 25 points, 10 points, 5 points, or 1 point. How many total scores are possible?

11. KYLE CRAVES CANDY

The corner convenience store sells candy in 5¢, 10¢ and 15¢ packages. List all of the ways in which Kyle can spend 40¢ *or less* on candy.

12. CAREERS

At the end of this chapter, two professionals, Joe and Jennifer, were profiled. They both use systematic lists in their jobs. Interview a relative or a friend who uses systematic lists or diagrams in his or her career.

13. WRITE YOUR OWN

Create your own systematic-list problem.

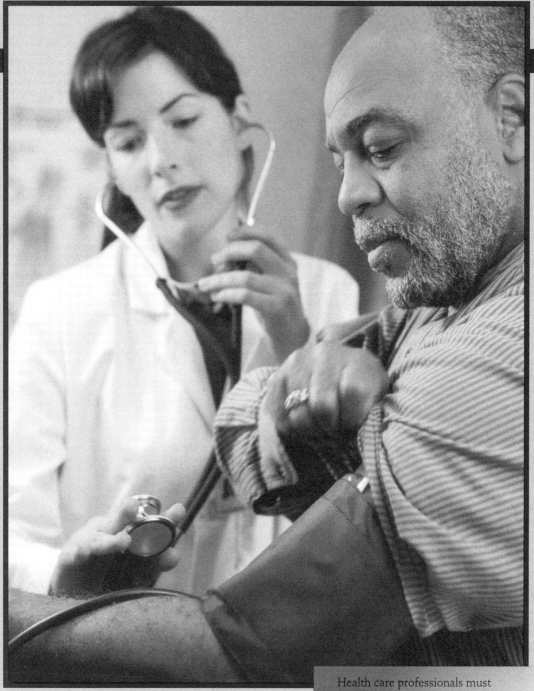

Health care professionals must conduct tests to eliminate possibilities when diagnosing an illness.

3

Eliminate Possibilities

AL: Well, his alibi checked out. It can't be Jerry who put the arsenic in the deceased's soup.

BETSY: Yeah, but who? We checked out everybody who went to the estate that day: the letter carrier, the gardener, the cook, the chauffeur—even the butler, though it was his day off. That eliminates everybody. I don't know who else it could be.

AL: I don't know. There has to be something . . . someone we overlooked.

Sounds like a tough case for Al and Betsy. They've been working hard on it for at least 10 minutes and must wrap it up in the next 47 minutes: Their show has just been canceled and there's no possibility for a two-part show. Al and Betsy are busy eliminating possibilities before they are eliminated from the airwaves—possibly forever.

Eliminating possibilities is a powerful problem-solving strategy. Sherlock Holmes used this strategy quite extensively. In his words, "Once you have eliminated the impossible, then whatever is left, no matter how improbable, must be the solution." In this chapter you will solve some problems by eliminating possibilities. Let's start with a made-up game of Twenty Questions.

The following game never actually took place, although you probably realize that every day, all over the world, real people are acting out very similar scenes.

Two people are playing this game. One player says, "I'm thinking of a number between 1 and 100, inclusive. You may ask whatever twenty questions you like, and I will respond with yes or no answers. To keep the game fair, I will always respond truthfully."

Question	Response	Comments
Is it greater than 50?	Yes	Good question. All numbers less than 51 are eliminated.
Is it 62?	No	Wasted guess. It eliminates only one number (62).
Is it 13?	No	Really wasted guess. The number 13 was eliminated earlier because the number we want is greater than 50.
Is it 3842?	No	
Is it greater than 75?	Yes	Good question. Eliminates about half the remaining numbers.
Is it odd or even?	Yes	
Is it odd?	No	Eliminates about half the remaining numbers.
Is it 83?	No	Bad guess. We know the number is not odd.
Is it less than 85?	Yes	Good, a further narrowing down.
Is it less than 80?	Yes	Again good.
Is it 76?	No	
Is it 78?	Yes	

When eliminating possibilities, it helps to remember the possibilities that have already been eliminated. Solve the following problem by eliminating possibilities.

Three brothers each arranged to spend an evening with a woman that he had never met before. Each wanted to show off how suave and debonair he could be, so each formed a plan.

By coincidence, each brother decided to buy a box of candy at the same store, and each bought tickets at the same ticket outlet.

Andy bought honey-based candies because he wanted to show what a sweet guy he could bee. Tooley bought chews because he wanted to show that he was a choosy guy. Marty bought nuts.

When it came time to leave, each brother grabbed the wrong candy box and ticket envelope. None of them took the candy or the tickets that belonged to him. Each took the tickets of one brother and the candy of the other. Andy didn't have Marty's candy. You'll have to figure out the rest.

Do this problem before continuing.

Kim drew the tree diagram shown below and then began to eliminate possibilities. Her diagram shows the candy and ticket possibilities for each brother. "I drew the diagram like this because it was given that each brother had the candy that belonged to one brother and the tickets belonging to the other."

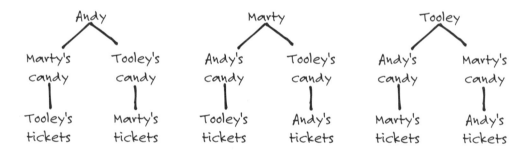

Here's Kim's explanation of her solution: "It was given that Andy did not have Marty's candy, so I crossed out the possibility that Andy had Marty's candy and Tooley's tickets. Therefore, Andy must have Tooley's candy. This also means that Andy must have Marty's tickets because each brother had the candy that belonged to one brother and the tickets belonging to the other. Because Andy has Tooley's candy, Marty can't be the one with Tooley's candy, so Marty must have Andy's candy. Then it is evident that Tooley doesn't have Andy's

candy, so he has Marty's candy, which is the only candy left after all other possibilities have been eliminated."

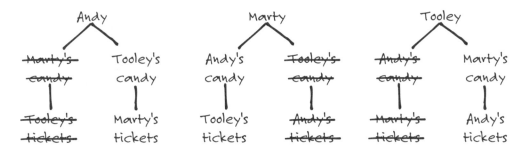

"Determining who has which candy automatically determines who has which set of tickets. So the answers are: Andy has Tooley's candy and Marty's tickets, Marty has Andy's candy and Tooley's tickets, and Tooley has Marty's candy and Andy's tickets."

PENNY'S DIMES, PART 2

Penny's favorite coin is the dime, as we saw in Chapter 2. Since we last saw Penny, she has spent some of her dimes and has acquired some more. She doesn't know how many she has now, but she knows she has fewer than 100. One day she was arranging them on her desk in different ways. She found that when she put them into piles of 2, there was 1 left over. When she put them into piles of 3, again there was 1 left over. The same thing happened when she put them into piles of 4. She then tried putting them into piles of 5 and found that there were none left over. How many dimes does Penny have? Solve this problem before continuing. (There is more than one correct answer.)

Five clues are given in this problem:

1. When divided by 2, the remainder is 1.

2. When divided by 3, the remainder is 1.

3. When divided by 4, the remainder is 1.

4. When divided by 5, the remainder is 0.

5. There are fewer than 100 coins.

This problem will clearly demonstrate that it's important to consider all possibilities before eliminating some. Here's how a group of students—Marli, James, Dennis, and Troy—solved this problem.

JAMES: Let's start with the first clue. I'll list all the numbers that give a remainder of 1 when divided by 2. (He wrote down the list shown below.)

3, 5, 7, 9, 11, 13, 15, 17, 19, 21, 23, 25, 27, 29, 31, 33, 35, 37, 39, . . .

MARLI: (interrupting him) Wait a minute, this can be done more efficiently. I like your list because it's systematic, but I think we can improve it. Instead of just considering one clue at a time, I think we can compress this by using two of the clues from the beginning.

DENNIS: Good idea, Marli. Let's try using clues 1 and 2.

TROY: I think we should use clues 4 and 5 instead.

DENNIS: Why not 1 and 2?

TROY: I chose 4 because it involves the fewest numbers, and 5 because it is so easy. So here is a list of all the numbers less than 100 that are divisible by 5. (He then wrote the list below.)

5, 10, 15, 20, 25, 30, 35, 40, 45, 50, 55, 60, 65, 70, 75, 80, 85, 90, 95

JAMES: Now we can go back and reconsider clue 1. My initial list showed us that the number we're looking for is odd. Because we're trying to eliminate possibilities, let's cross off all the even numbers in Troy's list. (He crossed off the numbers, as shown.)

5, ~~10~~, 15, ~~20~~, 25, ~~30~~, 35, ~~40~~, 45, ~~50~~, 55, ~~60~~, 65, ~~70~~, 75, ~~80~~, 85, ~~90~~, 95

MARLI: Now let's continue on through the clues. Clue 2 allows us to cross off any number that is not 1 greater than a multiple of 3.

DENNIS: Say what?

MARLI: Let me explain that more clearly. Clue 2 says, "When she put them into piles of 3, again there was 1 left over." That means if you divide the number of dimes by 3, the remainder would be 1. So we have to keep each number that is 1 more than a multiple of 3.

DENNIS: Oh, I see. That means we have to eliminate each number that is *not* 1 more than a multiple of 3.

JAMES: I don't get it. Can you give me an example?

MARLI: Okay. For example, 5 is 2 more than a multiple of 3, so we can cross it out. We can also cross out 15 because it's a multiple of 3. On the other hand, we can't cross out 25 because it's 1 more than 24, which is a multiple of 3. Thus, we can eliminate the multiples of 3 (15, 45, and 75) and numbers that are 2 more than a multiple of 3 (5, 35, 65, and 95). (She crossed off those numbers in the revised list.)

~~5~~, ~~15~~, 25, ~~35~~, ~~45~~, 55, ~~65~~, ~~75~~, 85, ~~95~~

TROY: This leaves us with 25, 55, and 85. Finally, we apply clue 3 and cross out any number that is not 1 greater than a multiple of 4. That means we can cross off 55 because it's 3 more than a multiple of 4 (because $52 = 4 \times 13$).

JAMES: That leaves us with the numbers 25 and 85. Each of these satisfies all the clues. Which is the correct answer?

MARLI: I guess we can't tell for sure.

This problem has more than one possible answer. You may be accustomed to math problems having only one answer. This is true for many types of equations and problems, but it won't always be true for the problems in this book. In this respect, this book mirrors life: There isn't always one correct answer for a problem, just as there isn't only one correct approach to finding an answer. In this class, when you solve a problem ask yourself whether or not you have the only answer or if there are others to consider. For this problem we warned you that there would be more than one answer. But **watch out:** We may not *always* warn you!

Eliminating possibilities is a way of organizing information. That is, you can eliminate certain possibilities after you organize the information given in a problem. It often helps to consider the possibilities systematically, as you did in the last problem. The strategy of eliminating possibilities also contains aspects of the guess-and-check strategy, which you'll explore more fully in Chapter 6.

One particular form of eliminating possibilities is a strategy that is often used in problem solving and in formal mathematics. This strategy is called **proof by contradiction** or **indirect proof**. In this book we will refer to this strategy as **seeking contradictions**. The following diagram shows the process of seeking contradictions:

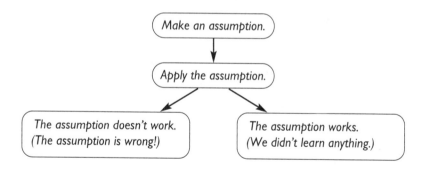

To seek contradictions, (1) make an assumption about the problem and (2) see what happens to the problem when you apply the assumption. There are two possible outcomes with this strategy: either it works or it doesn't work. "It doesn't work" is the contradiction we're seeking because it allows you to eliminate the assumption as a possibility. Although "it works" seems to be a good sign, all it really does is confirm that an existing possibility is still an existing possibility.

Seeking contradictions is a common strategy for eliminating possibilities, especially when other eliminations are not evident. You'll use this strategy in this chapter, especially when you solve the cryptarithmetic puzzles. You'll also see this strategy in Chapter 4.

The strategy of seeking contradictions is very useful in problems that involve truth tellers and liars. Variations of this type of problem have been around for years. Solve the next problem by seeking contradictions.

WHO IS LYING?

Jim tells lies on Fridays, Saturdays, and Sundays. He tells the truth on all other days. Freda tells lies on Tuesdays, Wednesdays, and Thursdays. She tells the truth on all other days. If they both say, "Yesterday I lied," then what day is it today? Solve this problem before continuing.

Danyell solved this problem by seeking contradictions. First she set up a chart of the two liars and the days of the week.

	MON	TUE	WED	THUR	FRI	SAT	SUN
JIM	T	T	T	T	L	L	L
FREDA	T	L	L	L	T	T	T

"Assume that today is Monday. Both people tell the truth on Monday, so the statement 'Yesterday I lied' must be true for both. But yesterday was Sunday, and only Jim was lying yesterday. Because Freda told the truth on Sunday, her statement is false. This is the contradiction we were seeking, because Freda is supposed to tell the truth on Monday. So today is not Monday.

"Assume today is Tuesday. Jim is telling the truth, so when he says, 'Yesterday I lied,' it is supposed to be true. But yesterday was Monday, and Jim tells the truth on Monday. So today can't be Tuesday. A similar argument can be made for Wednesday and Thursday, and in Freda's behalf on Saturday and Sunday.

"Now we have reached a contradiction for every day except Friday. So all days except Friday have been eliminated. So it seems that the answer is Friday. I'll check.

"Today must be Friday. Because Jim lies on Friday, his statement 'Yesterday I lied' is false. That works because on Thursday Jim tells the truth. Now consider Freda. She tells the truth on Friday, so her statement 'Yesterday I lied' must be the truth because she lies on Thursday. So I concluded that today is Friday, having reached contradictions for every other day and having shown that Friday worked."

In the next problem you'll eliminate possibilities, seek contradictions, and maybe guess a little bit. Problems like the one that follows are sometimes called **cryptarithms**. Doing math problems for pleasure may seem strange to you, but over the years many people have enjoyed cryptarithmetic problems just for fun. We hope you enjoy them, too.

LIFE ON THE FARM

Emil and Olive live on a farm with their father, Gordon. One day Emil asked his father, "Dad, what happened to that cat we used to have?" Olive overheard this and said, "Yeah, and we used to have a horse too." Gordon replied, "That tomcat and that old nag were no use. I traded them for our new goat."

Emil said, "Hey, that sounds like a good cryptarithmetic problem. Come on, Olive, let's see if we can solve it." They wrote down TOM + NAG = GOAT. Each letter stands for a different digit, 0 through 9. No two letters stand for the same digit. Determine which digit each letter represents. Do this problem before reading on. (**Note** that there are many solutions to this problem.)

A class of students presented many solutions on the board. Here are several of their solutions:

Jonathan solved the problem like this: "I started off realizing that G had to be 1 because it's impossible for two 3-digit numbers to add up to something more than 2000. Even if the two numbers were 999 and 999, the answer would be 1998. So G has to be 1. I wrote down 1 under G.

```
    T O M
  + N A G
        1
  -------
  G O A T
  1
```

"Then I was stuck. I wasn't really sure what to do next, so I started guessing numbers. I looked at O next and figured out that it had to be zero because in the tens place O + A = A.

```
    T  O  M
       0
 +  N  A  G
          1
 ─────────────
    G  O  A  T
    1  0
```

"Then I guessed numbers that added up to 10 for T and N. I picked 7 and 3, and everything worked out. M turned out to be 6, and then I just picked A to be 4."

```
    T  O  M
    7  0  6
 +  N  A  G
    3  4  1
 ─────────────
    G  O  A  T
    1  0  4  7
```

Here's how Jerri worked it out: "I did the same thing Jonathan did, but I picked a different set of numbers for T and N: I used 6 and 4. Then the problem works out like this:

```
    T  O  M
    6  0  5
 +  N  A  G
    4  9  1
 ─────────────
    G  O  A  T
    1  0  9  6
```

"Then I realized that A could be anything not used. So I got a few other solutions, too."

```
    T  O  M        T  O  M        T  O  M        T  O  M
    6  0  5        6  0  5        6  0  5        6  0  5
 +  N  A  G     +  N  A  G     +  N  A  G     +  N  A  G
    4  2  1        4  3  1        4  7  1        4  8  1
 ───────────   ───────────   ───────────   ───────────
    G  O  A  T     G  O  A  T     G  O  A  T     G  O  A  T
    1  0  2  6     1  0  3  6     1  0  7  6     1  0  8  6
```

Jack tried a chart. "I did what Jonathan and Jerri did, but I realized that T and N could be anything that added up to 10. Also, the choice for T automatically picked N. I came up with the following chart."

$$\begin{array}{llllllllll} N: & 1 & 2 & 3 & 4 & 5 & 6 & 7 & 8 & 9 \\ T: & 9 & 8 & 7 & 6 & 5 & 4 & 3 & 2 & 1 \end{array}$$

"I eliminated the combinations 1, 9 and 9, 1 because we already know that 1 is G. I also eliminated the 5, 5 combination because two different letters can't stand for the same digit.

$$\begin{array}{lllllll} N: & 2 & 3 & 4 & 6 & 7 & 8 \\ T: & 8 & 7 & 6 & 4 & 3 & 2 \end{array}$$

"Remember that we already know T is 1 greater than M. So I added M to the chart.

$$\begin{array}{llllll} N: & 2 & 3 & 4 & 6 & 7 \\ T: & 8 & 7 & 6 & 4 & 3 \\ M: & 7 & 6 & 5 & 3 & 2 \end{array}$$

"The last possibilities of N = 8 and T = 2 have been eliminated because if T were 2, M would have to be 1. But this is impossible because G = 1 and two different letters cannot represent the same digit.

"So the chart shows all of the possibilities for T, N, and M. This problem has five possible correct solutions. Actually this represents five families of solutions because A can be any digit not assigned to the other letters in the problem, as Jerri already explained."

Adrianne and Khue contributed some further insights to the problem. Adrianne said, "I didn't get as far as Jack did, but I noticed that a possibility for O could have been 9 if you carried from the ones column. It seemed to me this could happen a lot. You might think O had to be zero because O + A = A, but O could be 9 with a carry from the previous column. That is, 1 (carry) + 9 (letter O) + letter A will equal letter A (actually, this expression represents 10 + A). For example, if A = 2, then 1 + 9 + 2 would equal 12, making A = 2 and causing a carry of 1 to the hundreds column.

$$\begin{array}{lcccc} \text{CARRY} & 1 & 1 & & \\ & T & O & M & \\ & & 9 & & \\ + & N & A & G & \\ & & 2 & 1 & \\ \hline G & O & A & T & \\ 1 & 9 & 2 & & \end{array}$$

"But then I realized this was impossible. If O were 9, then the ones column would have had to carry. This would mean that M would have to be 9 because G is 1 and you would need 9 more to cause the carry. But that would mean M and O were both 9, and that's impossible."

Khue noticed, "Another reason that O can't be 9 is because the number for GOAT would have to be nineteen hundred something.

But that's also impossible because the only way that GO can be 19 is if T and N add to 19. Even if you carried from the tens column, T and N would both have to be 9, and that's impossible."

This problem illustrates a very important point about working in groups and presenting problems on the board. Each person who worked on the problem contributed something to its solution. It wasn't necessary that each person completely solve the problem for other people to benefit from their thinking. Share your thinking with each other, even if you haven't solved a problem or your work turns out to be wrong. You and other people will benefit from the exchange of information and thought processes.

Life on the Farm was another problem that had many possible solutions. When you solve a problem, **remember** to pursue alternative solutions unless you're sure there are none. Most cryptarithmetic problems have only one answer, or maybe two similar answers. However, the important points brought out in the Life on the Farm problem will show up in many cryptarithmetic problems. Try your hand at this next, rather famous, problem—it has one and only one correct solution.

THE LETTER FROM COLLEGE

The story goes that a young man away at college needed some extra cash. He sent his mother this plea. He wanted her to send the amount indicated by the following sum:

SEND + MORE = MONEY

Each letter stands for a different digit, 0 through 9. No two letters stand for the same digit.

How much money did the young man want? (Assume that there is a decimal point between N and E because his mother is probably not willing to send ten thousand or so dollars to her son on request.) Work this problem before continuing.

This problem and its solution are complex. Read through them slowly and try to work out the problem on a piece of paper as you read. Reread the explanation as many times as you need to.

First make a list of all the possible numbers and letters, as shown at the top of the next page. By listing the numbers, you can keep track of what numbers you've already used. By listing the letters, you'll see how many of the digits 0 through 9 are used in the problem.

Note that in this problem there are only eight different letters, so only eight of the ten digits 0 through 9 are used. As you match the letters to their correct digits, you can fill in the correct letter matches under the row of numbers, and you can fill in the correct number matches under the row of letters.

First, note that the maximum sum of two 4-digit numbers is 9,999 + 9,999 = 19,998. Also note that this maximum sum (19,998) is a five-digit number. Because the sum MONEY is also a five-digit number, we have to conclude that M = 1. (**Remember** that this is the same reasoning we used to figure out that G = 1 in the Life on the Farm problem.)

Now that we know M = 1, let's look at the sum S + M. It's clear that S + M = MO. Because M = 1, we know we need to carry a 1 over from the thousands column. (**Note** that the maximum carry for each column is 1 because we are adding only two numbers. Even if both of the numbers were 9, 9 + 9 = 18. And even with a carry, that sum would equal only 19.) Thus, S has to equal 9 *without* a carry from the hundreds column or S has to equal 8 *with* a carry from the hundreds column. In either case, O has to equal zero because 1 + 9 + (a carry) would mean MO = 11. But O can't equal 1 because M = 1. Thus, O = 0. So far, the solution looks like the figure shown at right.

```
    S  E  N  D
   8, 9
    M  O  R  E
    I  0
   ─────────────
    M  O  N  E  Y
    I  0
```

Now look at the hundreds column, E + 0 = N. Clearly, anything plus zero equals the same number. But because E and N cannot equal the same number, a 1 (the maximum carry) must have been carried from the tens column. Thus, E + 1 = N.

Next let's look to see if S equals 8 or 9. We will do this by seeking contradictions. S will equal 8 only if the hundreds column carries into the thousands column. Assume this is the case. The only way for the hundreds column to carry is if E = 9, because O already equals zero. That is, 9 + 1 (carry) + 0 = 10. But this would make N = 0, and because we already know that O = 0, this is impossible. We have reached a contradiction. Our assumption that the hundreds column carried is false, and S does not equal 8. Therefore, S must equal 9, and the hundreds column does not carry. Now the solution looks like the figure shown at the top of the next page, including the carries.

carries 0 1
    S E N D
    9
    M O R E
    1 0
    ———————
    M O N E Y
    1 0

0 1 2 3 4 5 6 7 8 9
O M   S
S E N D M O R Y
9   1 0

Here's how Georgia figured out which digit corresponds to R:

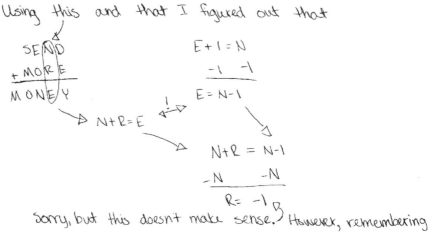

Using this and that I figured out that

$$SE(N)D$$
$$+ MO(R)E$$
$$\overline{M ON(E)Y}$$

$$N + R = E$$

$$E + 1 = N$$
$$-1 \quad -1$$
$$E = N - 1$$

$$N + R = N - 1$$
$$-N \qquad -N$$
$$R = -1$$

Sorry, but this doesn't make sense. However, remembering that N+R >10 (because we found a carry digit in the hundreds column.)

So, . . . $N + R = 10 + E$ and using $E = N - 1$

$$N + R = 10 + (N - 1)$$
$$-N \qquad\qquad -N$$
$$\overline{R = 10 \qquad -1}$$
$$R = 9$$

But this still doesn't work because R can't equal 9 since S is already equal to 9. There must be another alternative. Suppose there is a carry from the one's column . .

$$R + 1 = 9$$
$$R = 8$$

Up to this point, the solution looks like the figure shown below.

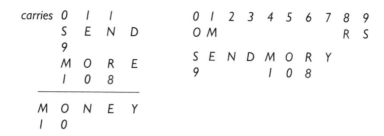

```
carries 0  |  |           0 | 2  3  4  5  6  7  8  9
        S  E  N  D         O  M                 R  S
        9
        M  O  R  E         S  E  N  D  M  O  R  Y
        |  0  8            9              |  0  8
       _____
        M  O  N  E  Y
        |  0
```

Now note that D + E in the ones column must carry. So D + E = 10 + Y. The minimum value for Y is 2 because 1 and 0 are already taken. Thus, D + E has to be at least 12. The possible combinations of values are listed at right. Note that 8 and 9 are not listed for D and E because these values are already taken by R and S (as we can see in our list of possibilities).

D: 6 7 7 5
E: 7 6 5 7
N: 8 7 6 8
Y: 3 3 2 2

Recall that E + I = N.

Which possibilities are valid? The first and fourth columns of values must be eliminated because N would equal 8, and 8 is already taken by R. The second column is eliminated because D and N would both be 7. Thus, the third column is correct, and the solution is as shown below.

```
carries 0  |  |           0 | 2  3  4  5  6  7  8  9
        S  E  N  D         O  M  Y           E  N  D  R  S
        9  5  6  7
        M  O  R  E         S  E  N  D  M  O  R  Y
        |  0  8  5         9  5  6  7  |  0  8  2
       _____
        M  O  N  E  Y
        |  0  6  5  2
```

The question asked how much money the young man wanted. Assuming that there is a decimal between N and E, he wanted $106.52.

Remember that many problems cannot be solved by using only one strategy. As you work through this book, you'll come across more and more problems that may require several strategies to solve. The next problem requires that you use two strategies together: making a systematic list and eliminating possibilities. The problem is tough and a little tricky. Take your time and be sure you consider all possibilities before eliminating some.

DOWNTOWN DELI

Seymour owns his own business. He makes deli sandwiches, which he wraps to retain freshness and then distributes to several convenience stores for resale. One of his favorite sandwiches is the Sausage and Meatball Combo, but it has a very low distribution. In fact, only three stores take deliveries of the Sausage and Meatball Combo: two Fast Stop stores and one Circle B store.

One morning, Seymour suffered an unfortunate accident. He slipped on the floor and banged his head. He seemed to be fine, except that when he was out on his delivery route, he couldn't remember which streets the three Sausage and Meatball Combo stores were on. The streets were numbered from 1st Street up to 154th Street, and he remembered that the two Fast Stop stores were on streets whose numbers added up to 50. He also remembered that the Circle B store was two streets away from one of the Fast Stop stores. And he remembered that he called the Sausage and Meatball Combo his "prime" favorite because all three stores were on prime-numbered streets. Unfortunately, the information he remembered wasn't enough to get him to the stores.

He called his friend Gus and, well, let's keep this short by saying Gus remembered that Seymour had told him the product of the numbers of the streets the stores were on, but Gus could remember only the last digit of the product. This proved to be enough for Seymour, who promptly double-parked, whipped out a pencil, made a systematic list, and eliminated possibilities to find the answer.

Now it's your turn to re-create Seymour's heroics.

Richard solved this problem as follows:

First he considered the streets that the Fast Stop stores could be on. He made a systematic list of all the pairs of odd numbers that add to 50. He used odd numbers because even numbers cannot be prime. (The exception to this is 2, but 2 would be paired with 48, which is obviously not prime.) He knew some of the odd numbers weren't prime, but he listed them anyway because he wanted to be careful not to accidentally eliminate any possibilities before he considered them.

FS #1	FS #2
1	49
3	47
5	45
7	43
9	41
11	39
13	37
15	35
17	33
19	31
21	29
23	27
25	25

Next he eliminated all the numbers that weren't prime: 1, 49, 45, 9, 39, 15, 35, 33, 21, 27, and 25. He also eliminated the numbers they were paired with, even if they were prime. He was left with four pairs: 3 and 47, 7 and 43, 13 and 37, and 19 and 31.

Now he had a better idea of the possible combinations of streets the Fast Stop stores could be on. However, he didn't know specifically which store was on which street. For instance, was the first store on 3rd Street and the second on 47th Street, or was it the other way around? To make sure he accounted for all possible combinations, he again added his four pairs to the list but in reverse order: 47 and 3, 43 and 7, 37 and 13, and 31 and 19. His revised list is shown at right.

FS #1	FS #2
3	47
47	3
7	43
43	7
13	37
37	13
19	31
31	19

Next he added a third number to represent the street the Circle B store was on. He knew that the Circle B store was two streets away from one of the Fast Stop stores. He didn't worry about *which* store the Circle B store was near because he'd already listed all the possible combinations of Fast Stop stores. But he did want to consider whether or not the Circle B store was two streets *up* or two streets *down* from a Fast Stop store. This meant that each third number he added would have to be 2 greater than or 2 less than the second number. He revised his list as shown at right, adding all possible combinations.

FS #1	FS #2	CB
3	47	45
3	47	49
47	3	1
47	3	5
7	43	41
7	43	45
43	7	5
43	7	9
13	37	35
13	37	39
37	13	11
37	13	15
19	31	29
19	31	33
31	19	17
31	19	21

However, Richard needed to consider only third numbers that were prime. For example, the first set of Fast Stop numbers was 3 and 47. The two possible third numbers for this pair were 45 and 49. But neither of these numbers is prime, so he didn't have to consider them. He eliminated all the third numbers that were not prime, which left him with the list shown at right.

FS #1	FS #2	CB
47	3	5
7	43	41
43	7	5
37	13	11
19	31	29
31	19	17

Now consider the last clue of the problem. When Gus told Seymour the last digit of the product of the three numbers, Seymour was able to figure out the answer. Richard didn't know the product, but it is enough for him to know that if *Seymour* knew the product, Seymour could figure it out. See if you can figure out the answer before reading on.

For each set of numbers in the list, Richard added the last digit of their product. **Note** that he needed only the last digit of the product. For instance, $47 \times 3 \times 5 = 705$ ends in 5. (To save himself from having to multiply all the numbers, he used a multiplication shortcut.

FS #1	FS #2	CB	Last Digit
47	3	5	5
7	43	41	1
43	7	5	5
37	13	11	1
19	31	29	1
31	19	17	3

He simply multiplied the digits in the ones places of the numbers to figure out what the last digit of the total product would be. For example, for $7 \times 43 \times 41$, he multiplied $7 \times 3 \times 1 = 21$, which ends in 1 and which is the last digit of the product of $7 \times 43 \times 41$.)

Richard noticed that 3 appears in the Last Digit column only once, while 5 appears twice and 1 appears three times. Thus, because Seymour was able to deduce the correct combination once he knew only the last digit of the product, the last digit must be 3. Otherwise, without more information he wouldn't have been able to figure out the combination. So Richard concluded that the streets were numbered 31, 19, and 17. This meant that the Fast Stop stores were located on 31st Street and 19th Street, and that the Circle B store was on 17th Street.

This problem contains a key element that appears in a lot of puzzle problems: You didn't have all the information that Seymour had. However, it was enough to know that if Seymour had the information, then he could solve the problem. This bit of knowledge allows you to solve the problem, too.

Eliminating possibilities, sometimes by seeking contradictions, is a valuable problem-solving strategy. By considering all the possibilities and eliminating the obviously incorrect ones, you can narrow in on the right answer. (In this chapter you used the strategy of systematic lists to help you consider and eliminate possibilities.) Sometimes not all possibilities can be eliminated right away. Detectives may run into this situation as they try to solve crimes. But sometimes many possibilities can be eliminated quickly. When detectives are able to quickly eliminate some potential suspects, they can concentrate their efforts on the remaining suspects. Thus, they can use their time more effectively and increase their chances of solving the crime.

You will probably begin noticing that you already use this strategy in your daily life. For example, you consider and eliminate possibilities when you decide what to watch on TV or what to have for dinner. Restaurant customers often use the strategy of eliminating possibilities when ordering dinner. Many people decide what to eat based not on what they want, but rather on what they don't want. After eliminating foods they obviously don't like, they often settle down to picking among three or four items. The decisive factor may come about something like this: Imagine that Artie is out to dinner with his family. "Let's see, the chicken sounds good, but so does the pasta, the steak, and the salmon. Well, the salmon comes poached with a white wine cream sauce, and I really would rather have it broiled with lemon, so I'll skip that. The chicken sounds great, but it comes with artichokes and the thought of artichokes makes me gag. The steak sounds really good, but my dad says I've been eating too much red meat lately. (I think what that really means is, it's too expensive.) So I'll go with the pasta."

You'll find that your problem-solving skills will increase if you make a conscious effort to eliminate possibilities when solving real-life problems.

Problem Set A

1. SQUARE ROOTS

The square root of 4356 is an integer. Without a calculator, determine what that integer is by eliminating possibilities. Do the same for 8464.

2. HOW MANY LINES?

Sam counted the lines of a page in his book. Counting by threes gave a remainder of 2, counting by fives also gave a remainder of 2, and counting by sevens gave a remainder of 5. How many lines were on the page?

3. EGGS IN A BASKET

If the eggs in a basket are removed two at a time, one egg will remain. If the eggs are removed three at a time, two eggs will remain. If the eggs are removed four, five, or six at a time, then three, four, and five eggs will remain, respectively. But if they are taken out seven at a time, no eggs will be left over. Find the least number of eggs that could be in the basket.

4. DARTBOARD

Juana threw five darts at a dartboard. The possible scores on the target were 2, 4, 6, 8, and 10. Each dart hit the target. Which of these total scores can be *quickly* identified as "not possible": 38, 23, 58, 30, 42, 31, 26, 6, 14, or 15? (Don't spend more than one minute on this problem.)

5. FIND THE NUMBER

If you multiply the four-digit number *abcd* by 4, the order of digits will be reversed. That is, *abcd* × 4 = *dcba*. The digits *a, b, c,* and *d* are all different. Find *abcd*.

6. WOW, WOW, SO COOK!

Denée was having an argument with her roommate, Frankie, about whether or not Frankie could cook. After arguing for a while, Denée said, "Wow, wow, so cook!" Frankie, who was a math teacher, noticed that what Denée said might be a cryptarithm. She sat down to work on it, and Denée ended up cooking dinner. Each letter in the cryptarithm stands for a different digit. **Hint:** K = 9.

```
    W  O  W
    W  O  W
+      S  O
----------
 C  O  O  K
```

7. NELSON + CARSON = REWARD

A story from the Old West tells the tale of two famous outlaws named Nelson and Carson. The wanted poster calling for their arrest indicated that a substantial reward would be offered to the person who caught up to both of them and brought them in for trial. Amazingly, it turned

out that the poster contained a great cryptarithm. All who saw the poster realized this and spent their time solving the puzzle rather than looking for Nelson and Carson! When Nelson and Carson heard all the ruckus about the poster, they also tried the problem. However, they weren't too bright and ended up visiting their local sheriff for a clue. He told them that N = 5, and then he arrested them. They solved the problem during the time they spent in jail. Each letter in the cryptarithm stands for a different digit. Find the digits that the other letters represent.

$$
\begin{array}{ccccccc}
  & N & E & L & S & O & N \\
+ & C & A & R & S & O & N \\
\hline
  & R & E & W & A & R & D \\
\end{array}
$$

8. THE THREE SQUARES

Three cousins, Bob, Chris, and Phyllis, were sitting around watching football on TV. The game was really boring, so they started talking about how old each of them were. Bob (the oldest) noticed that they were all between the ages of 11 and 30. Phyllis noticed that the sum of their ages was 70. Chris (the youngest) burst out, "Gee, if you write the square of each of our ages, all the digits from 1 to 9 will appear exactly once in the digits of the three squares." How old was each person?

9. TO TELL THE TRUTH

Many puzzle books contain puzzles that involve people or creatures who are either liars or truth tellers. You no doubt know from experience, for instance, that many talking dogs are notorious liars. Imagine that you have just encountered three talking dogs and you ask them if they are liars or truth tellers. Dog 1 says something that you do not understand. Dog 2 says, "He said he was a truth teller." Dog 3 says, "Joe is lying." You then ask, "Which one of you is Joe?" Dog 2 says, "I am the only Joe." Dog 3 points to Dog 1 and says, "He is the only Joe." Determine whether each dog is a liar, a truth teller, or whether it can't be determined.

10. RANKINGS

Thuy (the tallest) is older than Miguel (the lightest). Jerel (the oldest) is shorter than Nick (the heaviest). No one has the same rank in any category. For example, if someone is the second tallest, he can't also be the second heaviest or the second oldest. Rank the four boys in each category: age, height, and weight.

11. CONNECTIONS

Where have you used any of the problem-solving strategies you've learned so far in your daily life outside of school?

12. WRITE YOUR OWN

Create your own problem that has to be solved by eliminating possibilities. In your problem you may want to somehow use the systematic-list problem you created in Chapter 2: Systematic Lists. You may also want to try making up a cryptarithmetic problem.

Problem Set B

1. THE SIDEWALK AROUND THE GARDEN

We have a garden that measures 17 feet by 20 feet. We want to pour cement for a 3-foot-wide sidewalk around the garden. To make the forms for the cement, we will need to buy some 2-by-4-inch lumber. How many feet of lumber will we need just for the perimeter of the walk? (Consider both the inside and outside perimeter.)

2. A NUMBER OF OPTIONS

Dusty Rhodes is planning to buy a new dirt bike. The different available options are

a. She can choose either regular tires or extra heavy-duty tires.

b. She can choose to get plastic, vinyl, cloth, or leather for the seat.

c. She can choose a paint color: Bad Brown, Sick Silver, or Grease Black.

In how many different ways can she order her new bike?

3. GOOD DIRECTIONS?

I stopped at a street corner and asked for directions to Burger Jack. Unfortunately, the person I asked was Larry Longway, whose directions are guaranteed to be too complicated. He said, "You are now facing north. Go straight for two blocks. Turn left. Go straight for one block. Turn right. Go straight for three blocks. Turn right. Go straight for five blocks. Turn right. Go straight for three blocks. Turn left. Go straight for one block. Turn right. Go straight for four blocks. Turn left. Go straight for two blocks. Turn left. Go straight for one block. Turn left. Go straight for five blocks, and you are there." By the time I arrived I was out of breath and Burger Jack was closed. Please give me the directions for the shortest path from my original spot to Burger Jack. (Assume no streets have dead ends.)

4. HIGH SCORERS

The five starters for the Seaside Shooters scored all the team's points in the final basketball game of the season. Regina Reporter covered the game, but later her notes were accidentally destroyed. Fortunately she had taped some interviews with the players, but when she played them back, only a few quotes seemed relevant to the scoring. She knew the final score was 95–94. Using the players' observations, determine how many points each of them scored.

Kellene: Everybody's totals were odd.

Sara: Donna was fourth highest with 17 points. I scored 12 more points than Kellene.

Martina: Kellene and I scored a total of 30 points. I outscored her.

Heather: The last digit in everybody's score was different.

Donna: Our highest scorer had 25 points.

The Chicago Bears score 18 points in a football game. In how many different ways can the Bears score these points? Points are scored as follows: a safety is 2 points, a field goal is 3 points, a touchdown is 6 points, and a point after touchdown (PAT) is 1 point (a PAT can't be scored unless a touchdown is scored first).

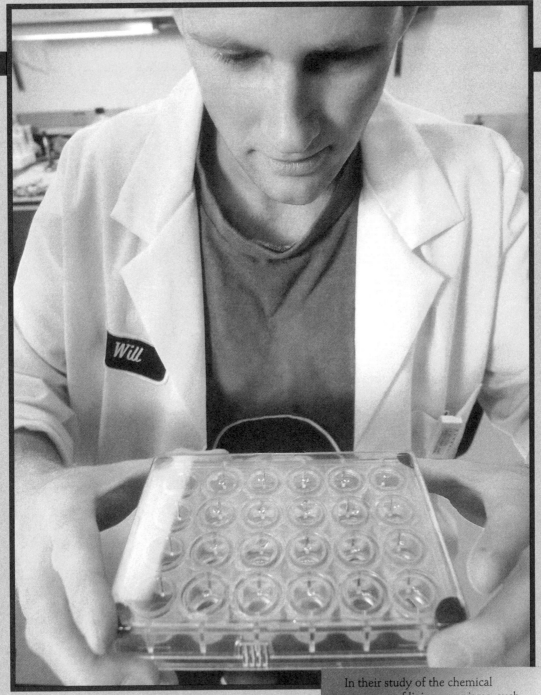

In their study of the chemical processes of living organisms, such as the regulation of metabolism, biochemists use matrix logic to create and organize various chemical compounds and reactions.

4

Matrix Logic

Our society values logical thinking and encourages people to think logically when they interact with other people. For example, decisions reached by thinking logically are often held in higher esteem than decisions made emotionally. And logical arguments are often more readily accepted than arguments based on emotion, which are discounted or disdained by some people.

A logical argument starts at some point and moves to another point by way of ordered steps. The argument must be developed sequentially or people will not give it credence. For example, a man might tell his daughter that she should go to the dentist because it looks like rain. This statement may seem utterly silly if we don't know that the man's daughter left her umbrella at her dentist's office last week. The man's conclusion that his daughter should go to the dentist is correct, but his statement seems ridiculous when we don't know the logical thinking behind it.

One way to improve your logical reasoning ability is to solve logic problems. This type of problem is fun and challenging. (Most grocery stores and drugstores carry booklets or magazines that are full of logic problems. Three such magazines are *Games* and *World of Puzzles*, published by Games Publications, and *Dell Math Puzzles and Logic Problems*, published by Dell Publications.) The basic idea of logic problems is to solve them by matching up items in various categories. For example, you might match up the first and last names of a list of people, their favorite foods, their favorite colors, and the pets they own. Or you might match up each person's name with a kind of car and an occupation. Generally speaking, these problems get harder as more people or more categories are added.

Most logic problems can be solved by a chart or a table that we will call a **matrix**. A matrix helps you organize the information in a problem in a useful way. And a matrix facilitates eliminating possibilities, which is an important strategy for solving logic problems. Many people use matrices to solve problems in their work. For example, the biochemist shown at the beginning of this chapter uses a matrix to organize answers to research data.

An example of a matrix is shown below. This matrix could be used for a problem that matches up names (John, Phil, Mary, and Alice) with pets (dog, cat, bird, and fish). Your task for this problem would be to match each person with the pet he or she owns.

FIRST NAMES

		John	Phil	Mary	Alice
	Dog				
	Cat				
PETS	Bird				
	Fish				

You can use the matrix to do two things: eliminate possibilities and show connections. When you eliminate a possibility, show it by marking an X in the matrix. An X shows a connection that is not correct. For example, suppose you determine that John doesn't own the dog. (You'll learn how to determine this later in this chapter.) You would then mark an X in the space that matches John and the dog as is shown in the following matrix. Suppose you also determined that Mary doesn't own the bird. You would place an X in the space that matches Mary and the bird.

FIRST NAMES

		John	Phil	Mary	Alice
	Dog	X			
	Cat				
PETS	Bird			X	
	Fish				

When you establish a definite connection, show it by marking an O in the matrix. An O shows a connection that is correct. (Some people use the words *yes* and *no* instead of X and O. Other people use other symbols.) For example, suppose you determine that Alice owns the fish. You would then mark an O in the space that matches Alice and the fish. **Note** that a standard feature of most logic problems is the **one-to-one correspondence** between things. For instance, in this Name/Pet matrix, each person owns one pet. Thus, once you are able to show a connection by marking an O, you can also show a lot of eliminated possibilities by marking X's. So if in our matrix Alice owns the fish, then nobody else does. Therefore, you can mark X's in the rest of the Fish row. And if Alice owns the fish, then she owns no other pet, so you can mark X's in the rest of Alice's column. Of course, keep all marks you've already made in the matrix so you can keep track of what information you do and do not have. This book will call attention to information added at each step of a solution by showing the new information in red.

FIRST NAMES

		John	Phil	Mary	Alice
	Dog	X			X
	Cat				X
PETS	Bird			X	X
	Fish	X	X	X	O

At this point in this problem, suppose you could deduce that Phil didn't own the dog. You would mark an X in the Phil-dog space.

FIRST NAMES

		John	Phil	Mary	Alice
PETS	Dog	X	X		X
	Cat				X
	Bird			X	X
	Fish	X	X	X	O

Eliminating the Phil-dog possibility would help tremendously. You can see in the matrix that neither John, Phil, nor Alice owns the dog. Therefore, Mary must own the dog. Now you can mark an O in the Mary-dog space and an X in the Mary-cat space (because if Mary owns the dog, she can't own the cat).

FIRST NAMES

		John	Phil	Mary	Alice
PETS	Dog	X	X	O	X
	Cat			X	X
	Bird			X	X
	Fish	X	X	X	O

Now you just need to determine who owns the cat and who owns the bird. Usually logic problems include some way to determine this, which allows you to finish the problem, but this example problem doesn't.

How do you determine a problem's various connections and eliminations? Each problem includes a set of clues. After you read them carefully, you'll be able to deduce the connections. Consider the next problem.

Ted, Ken, Allyson, and Janie (two married couples) each have a favorite sport: running, swimming, biking, and golf. Given the following clues, determine who likes which sport.

1. Ted hates golf. He agrees with Mark Twain that golf is nothing but a good walk spoiled.

2. Ken wouldn't run around the block if he didn't have to and neither would his wife.

3. Each woman's favorite sport is featured in a triathlon.

4. Allyson bought her husband a new bike for his birthday to use in his favorite sport.

Work this problem before continuing.

First set up the matrix like that shown below. Next label the top and left side of the matrix with the main categories given in the problem: names and sports. This matrix labels sports on top and names on the left side, but it could have been set up the other way around. If the problem featured more categories, you'd need more matrices. (You will see examples of this later in the chapter.)

		Running	Swimming	Biking	Golf
	Ted				
	Ken				
	Allyson				
	Janie				

SPORTS appears above the columns, *NAMES* labels the rows.

Here's how Jason solved the Favorite Sports problem:

"First I set up my chart [matrix], with the names on the side and the sports up on top. Then I read through the clues. Clue 1 said that Ted didn't like golf. So that eliminated Ted from being the golfer. I put an ✕ in the Ted-golf space. I also put a 1 next to this ✕ to show that I had eliminated this possibility by using clue 1.

"Clue 2 said that Ken wouldn't run around the block. So I figured that Ken wasn't the runner, and I put an X_2 in the Ken-running space.

The clue also said Ken's wife wasn't the runner, but I didn't know who his wife was, so I left this part of the clue alone for now.

"The third clue said that the women like sports featured in the triathlon. The only sport in the list that isn't featured in the triathlon is golf, so I put X_3's in the Allyson-golf and Janie-golf spaces."

SPORTS

NAMES	running	swimming	biking	golf
Ted				X_1
Ken	X_2			
Allyson				X_3
Janie				X_3

"Now Ken is the only person who can like golf, because all other people have been eliminated for golf. So I put an O in the Ken-golf space. This meant that Ken couldn't like any of the other sports, so I put X's in the Ken-swimming and Ken-biking spaces."

SPORTS

NAMES	running	swimming	biking	golf
Ted				X_1
Ken	X_2	X	X	0
Allyson				X_3
Janie				X_3

"Next I read clue 4. It said Allyson's husband likes biking. This meant that Ted had to like biking, since he was the only man left once I knew Ken liked golf. So Ted likes biking and is Allyson's husband. So I put an O_4 in the Ted-biking space. This meant that Ted could not be the runner or the swimmer, so I put X's in the Ted-running and Ted-swimming spaces. (The Ted-golf space already had an X in it.) I also put X's in the Allyson-biking and Janie-biking spaces, since if Ted was the bicyclist, then nobody else could be."

NAMES	running	swimming	biking	golf
Ted	X	X	O_4	X_1
Ken	X_2	X	X	O
Allyson			X	X_3
Janie			X	X_3

"Now I had to figure out who was the runner and who was the swimmer. But I didn't have any more clues. I read through all the clues again. Clue 2 said that Ken's wife wouldn't run around the block. I had skipped that part of the clue when I first read it, but now I thought I could use it. I knew that Allyson bought her husband a bike and that her husband turned out to be Ted. This meant that Ken is married to Janie, so Janie was the one who won't run around the block. (Substitute the name Janie for Ken's wife in clue 2.) So I put an X in the Janie-running space. This left Allyson as the runner and Janie as the swimmer."

SPORTS

NAMES	running	swimming	biking	golf
Ted	X	X	O_4	X_1
Ken	X_2	X	X	O
Allyson	$O_{2,4}$	X	X	X_3
Janie	X	O	X	X_3

"The answers are as follows: Allyson is the runner, Janie is the swimmer, Ted is the bicyclist, and Ken is the golfer. The chart really helped to solve this problem."

Here are a few things to **remember** about matrix logic problems:

First, although most people schooled in psychology will tell you to think positively, that's the wrong attitude for this kind of problem. (For personal problems, yes, do think positively. On matrix logic problems, don't.) It's far more helpful to "think negatively" for matrix logic problems. Negatives help eliminate possibilities. Matrix logic is a strategy based on things that cannot be. So you must think negatively to eliminate as many possibilities as you can.

Second, as soon as you know a connection, correct or incorrect, list it immediately and make the needed mark in your matrix. For example, in the Favorite Sports problem, as soon as you knew that Ted and Allyson were married to each other, you could have started a list with "Ted-Allyson (married)." Or maybe you could have put a little heart symbol in the matrix by their names so that you could easily remember their connection. Listing connections for a problem this simple isn't a big deal, but for a more difficult problem, it can be an asset to keep a careful list. A list like this is called an **adjunct list**. You'll use adjunct lists for some problems later in this chapter.

Finally, Jason had to reread a clue while solving the Favorite Sports problem. He skipped the part of clue 2 about Ken's wife, and came back to it later when he knew who Ken's wife was. Rereading clues is helpful in solving matrix logic problems.

Now consider a "partial" problem with more categories. ("Partial" problems, rather than real problems that you will solve, will be used in this book to help explain certain strategies.) This problem asks you to match up first names (Bob, Sara, Rick, and Jane), favorite colors (blue, red, white, and green), and home states (South Dakota, Missouri, New Jersey, and Texas). How many matrices will you need?

As with the Favorite Sports problem, you'd have to use matrices to match up each category with each other category. A good way to see how many matrices you'd need is to make a diagram. Write down the different categories and draw lines between them, as shown in the diagram at right. The number of lines tells you how many matrices you'd need and which matrices match which categories. The diagram shows that you'd need three matrices, one for matching first names with favorite colors, one for matching favorite colors with home states, and one for matching home states with first names.

Names

Colors ——————— States

Making another diagram helps you organize your matrices into one big matrix that is easier to work with. First draw a square to represent each of the three matrices you'd need. Then label them with their proper categories, as shown below.

Colors

Names   States

Colors   States

Names

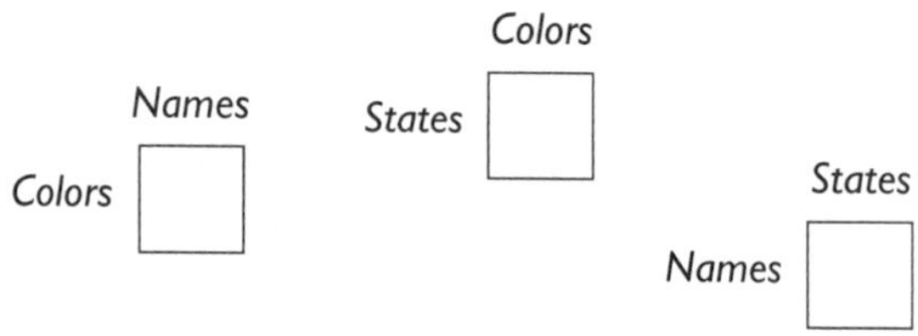

Match up like categories, as shown below. (You may have to rearrange some of the labels for each matrix box so that categories match up. In this diagram, the labels on the names-colors box were switched around so that both of the colors categories and both of the names categories could match up.)

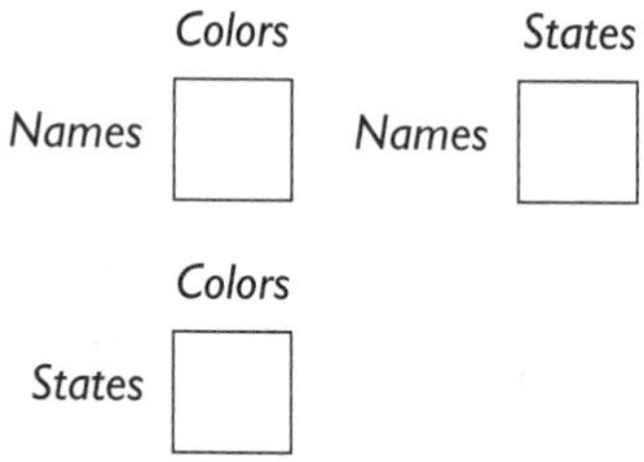

Colors   States

Names   Names

Colors

States

Now put your boxes together, making them into one figure, as shown below. Delete the category names that would be "squeezed" by putting the boxes together.

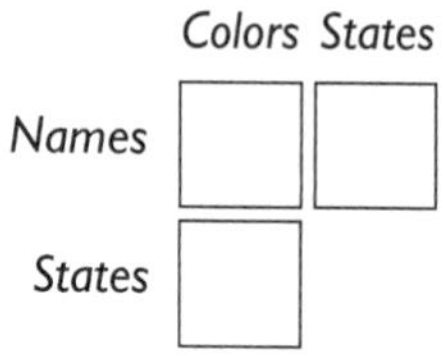

Colors States

Names

States

Now you have an idea of how your real Name/Color/State matrix would be organized. This is a good way to organize your matrix because, as you'll see in a moment, it helps you keep track of the information in a problem. Look at the final Name/Color/State matrix shown below. **Notice** that it contains all the categories given in the problem and that its labels correspond to the labels in the three-square diagram you just made.

		FAVORITE COLOR				HOME STATE			
		Blue	Red	White	Green	SD	MO	NJ	TX
FIRST NAME	Bob								
	Sara								
	Rick								
	Jane								
HOME STATE	SD								
	MO								
	NJ								
	TX								

After setting up your matrix, you would then use the problem's clues to solve it. Examine the Name/Color/State matrix shown below, which now shows information that has been gathered from this partial problem's "clues" so far.

		FAVORITE COLOR				HOME STATE			
		Blue	Red	White	Green	SD	MO	NJ	TX
FIRST NAME	Bob		X						X
	Sara		X						X
	Rick		X						X
	Jane	X	O	X	X	X	X	X	O
HOME STATE	SD								
	MO								
	NJ								
	TX								

Some problems can be solved just by carefully reading their clues. But most matrix logic problems require that you use a number of substrategies to solve them. You used the substrategies of rereading clues and making adjunct lists when you solved the Favorite Sports problem earlier in this chapter. Later in this chapter you'll learn other substrategies by looking at more partial problems. Then you'll practice with some real problems.

One substrategy is called **bouncing** or **cross-correlating**. Look again at the preceding matrix. It shows that Jane's favorite color is red. It also shows that Jane is from Texas. So far there are no marks on the Color/State matrix. But if you start at the O in the Texas-Jane space in the State/Name matrix, then move your finger left to the Name/Color matrix, you'll meet up with the O in the Jane-red space. Then you could move your finger down to the Color/State matrix and mark an O in red-Texas space. This would show that the person from Texas likes red. (A logician might say, "Jane likes red, and Jane is from Texas. Therefore, the person from Texas likes red." A mathematician would be sure to mention the use of the **transitive property**.) The new marks are shown in the following matrix.

		FAVORITE COLOR				HOME STATE			
		Blue	Red	White	Green	SD	MO	NJ	TX
FIRST NAME	Bob		X						X
	Sara		X						X
	Rick		X						X
	Jane	X	O	X	X	X	X	X	O
HOME STATE	SD		X						
	MO		X						
	NJ		X						
	TX	X	O	X	X				

This process is called bouncing because if you threw a ball from the State/Name matrix along the Jane row, it would come to the Jane-red space and bounce down to the red-Texas space. This process is also called cross-correlating because you correlate information from two separate matrices and cross them in a place that makes sense and is useful.

Another way you could have made the red-Texas connection would have been to keep an adjunct list, writing down the facts as soon as you knew them. Here's what an adjunct list for the preceding matrix would look like:

NAME	COLOR	STATE	
Jane	red		from Name/Color matrix
Jane		Texas	from State/Name matrix

Here's a more efficient way to list the facts:

NAME	COLOR	STATE
Jane	red	Texas

The substrategy of bouncing or cross-correlating works best when you bounce or cross-correlate positive information. This substrategy can also be used with negative information, but doing so can be a bit difficult. Consider the following matrix. (Because this is a partial problem, the matrix shown below does not contain the Jane-red-Texas information from the preceding matrix.)

		FAVORITE COLOR				HOME STATE			
		Blue	Red	White	Green	SD	MO	NJ	TX
FIRST NAME	Bob	X		X		O	X	X	X
	Sara					X			
	Rick					X			
	Jane					X			
HOME STATE	SD								
	MO								
	NJ								
	TX								

The State/Name matrix shows that Bob is from South Dakota. The Name/Color matrix shows that Bob does not like blue or white. Therefore, the person from South Dakota (Bob) does not like blue or white. Thus, X's can be marked in the South Dakota–blue and South Dakota–white spaces in the Color/State matrix. This process is called bouncing or cross-correlating with negative information. Bouncing with negative information is harder and less obvious than bouncing with positive information, but it is a very helpful technique to use when you seem to be stuck and unable to move forward with your solution.

| | | FAVORITE COLOR | | | | HOME STATE | | | |
		Blue	Red	White	Green	SD	MO	NJ	TX
FIRST NAME	Bob	X		X		O	X	X	X
	Sara					X			
	Rick					X			
	Jane					X			
HOME STATE	SD	X		X					
	MO								
	NJ								
	TX								

The next problem features three matrices, cross-correlation with both positive and negative information, and an adjunct list.

Tom, John, Fred, and Bill are friends whose occupations are (in no particular order) nurse, secretary, teacher, and pilot. They attended a church picnic recently, and each one brought his favorite meat (hamburger, chicken, steak, and hot dogs) to barbecue. From the clues provided below, determine each man's name, occupation, and favorite meat.

1. Tom is neither the nurse nor the teacher.

2. Fred and the pilot play golf together. The burger lover and the teacher hate golf.

3. Tom brought hot dogs.

4. Bill sat next to the burger fan and across from the steak lover.

5. The secretary hates golf.

Work this problem before continuing.

Millissent and Tami worked on this problem.

MILL: First we need to set up one of those matrix logic charts.

TAMI: That's right. We need three matrices. One matrix for Names/Occupations, one for Names/Meats, and one for Meats/Occupations. (She drew the matrix below.)

		Nurse	Scty	Tchr	Pilot	Burg	Chkn	Steak	Hdog
N A M E	Tom								
	John								
	Fred								
	Bill								
M E A T	Burg								
	Chkn								
	Steak								
	Hdog								

OCCUPATIONS: Nurse, Scty, Tchr, Pilot — MEAT: Burg, Chkn, Steak, Hdog

MILL: Now let's read the clues and start eliminating. The first clue says that Tom is neither the nurse nor the teacher. So put X's in the Tom-nurse and Tom-teacher boxes.

TAMI: Let's put little 1's next to the X's so we know we eliminated a box because of clue 1.

MILL: Okay. Now the next clue says that Fred and the pilot play golf together. That means that Fred is not the pilot, so put an X_2 in the Fred-pilot space.

TAMI: And then the burger lover and the teacher hate golf. So X_2 in the burger-teacher box.

MILL: Maybe we should start one of those adjunct lists.

TAMI: What are those?

MILL: When you have other things referred to in the clues, it helps to list them separately. So here we have two people who play golf and two people who don't. Listing information like this will help us keep everything straight. (She wrote down the adjunct list shown below.)

	Golfers		Non-Golfers	
Fred			burger	
	pilot			teacher

TAMI: How come you wrote Fred and the pilot down on different lines?

MILL: Because we know Fred is not the pilot, so "Fred" and "pilot" describe two different people. And I might get some more information about golfers that I could add next to "Fred" or "pilot."

TAMI: Oh, I see. And the burger lover and the teacher are written on different lines because they're different people as well. I'll bet we can use the list later, too. Wait a second. Fred can't like burgers or be the teacher.

MILL: How come?

TAMI: Fred likes golf and the burger lover and the teacher don't. So Fred can't be either one of them. Put an X_2 in the Fred-burger and Fred-teacher spaces.

MILL: That's right. And by the same reasoning we can cross off pilot-burger also.

OCCUPATIONS / MEAT

	Nurse	Scty	Tchr	Pilot	Burg	Chkn	Steak	Hdog
Tom	X_1		X_1					
John								
Fred			X_2	X_2	X_2			
Bill								
Burg			X_2	X_2				
Chkn								
Steak								
Hdog								

TAMI: Okay, let's go on. Clue 3 says "Tom brought hot dogs." That's easy. Put an O in the Tom–hot dog space.

MILL: And X's in the rest of that row and column because Tom couldn't have brought anything else and nobody else brought hot dogs. But watch out, don't put X's past the bold lines by accident.

OCCUPATIONS / MEAT

	Nurse	Scty	Tchr	Pilot	Burg	Chkn	Steak	Hdog
Tom	X_1		X_1		X_3	X_3	X_3	0
John								X_3
Fred			X_2	X_2	X_2			X_3
Bill								X_3
Burg			X_2	X_2				
Chkn								
Steak								
Hdog								

MILL: Now I think we can do some of that bouncing (or cross-correlating) with negative information we learned about. We know that Tom brought hot dogs. We also know that Tom is not the nurse or the teacher. So the nurse and the teacher didn't bring hot dogs. So put an X in the nurse–hot dog and the teacher–hot dog spaces.

		OCCUPATIONS				MEAT		
	Nurse	Scty	Tchr	Pilot	Burg	Chkn	Steak	Hdog
Tom	X_1		X_1		X_3	X_3	X_3	0
John								X_3
Fred			X_2	X_2	X_2			X_3
Bill								X_3
Burg			X_2	X_2				
Chkn								
Steak								
Hdog	X		X					

TAMI: That was good, Millissent. The next clue says Bill is not the burger fan or the steak lover, because he was sitting in different spots from them. So put X_4 in Bill-burger and Bill-steak.

MILL: Look, we can fill in that Bill must be chicken now. All the other possibilities are eliminated. Bill brought chicken, so nobody else could have brought chicken. Cross off the rest of the Chicken column.

TAMI: That gives us, John brought burgers and Fred brought steak.

MILL: Great, one of our matrices is done.

	OCCUPATIONS				MEAT			
	Nurse	Scty	Tchr	Pilot	Burg	Chkn	Steak	Hdog
Tom	X_1		X_1		X_3	X_3	X_3	0
John					0	X	X	X_3
Fred			X_2	X_2	X_2	X	0	X_3
Bill					X_4	0	X_4	X_3
Burg			X_2	X_2				
Chkn								
Steak								
Hdog	X		X					

MILL: Now we can do more bouncing with negative information. Look across Fred's row. Fred is the steak lover, and he isn't the teacher or the pilot. So the steak lover is not the teacher or the pilot. Put X's in the steak-teacher and steak-pilot spaces.

TAMI: And that gives us, the teacher is chicken.

MILL: It also shows that the pilot likes hot dogs after we cross off the rest of the Chicken row and the Teacher column.

	OCCUPATIONS				MEAT			
	Nurse	Scty	Tchr	Pilot	Burg	Chkn	Steak	Hdog
Tom	X_1		X_1		X_3	X_3	X_3	0
John					0	X	X	X_3
Fred			X_2	X_2	X_2	X	0	X_3
Bill					X_4	0	X_4	X_3
Burg			X_2	X_2				
Chkn	X	X	0	X				
Steak			X	X				
Hdog	X	X	X	0				

TAMI: Now let's do some bouncing with positive information. We know that Tom likes hot dogs. We also know that the pilot likes hot dogs. (The pilot probably *is* a hot dog.) So Tom must be the pilot. Put an O in the pilot-Tom space.

MILL: Great, Tami. We can do the same thing with Bill. We know Bill likes chicken and that the teacher likes chicken. So Bill must be the teacher.

		Nurse	Scty	Tchr	Pilot	Burg	Chkn	Steak	Hdog
	Tom	X_1	X	X_1	O	X_3	X_3	X_3	O
E M A N	John			X	X	O	X	X	X_3
	Fred			X_2	X_2	X_2	X	O	X_3
	Bill	X	X	O	X	X_4	O	X_4	X_3
	Burg			X_2	X_2				
T A E M	Chkn	X	X	O	X				
	Steak			X	X				
	Hdog	X	X	X	O				

(Column group headers: OCCUPATIONS over Nurse, Scty, Tchr, Pilot; MEAT over Burg, Chkn, Steak, Hdog)

MILL: We're almost there. The last clue says the secretary hates golf. How are we supposed to use that?

TAMI: We can use that. Remember that adjunct list we made before? Let's look at that again with the new information we've gained so far.

Golfers			Non-Golfers		
Fred	steak		John	burgers	
Tom	hot dogs	pilot	Bill	chicken	teacher

MILL: Okay, so the secretary hates golf. That means the secretary can't be Fred. So it has to be John.

TAMI: Right, so Fred is the nurse. Great job.

		OCCUPATIONS				MEAT			
		Nurse	Scty	Tchr	Pilot	Burg	Chkn	Steak	Hdog
N A M E	Tom	X_1	X	X_1	0	X_3	X_3	X_3	0
	John	X	0	X	X	0	X	X	X_3
	Fred	0	X_5	X_2	X_2	X_2	X	0	X_3
	Bill	X	X	0	X	X_4	0	X_4	X_3
M E A T	Burg	X	0	X_2	X_2				
	Chkn	X	X	0	X				
	Steak	0	X	X	X				
	Hdog	X	X	X	0				

TAMI: Let's be sure to answer the question.

MILL: Okay.

Tom	pilot	hot dogs
John	secretary	burgers
Fred	nurse	steak
Bill	teacher	chicken

Another substrategy you can use to help you solve matrix logic problems is rewriting a problem's clues as you gain more information. Let's look again at the Name/Color/State partial problem featured earlier in this chapter. Remember, this problem asks you to match up first names (Bob, Sara, Rick, and Jane), favorite colors (blue, red, white, and green), and home states (South Dakota, Missouri, New Jersey, and Texas).

Suppose you've already determined that the New Jersey native's favorite color is green. Consider this problem's "clues."

1. The person whose favorite color is green went to the movie with Sara and the person whose favorite color is white.

2. The person from New Jersey is not Bob.

Since you've determined that the New Jersey native's favorite color is green, the clues become

1. The person whose favorite color is green (person from New Jersey) went to the movie with Sara and with the person whose favorite color is white.

2. The person from New Jersey (green) is not Bob.

This new information allows you to mark off two more spaces in your matrix: from clue 1 you know that Sara is not from New Jersey, and from clue 2 you know that green is not Bob's favorite color.

This substrategy of rewriting clues is called **substitution**. The results you get with substitution are very similar to those you get with the substrategy of cross-correlating with negative information. For example, in the Outdoor Barbecue problem you just solved, clues 1 and 3 allowed some cross-correlating with negative information:

1. Tom is neither the nurse nor the teacher.

3. Tom brought hot dogs.

Millissent and Tami cross-correlated with negative information in their solution. They could have accomplished the same results with substitution: clue 3 said that Tom brought hot dogs, so clue 1 could have been rewritten to read, "The person who brought hot dogs is neither the nurse nor the teacher." This rewritten clue would have allowed them to mark off the hot dogs–teacher and the hot dogs–nurse spaces. Although these substrategies are similar, it's a good idea to learn both of them because one may work when the other doesn't.

Another useful substrategy is **combining clues**. What do the following two clues have in common?

3. Bob, the person from New Jersey, and the person who likes blue love going to the movies each week.

4. Jane does not like the movies.

Both clues deal with people going to the movies. If you combined the two clues, you'd see that Jane could not be one of the people who went to the movies, and therefore could not be from New Jersey and could not be the person who likes blue.

Millissent and Tami used this substrategy in the Outdoor Barbecue problem with the help of an adjunct list. If they hadn't made an adjunct list of golfers, they could have combined clues 2 and 5 to get the same results:

2. Fred and the pilot play golf together. The burger lover and the teacher hate golf.

5. The secretary hates golf.

Millissent and Tami could have combined the clues and used substitution: They knew that John was the burger lover, so John and the teacher hated golf. The secretary also hated golf, and because the secretary and the teacher couldn't be the same person, the secretary was John.

Here's a **word of caution** about combining clues: Make sure your conclusion accounts for *all* the people in the problem. For example, clue 2 in the Outdoor Barbecue problem describes four people: Fred, the pilot, the burger lover, and the teacher. This clue includes each person mentioned in the entire problem. But if the Outdoor Barbecue problem had been about *five* people instead of four, then *three* people may have hated golf (hard to imagine), and the secretary and the burger lover could have been different people. Consider these clues to the Name/Color/State partial problem:

5. The person from South Dakota and Rick like dinners out.

6. The person who likes blue likes dinners out.

Do these clues tell you that the person who likes blue is either Rick or the person from South Dakota? No, they don't. They could be referring to three different people. Now consider these clues again, along with another clue:

5. The person from South Dakota and Rick like dinners out.

6. The person who likes blue likes dinners out.

7. Bob and Sara hate dinners out.

These clues seem to describe five people: the person from South Dakota, Rick, the person who likes blue, Bob, and Sara. But remember that the problem includes only four people: Bob, Sara, Rick, and Jane. Therefore, two of the people described in the clues are actually the same person. So, two of four people like dinners out, two people don't, and clue 6 refers to one of the people in clue 5. (Don't forget, making an adjunct list is another way to make sense of these clues about dinners out.)

Here are a couple of things to **remember** about the introductions to problems:

Some introductions tell you exactly who all the people in the problem are and what you are supposed to find. For example, "Len, Howard, and Raymond are a grocer, a chemist, and a model, and each have dogs, named Clio, Fido, and Spot. Match each man's name, job, and dog." In other problems, introductions are a little bit vague. For example, "Three men (one is named Len) have different jobs (one is a model). Each also has a dog (one dog is named Fido). From the clues below, determine each man's name, job, and dog." In this case, you would have to read the clues to find the names of the other men, the names of the other dogs, and the other occupations. You would then mark that information in your matrix. (Of course, you would hope to be able to tell the difference between a man's name and a dog's name. For example, what would you do with the name Rex?)

Sometimes introductions hide pieces of information you need to solve the problem. For example, "Ivan and three friends (one is a mechanic) like different sports." This sentence tells you that the problem is about four people, one of whom is named Ivan. As with other matrix logic problems, you can probably assume that the people have different jobs unless the problem states otherwise. What you may not notice right away is that the mechanic is not Ivan, because the mechanic is referred to as one of Ivan's friends. But if you read the sentence carefully, you'll notice this kind of clue and you can mark off the Ivan-mechanic space in your matrix.

The next problem features many of the substrategies you've read about so far.

Four high school friends (one is named Cathy) are about to go to college. Their last names are Williams, Burbank, Collins, and Gunderson. Each is enrolled in a different college (one is a state college). From the clues below, determine each person's full name and the college he or she will attend.

1. No student's first name begins with the same first letter as her or his last name. No student's first name ends with the same letter as the last letter of her or his last name.

2. Neither Hank nor Williams is going to the community college.

3. Alan, Collins, and the student who is going to the university all live on the same street. The other student lives two blocks away.

4. Gladys and Hank live next door to each other.

5. The private college accepted Hank's application, but he decided he couldn't afford to go there.

Work this problem before reading on.

The first thing you must do is determine the other three names and colleges. The clues give you a lot information: the first names Hank, Alan, and Gladys are mentioned in clues 2, 3, and 4; and community college, university, and private college are mentioned in clues 2, 3, and 5. Rochelle's matrix for this problem is shown below.

		LAST NAMES				COLLEGES			
		Wlms	Bbnk	Clns	Gdsn	CC	State	Univ	Priv
FIRST NAME	Hank								
	Alan								
	Gladys								
	Cathy								
COLL	CC								
	State								
	Univ								
	Priv								

Rochelle explained her solution:

"I made my matrix, and then I read the clues. The first clue said that the first letter of the first and last name could not be the same, and that the last letter of the first and last name could not be the same either. So I went through each first name and compared the first and last letters with the different possible first and last letters of the last names. Hank started with an *h* and ended with a *k,* so his last name couldn't be Burbank because that ends with a *k.* I saw that Alan's last name couldn't be Gunderson because that name ends with an *n.* Gladys' last name also couldn't be Gunderson because it starts with a *g,* and it couldn't be Collins or Williams because they end with *s.* Cathy's last name couldn't be Collins because Collins starts with a *c.* I put X_1's in all these spaces to signify they were eliminated by clue 1.

"This meant that Gladys was Burbank, because that was the only last name left for her. So I put an O in the Gladys-Burbank space and X's in the rest of the Burbank column. I started writing down known results in the matrix's blank space."

		LAST NAMES				COLLEGES			
		Wlms	Bbnk	Clns	Gdsn	CC	State	Univ	Priv
FIRST NAME	Hank		X_1						
	Alan		X		X_1				
	Gladys	X_1	0	X_1	X_1				
	Cathy		X	X_1					
COLL	CC								
	State								
	Univ								
	Priv								

Known results:
Gladys Burbank

"Next I read the second clue. Hank and Williams did not go to the community college. I could obviously put X_2's in the Hank-CC space and the Williams-CC space. And because Hank and Williams were referred to as two people, I knew that Hank's last name could not be Williams. So I also put an X_2 in the Hank-Williams space. (Sorry, all you country-western fans.)

"Reading the third clue, I saw that Alan and Collins did not go to the university because the clue refers to three people who live on the same street. I also knew that Alan was not Collins."

		LAST NAMES					COLLEGES		
		Wlms	Bbnk	Clns	Gdsn	CC	State	Univ	Priv
FIRST NAME	Hank	X_2	X_1			X_2			
	Alan		X	X_3	X_1			X_3	
	Gladys	X_1	O	X_1	X_1				
	Cathy		X	X_1					
COLL	CC	X_2							
	State								
	Univ			X_3					
	Priv								

Known results:
Gladys Burbank

"Looking at the matrix, I saw that Alan had to be Williams because that was the only space left. I put an O in the Alan-Williams space. This meant I had to put an X in the Cathy-Williams space. That meant that Cathy was Gunderson, which forced Hank to be Collins. So now I knew all the first and last names. I wrote all this down in my known-results space."

		LAST NAMES					COLLEGES		
		Wlms	Bbnk	Clns	Gdsn	CC	State	Univ	Priv
FIRST NAME	Hank	X_2	X_1	O	X	X_2			
	Alan	O	X	X_3	X_1			X_3	
	Gladys	X_1	O	X_1	X_1				
	Cathy	X	X	X_1	O				
COLL	CC	X_2							
	State								
	Univ			X_3					
	Priv								

Known results:
Gladys Burbank
Hank Collins
Alan Williams
Cathy Gunderson

"At this point I had some definite connections. I reread the second and third clues and used substitution. Because I knew that Hank was Collins and that Alan was Williams, the second clue read, 'Neither Hank (Collins) nor Williams (Alan) went to the community college.' This allowed me to mark off the Collins-CC and the Alan-CC spaces. I put $X_{2,3}$'s in those spaces.

"Clue 3 now read, 'Alan (Williams), Collins (Hank), and the student who went to the university all live on the same street. The other student lives two blocks away.' I now knew that Williams and Hank did not go to the university. So I put $X_{2,3}$'s in those spaces also."

		LAST NAMES				COLLEGES			
		Wlms	Bbnk	Clns	Gdsn	CC	State	Univ	Priv
FIRST NAME	Hank	X_2	X_1	0	X	X_2		$X_{2,3}$	
	Alan	0	X	X_3	X_1	$X_{2,3}$		X_3	
	Gladys	X_1	0	X_1	X_1				
	Cathy	X	X	X_1	0				
COLL	CC	X_2		$X_{2,3}$					
	State								
	Univ	$X_{2,3}$		X_3					
	Priv								

Known results:
Gladys Burbank
Hank Collins
Alan Williams
Cathy Gunderson

"Then I read clue 4. It said that Gladys and Hank live next door to each other. I combined this clue with the substituted form of clue 3: 'Alan Williams and Hank Collins live on the same street as the student who went to the university, and the other student lives two blocks away.' So Gladys must be the student who went to the university because clearly Gladys lives on the same street as Hank. I put an O_4 in the Gladys-university space, and because Gladys' last name is Burbank, I also put an O_4 in the Burbank-university space (cross-correlating with positive information). Doing this filled in a whole bunch of X's for university, Burbank, and Gladys. When I finished filling in all those X's, I saw that Cathy Gunderson went to the community college."

LAST NAMES   COLLEGES

		Wlms	Bbnk	Clns	Gdsn	CC	State	Univ	Priv
FIRST NAME	Hank	X_2	X_1	0	X	X_2		$X_{2,3}$	
	Alan	0	X	X_3	X_1	$X_{2,3}$		X_3	
	Gladys	X_1	0	X_1	X_1	X_4	X_4	0_4	X_4
	Cathy	X	X	X_1	0	0	X	X_4	X
COLL	CC	X_2	X_4	$X_{2,3}$	0				
	State		X_4		X				
	Univ	$X_{2,3}$	0_4	X_3	X_4				
	Priv		X_4		X				

Known results:
Gladys Burbank—Univ.
Hank Collins
Alan Williams
Cathy Gunderson—CC

"Now I just had to figure out whether Hank or Alan went to the state college or the private college. The last clue said that Hank did not go to the private college. So Alan must have gone to the private college, and therefore Hank went to the state college."

LAST NAMES   COLLEGES

		Wlms	Bbnk	Clns	Gdsn	CC	State	Univ	Priv
FIRST NAME	Hank	X_2	X_1	0	X	X_2	0_5	$X_{2,3}$	X_5
	Alan	0	X	X_3	X_1	$X_{2,3}$	X_5	X_3	0_5
	Gladys	X_1	0	X_1	X_1	X_4	X_4	0_4	X_4
	Cathy	X	X	X_1	0	0	X	X_4	X
COLL	CC	X_2	X_4	$X_{2,3}$	0				
	State	X_5	X_4	0_5	X				
	Univ	$X_{2,3}$	0_4	X_3	X_4				
	Priv	0_5	X_4	X_5	X				

The answers to the problem are

Hank Collins: state college

Alan Williams: private college

Gladys Burbank: university

Cathy Gunderson: community college

The X's and O's in the completed matrix include many subscripts. These subscripts indicate the numbers of the clues that allowed Rochelle to mark them off in the matrix. The subscripts are useful for two reasons:

First, if you make a mistake while solving a problem, you will have to do part of the problem over again. The subscripts will help you remember the information you already had before you made the mistake. Without them, you'd have to start the whole problem over again. With them, you can probably just erase a few marks and start from where you made the mistake.

Second, the subscripts are extremely useful when you re-create your reasoning after you've solved the problem. If you saw only X's and O's in the matrix, you'd have to do the problem again to explain your reasoning. The subscripts remind you why you marked each X and O in the matrix, and thus make your explanation easier to write.

Just as it helps to use subscripts to keep track of information in a problem, sometimes it also helps to add information to the labels of your matrix. For example, this information might be in an adjunct list but would also be helpful to see in the labels. Let's look again at the Name/Color/State partial problem, which matches up first names (Bob, Sara, Rick, and Jane), favorite colors (blue, red, white, and green), and home states (South Dakota, Missouri, New Jersey, and Texas). Consider these new clues, paying attention to each person's gender:

8. The person from Missouri sold his skis.

9. The person who likes blue gave birth last month.

These clues tell you that the person from Missouri is male (sold *his* skis) and that the person who likes blue is female (gave birth). You can add this information to the matrix labels: **Notice** that Missouri is marked M (male) in the state matrices shown below, and that blue is marked F (female) in the color matrix. Each first name is also marked M or F. Adding the information about gender to a couple of the labels lets you immediately eliminate some spaces.

| | | FAVORITE COLOR | | | | HOME STATE | | | |
		Blue (F)	Red	White	Green	SD	MO (M)	NJ	TX
FIRST NAME	Bob (M)	X_9							
	Sara (F)						X_8		
	Rick (M)	X_9							
	Jane (F)						X_8		
HOME STATE	SD								
	MO (M)	$X_{8,9}$							
	NJ								
	TX								

Notice what we eliminated: In the State/Name matrix, knowing that the person from Missouri is male doesn't yet determine who he is. Rather, this information helps us determine that a couple of people are *not* from Missouri: the women. (Remember, think negatively.) Next, in the Name/Color matrix we can conclude that neither Bob nor Rick prefers blue because we have already established that the person who likes blue is a woman. And in the Color/State matrix, we can determine that the person who likes blue (our label tells us she's a woman) is not from Missouri (we know he's a man).

But be careful about assigning gender with certain names. In this problem it's pretty clear that Bob and Rick are men and that Sara and Jane are women. However, some problems deliberately include names that could be used by either gender. For example, in a problem about four people named Kelly, Pat, Sam, and Chris, it wouldn't necessarily be clear whether they were female or male—figuring out genders might turn out to be an important part of solving the problem. And if a problem included names from a culture unfamiliar to you, you might have trouble determining gender from the names. The moral of this story is beware of assuming anything.

With that warning about assumptions, let's consider one more substrategy: **making an assumption**. Making an assumption is tricky because, in keeping with the idea of thinking negatively, the most important part of making an assumption is proving your assumption *incorrect*. In fact, this substrategy works *only* if you can prove you made an incorrect assumption. The solution to the next problem uses this substrategy.

COAST TO COAST

Four women live in different cities. One of the cities is San Francisco. Determine which city each woman lives in.

1. Riana, the woman from Charleston (South Carolina), and the woman from Gainesville (Florida) are not related.

2. Wendy and the woman from Provo are cousins.

3. Neither Phyllis nor Wendy is from the West Coast.

4. Ann is from a coastal city.

Solve this problem before reading on.

		Ann	Phyllis	Wendy	Riana
	SF		X_3	X_3	
CITIES	Gain	X_4			X_1
	Chrl				X_1
	Provo	X_4		X_2	

NAMES

Right away, the problem's clues allow us to mark X's in the matrix shown above. Now let's use the substrategy of making an assumption. We'll assume that Riana is from Provo. The new chart that follows has a light blue O marked in the Riana-Provo space. If Riana is from Provo, then she's not from San Francisco, so mark an X in the Riana–San Francisco space. Thus, Ann must be from San Francisco, because Ann's space is the only space left for San Francisco. We already know that Wendy is from either Charleston or Gainesville (clue 3: Wendy is not from the West Coast). The matrix below shows all of our original marks in red and all of our new marks, based on our assumptions, in light blue.

NAMES

CITIES		Ann	Phyllis	Wendy	Riana
	SF	○	X_3	X_3	X
	Gain	X_4			X_1
	Chrl	X			X_1
	Provo	X_4	X	X_2	○

Now reread the clues to look for a contradiction. Clue 2 says that Wendy and the woman from Provo are cousins. We assumed that Riana is from Provo, which means that Wendy and Riana are cousins (clue 2). But clue 1 says that Riana and the women from Charleston and Gainesville are not related. Because Wendy is from either Charleston or Gainesville (clue 3), clue 1 tells us that she should not be related to Riana. But according to clue 2, Wendy and the woman from Provo (who we assumed was Riana) are cousins. This contradiction arose from our assumption. So our assumption that Riana is from Provo is false. (And proving an assumption wrong is cause for celebration: Hooray!) Therefore, Riana is not from Provo. Knowing this fact allows us to mark off the Riana-Provo space.

NAMES

CITIES		Ann	Phyllis	Wendy	Riana
	SF		X_3	X_3	
	Gain	X_4			X_1
	Chrl				X_1
	Provo	X_4		X_2	X

Now the matrix clearly shows that Riana is from San Francisco. From this point on, we can simply mark spaces in the matrix to solve the entire problem, as shown in the next matrix.

	NAMES			
	Ann	Phyllis	Wendy	Riana
SF	X	X_3	X_3	O
Gain	X_4	X	O	X_1
Chrl	O	X	X	X_1
Provo	X_4	O	X_2	X

At this point, be sure to recheck who is related to whom. The women from Gainesville and Charleston are Wendy and Ann, and they are unrelated to Riana. Wendy's cousin is Phyllis (the woman from Provo), so that connection works.

The substrategy of making an assumption can be very dangerous. If your assumption does *not* result in a contradiction, then it proves nothing. Use this substrategy only as a last resort when you are completely stuck on a problem and need to try something drastic. But first try the other substrategies you explored in this chapter. You'll be able to solve most logic problems without making any assumptions.

Here's a tip when you do want to use this substrategy: Before making an assumption, mark in pen every known connection in the matrix. Then, from the point at which you make the assumption, mark in light pencil all further connections. If you determine that the assumption is wrong, that's great. If you don't find any contradictions, you can erase all your pencil marks and your earlier connections will still be marked in pen. We tried to illustrate this idea in the second matrix of the Coast to Coast problem by using light and dark colors.

Many logic problems feature more people or categories than you've seen so far in this chapter. For example, a problem may ask you to match up first names, last names, cities, and jobs. As with problems that include fewer categories, your first step in solving this problem would be to determine how many matrices to combine into your final matrix. A diagram like the one you used for the Name/Color/State problem can help.

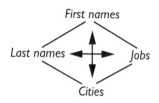

First names

Last names ←——→ Jobs

Cities

You must have a matrix that matches each category with each other category. From the diagram, you can see that you need the following matrices:

First names/Last names

First names/Cities

First names/Jobs

Last names/Cities

Last names/Jobs

Cities/Jobs

You could also have made a systematic list to determine the category matchups, matching two of the categories at a time. In fact, the list above is such a list and could have been made without the diagram. Just make sure you match up every possible pair of categories.

Setting up the form of the matrix is the next important step in solving the problem. Look at the preliminary matrix shown below. (**Note** that in your final matrix, each category space, such as the cities-jobs space, will be a complete matrix that includes its own spaces for each person in the problem.)

	First names	Last names	Cities	Jobs
First names				
Last names				
Cities				
Jobs				

This preliminary matrix certainly contains too many category spaces. In your final matrix you won't need matrices that match up categories with themselves, such as first names with first names. To make your final matrix efficient and easy to work with, get rid of the unnecessary spaces, rows, and columns. In this case, you could take out the First names row and the Last names column, then "squeeze together" the remaining rows and columns. Consider the matrix shown below.

	First names	Cities	Jobs
Last names			
Cities			
Jobs			

This new matrix is definitely an improvement, but it still contains too many category spaces. Again, you won't need to match categories to themselves, such as cities to cities and jobs to jobs. Also, this new matrix has two jobs-cities spaces. By getting rid of a few more unnecessary spaces, we have a matrix that is really useful.

	First names	Jobs	Cities
Last names			
Cities			
Jobs			

Note that in the top row of labels, we've switched the order of the cities and the jobs labels so that we wouldn't have a cities-cities space. And **note** that putting the cities and jobs labels in an order on the *top* that is different from the order they're in on the *left* is a way to make your matrix turn out really well. Now your final matrix will look nice, and will be efficient and easy to work with. Ordering your category labels carefully is an important part of setting up your matrix. Generally, it's helpful to order your category labels like this: Label the left-most column with one main category (see the First names label in the preceding matrix). Label the top row with another main category (see the Last names label in the matrix). (**Note** that when two of your categories are first and last names, they should *always* be placed in the first column and first row.) Then label the other columns with the rest of the categories, and repeat the labels in reverse order in the other rows (as the jobs and cities labels are in the matrix, the repeated categories should *always* be in reverse order in the rows and columns). You need to repeat labels in the columns and rows so that each category matches up with each other category.

Now you try one. Draw a matrix for a problem asking that you match first names, jobs, hair color, eye color, and height.

This problem would need ten matrices: Name/Job, Name/Height, Name/Eyes, Name/Hair, Job/Hair, Job/Eyes, Job/Height, Height/Hair, Height/Eyes, and Eyes/Hair. A typical matrix for this problem might look like this:

	Name	Hair	Eyes	Height
Job				
Height				
Eyes				
Hair				

Be sure to experiment a little bit with your preliminary matrices so that they will be really functional before you draw your final matrix. Use graph paper so that it's easier to draw the matrix lines. And, of course, you can apply all the substrategies you've learned in this chapter to problems that require more than three matrices.

As you read at the beginning of this chapter, solving logic problems can improve your reasoning abilities. You must solve the problems step by step, using a process similar to developing arguments based on logic. Logic problems are also fun and challenging, as all those people who buy problem-solving magazines have discovered. Enjoy the challenge!

Problem Set A

1. **CLASS SCHEDULES**

The master schedule for River High School is shown below. The dots indicate the period(s) in which a class is offered. All students must take the classes marked with asterisks. The other classes are electives.

	1	2	3	4	5	6	7
*English	•		•			•	
*Math		•		•	•		
*Science			•	•			
*PE	•	•			•		
History		•					•
Drama			•				
Typing						•	•
Band	•						
*Lunch				•	•		

a. Make up a schedule for Jill. She wants to take Band and History as her electives. She needs Lunch during fifth period because the science club meets then.

b. Make up a schedule for Tom. He wants to take Drama and Typing. He would like to have Lunch during fourth period, but he doesn't care that much.

c. Make up a schedule for Leanne. She wants to take Band and Drama.

d. Make up a schedule for Mea. She wants to take History and Typing.

e. Part 1: Jose wants to take Drama and History. Make up his schedule.

(This problem is continued on the next page.)

Part 2: Jose had his schedule all figured out, but when he went to sign up for first-period PE, he found out that the class was closed. However, the other two periods of PE were still open. What should he do?

Part 3: After making a new schedule that he wasn't too happy with, Jose found out that the school was opening a new sixth-period Science class. Now what should he do?

2. THE FISHING TRIP

Several friends take a fishing trip every year. Each year they have a contest to see who catches the heaviest fish. The loser has to pay for all of the junk food they eat on the trip. (Second and third places are also expected to chip in token amounts.) Determine each friend's standings in this year's contest by using the following clues. By the way, in the tradition of fishing trips, every statement quoted here is a falsehood.

Marta: Larry was first.   Woody: I beat Sally.

Sally: Marta beat Woody.   Larry: Woody was second.

3. CABINET MEMBERS

The president was discussing some politics with the vice president and three of her cabinet members: the secretaries of state, education, and the treasury. Using the clues in the conversation below, determine which woman (one is named Norma) holds which position.

Paula said, "Ms. President, I don't think the secretary of state knows what she is talking about. I think our foreign policy has really deteriorated lately."

The secretary of state shook her head. So did the vice president.

The secretary of the treasury said, "I agree with Paula. We haven't even talked to Japan lately."

The vice president jumped in. "Will you two leave Inez alone? She is doing a fine job."

Georgianne, who had been silent so far, finally said, "Okay, let's get on to something else."

(This problem is continued on the next page.)

The secretary of education said, "I'm sorry, Inez. Nothing personal."

Colleen said, "I'm sorry too, Inez. I guess we just got carried away."

Inez replied, "That's okay. I know we've all been under a lot of stress lately."

4. VOLLEYBALL TEAM

Three friends—Elaine, Kelly, and Shannon—all start for their college volleyball team. Each plays a different position: setter, middle blocker, and outside hitter. Of the three, one is a freshman, one a sophomore, and the other a junior. From the clues below, determine each woman's position and year in school.

1. Elaine is not the setter.

2. Kelly has been in school longer than the middle blocker.

3. The middle blocker has been in school longer than the outside hitter.

4. Either Kelly is the setter or Elaine is the middle blocker.

5. MUSIC PREFERENCES

Two men (Jack and Mike) and two women (Adele and Edna) each like a different type of music (one likes jazz). Their last names are Mullin, Hardaway, Richmond, and Higgins. From the clues below, find each person's full name and favorite type of music.

1. Hardaway hates country-western music.

2. The classical-music lover said she'd teach Higgins to play the piano.

3. Adele and Richmond knew the country-western fan in high school.

4. Jack and the man who likes rock music work in the same office building.

5. Richmond and Higgins are on the same bowling team. There are no men on their team.

6.   SUSPECTS

The police department arrested four suspects—two men and two women—on suspicion of petty theft. The sergeant on duty who processed the suspects was having a bit of a bad day. He produced this list of suspects and descriptions:

Robin Wilde: scar on left cheek

Cary Steele: purple hair

Pat Fleece: tall and blonde

Connie Theeves: birthmark on left wrist

When the list landed on the arresting detective's desk, he was furious. He went to the sergeant and said, "Paul, you might be having a bad day, but this list is full of mistakes. The first and last names are all mismatched. And none of the descriptions matches either the first or the last name it is listed with. Do you think you can fix this?"

The sergeant replied, "Sorry, Dick. I *am* having a bad day. But I think I need a little bit more information."

The detective answered, "Okay, Paul. Here's some more info. Connie has purple hair to match her purple high tops. The men are Steele and Fleece. A woman has the scar. Do you think you can straighten this mess out now?"

The sergeant now determined the first and last names of each suspect, as well as their descriptions. You work it out, too.

Three couples are good friends. At a dinner party one night, they discovered that their anniversaries were in different months: May, June, and July. They also discovered that they had each been married a different number of years: 11, 12, and 13. From the clues below, match up each husband (one is Pete) with each wife (one is Lorna), the month of their anniversary, and the number of years each couple has been married.

1. Jorge and his wife have three kids. Their anniversary is not in July. They have not been married as long as Tori and her husband have.

2. Nylia and her husband have four kids. Their anniversary is in June. They have been married longer than Ahmed and his wife.

8. **WRITE YOUR OWN**

Create your own matrix logic problem. First come up with the people in the problem and what their characteristics are. In other words, start with the answer. We suggest you use only one chart for your first made-up problem. Then write the clues and solve the problem as you are writing clues. In this way, you will know when you have enough clues.

Problem Set B: Introducing the Family Family

1. **THE PHONE NUMBER**

Ed, the eldest child of the Family family, met a new girl named Candy at the beginning of his senior year in school. He really liked her, so he wanted her phone number. He knew the first three digits of the number were 492 because the town was so small that everyone had the same telephone prefix. She wouldn't give him the rest of the number at first, but he persisted. Finally, at the beginning of the lunch period, she handed him a piece of paper with several numbers on it.

"The last four digits of my phone number are on this page," she explained.

3257   4682   8824   0626   4608

    8624   4632   6428   8604   8428

8064   3195   8420   4218   8240

    7915   6420   4602   2628   4178

3281   2804   4002   4826   0846

    4718   4680   6402   0428   2406

Ed protested, "But there must be thirty numbers here."

Candy laughed, "That's right. But I'll give you some clues. If you really want my number, you'll figure it out."

"Okay," he said. "Shoot. I'm ready."

Candy listed her clues:

1. All the digits are even.

2. All the digits are different.

3. The digit in the tens place is less than the other digits.

4. The sum of the two larger digits is 10 more than the sum of the two smaller digits.

During lunch, Ed frantically worked away and tried to figure out which number was Candy's. He looked up with only a few minutes left in the lunch period. "I don't have enough information," he protested. The bell rang, so they walked out of the lunchroom together. She said, "Okay, I'll tell you the sum of all the digits." She whispered the information in his ear.

"Thanks!" Ed said, because this gave him enough information to figure out the number. "I'll call you tonight."

What was Candy's phone number?

2.   THE BILLBOARD

Ed went to work for an advertising company after school and on Saturdays. For his first assignment, he hired himself to create a billboard. The billboard will be 20 feet high and will proclaim his love for Candy (the girl, not the sweets). He decided that each letter should be 2 feet high and that there will be a 1/2-foot space between the bottom of one line of words and the top of the next line of words. In addition, he wants borders measuring 1 1/2 feet at both the top and the bottom of the billboard. How many lines of words can Ed fit onto the billboard?

3. A WORTHY SUITOR

Lisa, the eldest daughter in the Family family, is a junior at the same high school that her brother attends. Ed told her about the incident with the phone number, and she decided that she might do something similar sometime. Her opportunity came the next day when Ernie asked her for a date. She liked Ernie, but she couldn't resist a good puzzle. She decided to test Ernie's skill as a puzzler.

"Okay, Ernie, I'd like to go out with you, but I need to see if we're compatible puzzlers. Can you find five ways to add up four even, positive numbers (not including zero) and get a sum of 16?"

Ernie replied, "Oh sure, I can do that." He whipped out a piece of paper and a pencil and wrote down

$$2 + 2 + 2 + 10 = 16$$
$$2 + 2 + 4 + 8 = 16$$
$$2 + 2 + 6 + 6 = 16$$
$$2 + 4 + 4 + 6 = 16$$
$$4 + 4 + 4 + 4 = 16$$

"Good job," said Lisa. "Now, if you can do this next problem, I'll go out with you. How many ways are there to add up six even, positive numbers (again, not including zero) to get a sum of 26?"

Ernie did it. Now you do it too.

4. THOSE AMAZING NAMES

Papa Family was sitting at the kitchen table one day, looking at a piece of paper that had his children's names written on it. The paper read

LISA
JUDY
EDWARD

He said to Mama Family, "You know, the names of our kids almost make one of those cryptarithm word-arithmetic problems."

Mama said, "Let me see." She looked at the paper. "Papa, you forgot: Ed's name is Eduard with a *u,* not a *w.* And Lisa's name is really Elisa, but we don't call her that much anymore since she went to high school and decided that Lisa is prettier. And don't you remember about Judy's name? It's really Ajudy."

"Oh, yeah," Papa said. "I forgot about that. The nurse came into the delivery room and said, 'Well, what do we have here: a Kathy?' And you said, 'No, a Judy.' What a surprise when the birth certificate actually had 'Ajudy' written on it."

Mama said, "Look, Papa, if you use their real names, it does work as a word-arithmetic problem." She wrote down

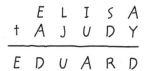

Together, she and Papa solved the problem in a few minutes. You solve it, too. Each letter stands for one of the digits 0 to 9, and no two letters stand for the same digit.

5. THE SPORTING EVENTS

Papa Family just got a new job at the recreation department. His first task is to schedule the playing field for the afternoons of the upcoming week. His first priority in scheduling is to make his three children—Ed, Lisa, and Judy—happy. They all play various sports, and their teams are supposed to play after school during this week. Papa also wants to make his wife, Mama Family, happy. She is taking a golf class and also needs to use the field this week. Use the information below to help Papa figure out a schedule that will satisfy all of the desires of all the members of his family.

1. The field is available only on Monday, Tuesday, Thursday, and Friday.

2. Lisa wants to watch the baseball game, but she's in the school play and has rehearsal after school on Tuesday and Thursday.

3. Lisa and Judy have no interest in seeing each other play.

4. One daughter wants her ultimate-Frisbee event to precede the soccer game and the golf class because soccer players and golfers tear up the field.

5. Ed is going to visit colleges on the weekend, so he wants to get an early start immediately after school on Friday.

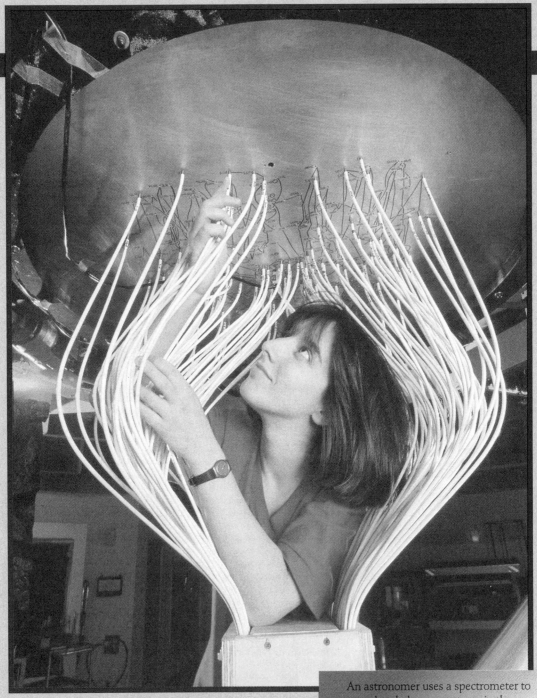

An astronomer uses a spectrometer to record and observe patterns in the frequencies of light radiated from a distant star. In doing so, she can determine what type of star it is by determining its chemical composition.

5

Look for a Pattern

The study of mathematics is often called the study of **patterns**. Patterns show up everywhere around us. In everyday life, there are thousands of patterns: wallpaper, traffic, automobile designs, weekday afternoon TV schedules, cabinet door arrangements, swimming pool tiles, fence links, and much, much more. In mathematics, patterns can repeat and extend indefinitely. In this chapter you will develop your ability to recognize and extend patterns, which is a very valuable problem-solving skill.

Recognizing patterns is extremely useful for real-world problems. Detectives look for established patterns of behavior so they can determine the characteristics of the person who committed a crime. By doing this, they can narrow down their list of suspects. After they catch the criminal, they also attempt to link together similar crimes that person may have committed so they can strengthen existing evidence. Researchers need to be able to detect patterns so they can isolate variables and reach valid conclusions. A child uses patterns to learn about the world. For example, children learn to differentiate between positive and negative behavior as they recognize patterns in their parents' reactions.

As a problem-solving strategy, recognizing patterns enables you to reduce a complex problem to a pattern and then use the pattern to find a solution. Often the key to finding a pattern is organizing information.

Let's begin this chapter with mathematical sequences. A **sequence** is an ordered string of numbers tied together by a consistent rule, or set of rules, that determines the next term in the sequence. A **term** is an individual member of a sequence.

Consider this sequence: 3, 7, 11, 15, __, __, __, __.

The rule that ties these numbers together appears to be "Add 4 to each term to generate the next term in the sequence," giving 3, 7, 11, 15, **19, 23, 27, 31.**

Note that you could continue this sequence by repeating the first four terms: 3, 7, 11, 15, **3, 7, 11, 15,** . . . . However, for the purposes of this text, the repeating pattern in a sequence is declared null, void, illegal, invalid, unconstitutional, unpatriotic, immoral, corrupt, and not at all nice. In other words, don't take the easy way out on these sequence problems. Instead, find the pattern and apply it to find subsequent terms in the sequence.

The following problem features examples of mathematical sequences.

SEQUENCES

Find the pattern and predict the next four terms. Then write a sentence that explains your pattern. Solve each problem before continuing on.

1. 1, 2, 4, _____, _____, _____, _____

2. 1, 3, 5, 7, _____, _____, _____, _____

3. 1, 6, 11, 16, _____, _____, _____, _____

4. 1, 4, 9, 16, _____, _____, _____, _____

5. 1, 3, 6, 10, _____, _____, _____, _____

6. 3, 6, 5, 10, 9, 18, 17, 34, _____, _____, _____, _____

7. 77, 49, 36, 18, _____ (This sequence ends here.)

1. Sequence 1 in this problem illustrates an important point. Here are two possible answers with the patterns explained:

   a. 1, 2, 4, **8, 16, 32, 64,** . . . (Double each term to find the next term in the sequence.)

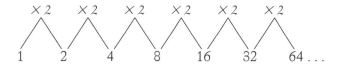

   b. 1, 2, 4, **7, 11, 16, 22,** . . . (Start by adding 1 to the first term, then add one greater number to each successive term. That is, add 1, then add 2, then add 3, and so on.)

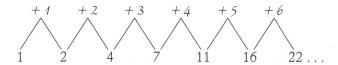

As you can see, there is more than one reasonable, correct answer to this sequence. And each answer follows a consistent rule. Therefore, from this point on check your answers very carefully. If you come up with the same answers as the authors of this book did, you are obviously a genius. If you come up with different answers, double-check to make sure you're applying your rules consistently. It is quite possible that some of the sequences in this problem have more than one verifiable correct answer. It's also possible that you could use different patterns to arrive at the same answers, as you'll see in the solutions for sequences 2 and 4.

Here are the most common answers to each problem, although you may be able to justify a different set of answers:

2. 1, 3, 5, 7, **9, 11, 13, 15,** . . .

3. 1, 6, 11, 16, **21, 26, 31, 36,** . . .

4. 1, 4, 9, 16, **25, 36, 49, 64,** . . .

5. 1, 3, 6, 10, **15, 21, 28, 36,** . . .

6. 3, 6, 5, 10, 9, 18, 17, 34, **33, 66, 65, 130,** . . .

7. 77, 49, 36, 18, **8** (no further terms)

Before you go on to read the explanations below, see if you can decipher the patterns that you didn't get.

2. 1, 3, 5, 7, 9, 11, 13, 15, . . .

The pattern in sequence 2 clearly involves odd numbers. But many different patterns could be used to arrive at this answer:

a. The pattern is a sequence of odd numbers.

b. Add 2 to each term to get the next term.

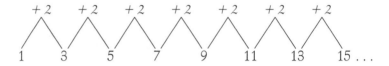

c. The table below shows each term in this sequence in its position in the sequence.

Position in the sequence	1	2	3	4	5	6	7	8
Term	1	3	5	7	9	11	13	15

Take the position of each term, double that number, and subtract 1. For example, term number 3 in this sequence is 5. We get 5 by doubling the term number, 3, and subtracting 1. That is, $2 \times 3 - 1 = 5$. Similarly, the eighth term is 15 because $2 \times 8 - 1 = 15$.

3. 1, 6, 11, 16, 21, 26, 31, 36, . . .

To get the next term in sequence 3, add 5 to the previous term:

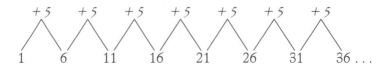

4. 1, 4, 9, 16, 25, 36, 49, 64, . . .

Most people see the pattern in sequence 4 in one of these ways:

a. To get from one term to the next, add an odd number. To get the term after that, add the next greatest odd number. Continue in this way, adding successive odd numbers. That is, first add 3, then 5, then 7, and so on, always adding the next odd number.

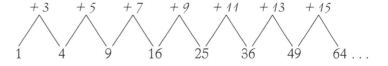

b. Begin by adding 3 to the first term. Then add 2 to each successive addition:

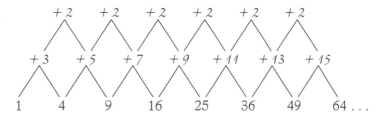

(**Note** that this pattern is essentially the same as adding successive odd numbers, but it is explained in a slightly different way.)

c. This sequence is a sequence of **square numbers**. So, the first term is 1×1, or 1^2. And the second term is 2^2, the third term is 3^2, the fourth term is 4^2, and so on. **Note** that these numbers are called "square" because sets of dots corresponding to these numbers can be arranged in squares:

$1^2 = 1$ $2^2 = 4$ $3^2 = 9$ $4^2 = 16$ $5^2 = 25$

The pattern of adding odd numbers is shown in this diagram of squares. In each successive diagram, a new bottom row and right-most column have been added. The number of dots required for these additions always corresponds to the next odd number.

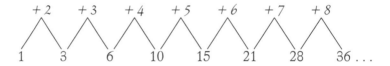

$1^2 = 1$　　　$2^2 = 4$　　　$3^2 = 9$　　　$4^2 = 16$　　　$5^2 = 25$

5. 1, 3, 6, 10, 15, 21, 28, 36, . . .

In sequence 5, start by adding 2 to the first term. Then add 3. Then add 4. That is, add 1 to each successive addition:

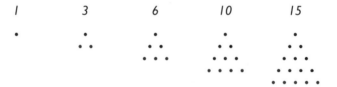

This sequence is often referred to as one of **triangular numbers** because sets of dots corresponding to these numbers can be arranged in triangles. In each successive diagram shown below, one more dot has been added to the bottom row.

1　　　　　3　　　　　6　　　　　10　　　　　15

6. 3, 6, 5, 10, 9, 18, 17, 34, 33, 66, 65, 130, . . .

Sequence 6 shows a different kind of a pattern. First, multiply the first term by 2 to get the second term. Then subtract 1 to get the third term. Then again multiply by 2 to get the fourth term. Then again subtract 1 to get the fifth term. Continue in this way, alternately multiplying by 2 and subtracting 1. Thus, $2 \times 3 = 6$.

Then $6 - 1 = 5$, then $5 \times 2 = 10$, and then $10 - 1 = 9$. After that, $9 \times 2 = 18$, and $18 - 1 = 17$. The pattern continues in this way.

7. 77, 49, 36, 18, 8 (no further terms)

The pattern for sequence 7 may seem strange compared with the patterns you've looked at so far. This pattern illustrates the need to be mentally flexible when dealing with patterns. For this sequence, treat the digits in each term as separate numbers, then multiply them together. So for the first term, $7 \times 7 = 49$. Then $4 \times 9 = 36$. Then $3 \times 6 = 18$. Then $1 \times 8 = 8$, and the pattern is over. Try making up your own problem like this. Start with a two-digit number and see if you can come up with a longer sequence than sequence 7.

Need some help with sequences? Try the following process:

1. Write down the sequence you're working with:

   3, 4, 6, 9, 13, 18, 24, . . .

2. Write down each term of the sequence and its position in the sequence, as shown in the table below.

Position	1	2	3	4	5	6	7
Term	3	4	6	9	13	18	24

3. Write down the difference between the terms of the sequence:

Position	1	2	3	4	5	6	7
Term	3	4	6	9	13	18	24

   $+ 1 \quad + 2 \quad + 3 \quad + 4 \quad + 5 \quad + 6$

4. Look for a way to relate the terms to their positions. Look for a way to relate the differences between terms to the positions.

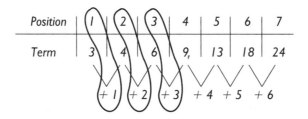

In this sequence, you add the position of the term to the term itself to get the next term. For example, with the third term in this sequence, you add 3 (the position of the term) to 6 (the term) to get 9 (the next term).

5. If figuring the differences between terms doesn't seem to work, try using other operations, such as multiplication, division, and so on.

Finding patterns in sequences is a skill that you can develop by following some standard procedures: writing down both the terms and their positions in the sequence, writing down the differences between terms and, if necessary, writing down the differences between the differences. **Remember** that patterns can be identified on different levels of complexity. That is, sometimes the pattern lies in the differences between the numbers, sometimes it lies in the differences between the differences, and so on. Following these procedures will help you develop your pattern-detection skills.

Now that you've practiced finding patterns in number sequences, try using patterns to solve problems. Often problems are easier to solve after you find a pattern in them—patterns can reduce a complex problem to a simple one.

Radio broadcasters joke about the number of people who start leaving Dodger Stadium during the seventh inning of baseball games. One evening, during a particularly boring baseball game in which the Dodgers were trailing by six runs after six innings, the fans began to leave at a record pace. After the first out in the top of the seventh inning, 100 fans left. After the second out, 150 fans left. After the third out, 200 fans left. The pattern continued in this way, with 50 more fans leaving after each out than had left after the previous out. The ridiculous thing was, the Dodgers tied up the game in the bottom of the ninth inning, and people still kept leaving early. The game lasted ten innings (the Dodgers lost anyway), and the pattern continued through the bottom of the tenth inning. How many fans left early? Work this problem before continuing.

Chemene wrote the following solution:

"My first reaction was, 'Holy cow, there won't be any fans left at the end of the game.' But after the panic subsided, I was ready. And as I thought about my visit to Dodger Stadium a few summers ago when we visited L.A., I realized that the problem was probably accurate. Anyway, I made a chart [also called a table]."

LOOK FOR A PATTERN

Inning	Out	Fans leaving	Fans who've left so far
top 7th	1	100	100
top 7th	2	150	250
top 7th	3	200	450
bot 7th	1	250	700
bot 7th	2	300	1000
bot 7th	3	350	1350
top 8th	1	400	1750
top 8th	2	450	2200

"At this point, I realized that this was going to take forever and that there had to be a more efficient way. After I thought about it a little more, I realized that from the top of the seventh inning to the bottom of the tenth, there were going to be 24 outs. So in my next chart, I just counted outs instead of writing the inning too. This was my next chart."

Out	Fans leaving	Fans who've left so far
1	100	100
2	150	250
3	200	450
4	250	700
5	300	1000

"At this point, I realized I could do this in a different way. I made a third chart. This time I set up the chart so that I could easily see the total number of fans leaving after each out. I broke up each out into the 100 fans that leave every time, plus the 50 more fans that leave for each out after the first out. For example, after the fourth out, 250 fans had left. This breaks down into 100 + 50 + 50 + 50, which is the way it is shown in the chart shown below. For each successive out, I just added another row of 50 fans leaving from that out until the end."

Out #	1	2	3	4	5	6	7	...	Total
Base fans leaving	100	100	100	100	100	100	100	...	2400
Additional fans leaving		50	50	50	50	50	50	...	1150
Additional fans leaving			50	50	50	50	50	...	1100
Additional fans leaving				50	50	50	50	...	1050

"To get the totals on the right, I just multiplied. There were 24 outs of 100 people leaving. Then 23 outs of 50 people leaving. Then 22 outs of 50 people leaving, and so on. I then totaled the amounts at the side, which, of course, showed a pattern after the first 2400 (1150 + 1100 + 1050 + 1000 + . . .). I then totaled the subtotals to get my answer. So 16,200 people left early. But that includes the people who left after the last out, which technically isn't early. If we don't include the 1,250 people who left right after the last out, then 14,950 people left early."

Chemene realized that her first few attempts would have worked but would have taken forever. She didn't hesitate to abandon one chart in favor of another. Her third chart clearly showed a pattern, which she used to solve the problem.

~~~~~~

All the work in this chapter deals with some sort of sequence that shows a pattern. Sequences taken from algebra are featured in the next set of problems. These problems are models of functions. A **function** assigns an output to each input. For each function there is a consistent rule that uses the input number to generate the output number. For example, consider the following function: multiply the input number by 5, then add 4. If you began with the set of input numbers 0, 1, 2, 3, 4, . . . , this function would produce the table of values shown at right. If 8 were the input, what would be the output?

It's usually quite easy to use the rule for a function to figure out a table of values. It's another matter to start with a table of values and figure out the rule for the function. Patterns can help you do this.

In	Out
0	4
1	9
2	14
3	19
4	24

TABLES OF VALUES

Determine the rule for each function shown below. Then fill in the outputs for the inputs 5 and 895. (**Note** that these are four separate problems.)

1.

In	Out
M	–?–
0	5
1	6
2	7
3	8
4	9
5	–?–
895	–?–

2.

In	Out
N	–?–
0	0
1	2
2	4
3	6
4	8
5	–?–
895	–?–

3.

In	Out
P	–?–
0	–3
1	–1
2	1
3	3
4	5
5	–?–
895	–?–

4.

In	Out
Q	–?–
0	0
1	–1
2	–2
3	–3
4	–4
5	–?–
895	–?–

Hint: If you can't figure out what the rules are, simply treat each problem as if it were a sequence written vertically.

In each of these problems, the pattern you're looking for depends on the terms. In problem 1, the pattern could have been written as a sequence of the output numbers.

5, 6, 7, 8, 9, . . .

To find each successive term, you'd simply add 1 to each previous term.

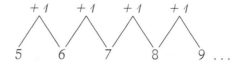

So to find the next four terms, you'd continue this pattern to get 10, 11, 12, and 13.

However, looking at problem 1 in the form of a table of values allows you to find a rule that you can apply to a *certain* term to find every other term. Let M represent that certain term, or input. The table shows that when M is 2, the output is 7. When M is 4, the output is 9. So the rule of adding 5 to the input seems to work for the inputs 2 and 4. Experimenting further shows you that this rule works for *all* the inputs. Now that we know that $M + 5$ is the function rule to apply to each input, determining the output for an input of 895 is easy: $895 + 5 = 900$.

In	Out
M	–?–
0	5
1	6
2	7
3	8
4	9

In problem 2, the outputs for N are simply twice N, so the function rule is $2N$. Thus, the output for 895 is 1790.

Clearly there is a big difference between finding patterns in tables of values and finding patterns in simple sequences. When finding patterns in sequences, you attempt to go through the entire sequence, always trying to find the next term in the sequence. When looking for a pattern in a table of values, you try to find a relationship between the input number and the output number. Finding this relationship allows you to jump way ahead in the sequence and find the output number for a large number (such as 895) without having to extend the sequence all the way to the 895th term. However, this method won't *always* work, because there may not be a way to find the relationship and a rule to apply. But this method does work for all the problems in this Tables of Values problem. The difference between the two methods becomes more apparent with more difficult patterns.

Problem 3 is the most difficult of these problems. Compare extended tables of values for problems 3 and 2. The output columns for each problem are related. The output numbers for problem 3 are 3 less than the output numbers for problem 2. Because the function rule for problem 2 was $2N$, the function rule for problem 3 must be $2P - 3$. Therefore, the output for $P = 895$ is $2(895) - 3 = 1787$. (**Note** that what the functions of problems 2 and 3 have in common is that the output numbers successively increase by 2.)

In	Out	In	Out
P	–?–	N	–?–
0	–3	0	0
1	–1	1	2
2	1	2	4
3	3	3	6
4	5	4	8
5	7	5	10
6	9	6	12
7	11	7	14

The rule for problem 4 is quite obvious: Change the sign of the number. So the output for $Q = 895$ is -895.

When trying to discover the rule for functions, you must look for patterns in the numbers and employ some guess-and-check. Guess a possible function rule, then check it with all the input numbers. If the rule works for every input-output pair you're given, then you've discovered the correct rule.

Jamie wanted to buy a rabbit. She had liked the Easter bunny when she was a kid, so she decided to raise some bunnies of her own. She went to the store with the intention of buying one rabbit, but she ended up with two newborn rabbits, a male and a female. She named them Patrick and Susan. Well, rabbits being what they are (rabbits), it is fairly impossible to have just two rabbits for an extended period of time. She bought them on April 1, 1999, which happened to be three days before Easter that year. On June 1, she noticed that Patrick and Susan were the proud parents of two newborn rabbits, again one male and one female. She named these new arrivals Thomas and Ursula.

On July 1, Patrick and Susan again gave birth to a male and a female rabbit. She named these Vida and Wanda.

On August 1, Patrick and Susan again gave birth to a male and a female. But Jamie was really surprised to see that Thomas and Ursula also gave birth to a male and a female. Jamie was running out of names, so she didn't bother giving them any.

On September 1, Patrick and Susan gave birth to a male and a female, and so did Thomas and Ursula, and so did Vida and Wanda. (Actually, Vida was no longer Vida, and Thomas was no longer Thomas. Jamie was worried about maintaining a diverse genetic pool among her bunnies, so she traded the original Thomas and Vida to other breeders and named their replacements with the same names.)

Jamie noticed a pattern to the breeding. A pair of rabbits was born. Two months later they bred a pair of rabbits, and continued to breed a pair of rabbits every month after that. Jamie wondered, "If this keeps up, how many rabbits am I going to have on April 1 of 2000?"

Do this problem before continuing on.

Four students—whose names just happened to be Pat, Sue, Tom, and Ula—worked on this problem.

PAT: Wow, this is weird. These rabbits have the same names that we do.

TOM: Let's try and do this problem, okay? We don't need to know whether the rabbits are named after us.

PAT: I just thought it was interesting.

ULA: How are we going to do this? I'm totally confused.

SUE: Let's try making a systematic list.

PAT: Okay, let's see, we've got adult rabbits and baby rabbits.

SUE: Yeah, but we also have teenaged rabbits. After Thomas and Ursula were born on June 1, they didn't have babies until August 1. So in July, they were just teenagers.

ULA: Let's get all this down in a table. Then maybe we can find a pattern. (Ula began writing a table. All numbers represent pairs of rabbits.)

Month	Adults	Teenagers	Babies	Total
April	0 pr	0 pr	1 pr	1 pr

TOM: That's great, Ula. Okay, so in May, Patrick and Susan grow to be teenagers. And then in June they become adults and have babies, Thomas and Ursula. And in July they have more babies.

Month	Adults	Teenagers	Babies	Total
April	0 pr	0 pr	1 pr	1 pr
May	0	1	0	1
June	1	0	1	2
July	1	1	1	3
August	2	1	2	5

SUE: Wait, how did you get August?

ULA: Well, in August, Thomas and Ursula grew up to be adults, and they had babies. So did Patrick and Susan.

PAT: Who are the teenagers?

TOM: Vida and Wanda. They were babies in July, so they are teenagers in August.

PAT: Oh, I think I see a pattern. The adults is the same number as the babies because each pair of adults has a pair of babies.

SUE: Yeah, and the ones who are babies this month become teenagers next month.

ULA: Right. And the adults are whoever were adults last month plus whoever were teenagers last month.

TOM: I think we can figure this out now.

Month	Adults	Teenagers	Babies	Total
April	0 pr	0 pr	1 pr	1 pr
May	0	1	0	1
June	1	0	1	2
July	1	1	1	3
August	2	1	2	5
September	3	2	3	8
October	5	3	5	13
November	8	5	8	21
December	13	8	13	34
January	21	13	21	55
February	34	21	34	89
March	55	34	55	144
April	89	55	89	233

TOM: I think we're done. Jamie has 233 pairs of rabbits on April 1 of 2000. Great job, guys.

SUE: Wait a second. I see a pattern here. Look down the Total column. You just have to add the two numbers above it to get the next number.

PAT: What?

TOM: I see what she means. Look at the top of the Total column. The first two numbers are 1 and 1. The next number is 2, which is 1 + 1. The next number is 3, which is 1 + 2. The next number is 5, which is 2 + 3. Then look, 8 is 3 + 5. So just add the two numbers above to get the next number.

ULA: Neat. And look, the same thing happens in all of the other columns, but the pattern starts later. And the numbers in each column are the same: 1, 1, 2, 3, 5, 8, 13, 21, 34, ...

PAT: Wow, that's cool. I think this sequence has a name. The Liberace sequins, maybe?

TOM: Not sequins. *Sequence.*

ULA: I think it's the Fibonacci sequence. It's named after an Italian.

TOM: I guess when you think you're done, maybe you're not. It's kind of neat to look back and find the pattern. With the pattern in our table, it would be really easy to keep going.

SUE: Yeah, but let's not. But we might see that pattern again someday.

This problem illustrates the effectiveness of finding patterns. The group found a pattern in what was going on as they worked the problem, but they didn't catch the number pattern until they were all done. And Tom is right: It's always good to look back at your work and notice things you might have missed, and to make sure your answer is reasonable.

～～～～～

The Fibonacci sequence is named after Italian mathematician Leonardo of Pisa (ca 1170–1240), called Fibonacci (son of Bonaccio) by an editor of his works in the nineteenth century. The sequence that bears his name shows up in some surprising places in nature. For instance, if you count the two sets of spirals on a pinecone, you will always get consecutive Fibonacci numbers such as 5, 8 or 8, 13 or 13, 21. For example, a pinecone might have eight spirals going in one direction and thirteen in the other. The same pattern also occurs in sunflowers, pineapples, cacti, and other plants. Read more about Fibonacci in an encyclopedia or a book on the history of mathematics.

FIBONACCI SEQUENCES

Find the four missing terms of each sequence. Work this problem before continuing.

1. 2, 2, 4, 6, 10, 16, 26, _____, _____, _____, _____
2. 1, 3, 4, 7, 11, 18, 29, _____, _____, _____, _____
3. 3, 1, 4, 5, 9, 14, _____, _____, _____, _____
4. 1, 2, 3, 6, 11, 20, 37, _____, _____, _____, _____
5. _____, _____, _____, _____, 16, 25, 41, 66, 107

1. 2, 2, 4, 6, 10, 16, 26, **42, 68, 110, 178,** . . .

   This is an ordinary, straight Fibonacci sequence for which you add two terms to find the next one in the sequence. This sequence starts with a "seed" of 2, 2.

2. 1, 3, 4, 7, 11, 18, 29, **47, 76, 123, 199,** . . .

   This sequence is also formed by adding two terms together. In this case it starts with a seed of 1, 3. This sequence is often referred to as the Lucas sequence, named after French mathematician Edouard Anatole Lucas (1842–1891).

3. 3, 1, 4, 5, 9, 14, **23, 37, 60, 97,** . . .

   This sequence is formed by reversing the seed of sequence 2. Again, each term is formed by adding the two previous terms.

4. 1, 2, 3, 6, 11, 20, 37, **68, 125, 230, 423,** . . .

This sequence turns out to be a variation of the Fibonacci sequence. The seed in this case is 1, 2, 3, and these three terms are added to form the fourth. This could be mistaken for a "sum of two terms" Fibonacci sequence at first because the first two terms in the seed sum to the third.

5. **5, 2, 7, 9,** 16, 25, 41, 66, 107, . . .

Again, this sequence is based on adding two terms. But the process is reversed because the seed and the next two terms are missing. However, it's not too difficult to reverse the process and find the missing terms.

MORE SEQUENCES

Find the next four terms of each sequence. Work this problem before continuing.

1. 2, 3, 5, 9, 17, 33, _____, _____, _____, _____

2. 1, 5, 13, 29, 61, 125, _____, _____, _____, _____

3. 1, 4, 13, 40, 121, 364, _____, _____, _____, _____

1. To solve sequence 1, write the difference between each pair of terms, that is, the number you add to a term to get the next term:

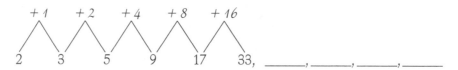

+1   +2   +4   +8   +16

2   3   5   9   17   33, _____, _____, _____, _____

The difference between each pair of terms forms an exponential sequence that features powers of 2: 1, 2, 4, 8, 16. This sequence shows up very well if you place one sequence above the other:

1   2   4   8   16

2,   3,   5,   9,   17,   33,   _____,   _____,   _____,   _____

The top sequence is a pure exponential sequence. The bottom sequence is also exponential, but 1 is added to each term:

2, 3, 5, 9, 17, 33, **65, 129, 257, 513**

Let's take a minute here to talk about finding rules in sequences. Sequences are studied in many mathematics courses, and calculating the ***n*th term** of a sequence is an important mathematical concept. "Calculating the *n*th term" means to figure out a rule for all the terms in a sequence, then relate that rule to each term number (this is very similar to what you did in the Tables of Values problem earlier in this chapter). In the top sequence shown on the previous page, the first term is 1, the second term is 2, the third term is 4, and so on. Each term is a power of 2. The exponent for each of these powers of 2 is 1 less than the term number. For example, the first term is 2^0, the second term is 2^1, the third term is 2^2, and so on. So the *n*th term is $2^{(n-1)}$. Thus, the sixth term in the top sequence is $2^5 = 32$ (note that the exponent of the sixth term equals $6 - 1 = 5$).

Each term in the bottom sequence shown on the previous page is 1 more than its corresponding term in the top sequence. So the *n*th term for the bottom sequence is $2^{(n-1)} + 1$. Thus, the sixth term for the bottom sequence is $2^5 + 1 = 33$.

2. Now let's move on to the solution for sequence 2. This sequence is also related to an exponential sequence, which becomes evident when you look at the differences:

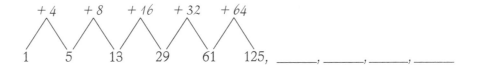

Again, powers of 2 show up in the differences but this time starting with 2^2: **1, 2,** 4, 8, 16, 32, 64. (This sequence of powers of 2 has been truncated—that is, the first two terms have been cut off—so that it starts with 4 instead of 1.) By placing one sequence over the other, we can examine how the sequences are related:

4   8   16   32   64

1,   5,   13,   29,   61,   125,   _____,   _____,   _____,   _____

By extending the sequence of differences a few more terms and adding the position of each term, we find that the pattern becomes more obvious:

Position	1	2	3	4	5	6	7	8	9	10
	2^2	2^3	2^4	2^5	2^6	2^7	2^8	2^9	2^{10}	2^{11}
	4	8	16	32	64	128	**256**	**512**	**1024**	**2048**
Term	1,	5,	13,	29,	61,	125,	**253,**	**509,**	**1021,**	**2045**

If we want to go from one term to the next, we just have to add the next power of 2. But suppose we want to find a particular term without having to find all the terms before it. To predict any term without using addition, **note** that each term is 3 less than the next power of 2. For example, the *fourth* term is 29, which is 3 less than 2 to the *fifth* power ($2^5 - 3 = 32 - 3 = 29$):

Position	1	2	3	4	5	6
	2^2	2^3	2^4	2^5	2^6	2^7
	$\downarrow$	$\downarrow$	$\downarrow$	$\downarrow$	$\downarrow$	$\downarrow$
	+ 4	+ 8	+ 16	+ 32	+ 64	+ 128
Term	1	5	13	29	61	125 ...

So we can conclude that the *n*th term for this sequence is $2^{(n+1)} - 3$.

3. Use the same approach for sequence 3. Look at the differences between terms in the sequence:

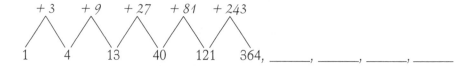

$+3$ $+9$ $+27$ $+81$ $+243$

1   4   13   40   121   364, _____, _____, _____, _____

In this case, the sequence of differences looks suspiciously like powers of 3. You can use this pattern to continue the sequence:

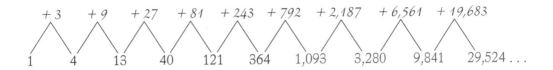

$$+3 \quad +9 \quad +27 \quad +81 \quad +243 \quad +792 \quad +2,187 \quad +6,561 \quad +19,683$$

1   4   13   40   121   364   1,093   3,280   9,841   29,524 . . .

The actual rule for the nth term of this sequence is difficult to derive, so we won't worry about it for this problem.

RETURN OF THE HOWLING DOGS

Shawna liked to jog in the late afternoon. One day she noticed an unusual phenomenon. As she jogged, dogs would hear her and bark. After the first dog had barked for about 15 seconds, two other dogs would join in and bark. And then in about another 15 seconds, it seemed that each barking dog would "inspire" two more dogs to start barking. Of course, long after Shawna passed the first dog, it continued to bark, as dogs are inclined to do. After about 3 minutes, how many dogs were barking (as a result of Shawna passing the first dog)? Work this problem before continuing.

Joan solved the Return of the Howling Dogs problem:
"This sounds like my neighborhood, 24 hours a day. I started out by trying to draw a diagram of what was going on. It was a mess."

ROVER (DOG #1)

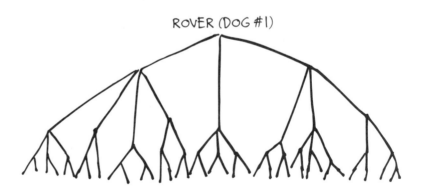

"The biggest problem seemed to be that the first dog doesn't just stop, but continues barking and continues inciting more dogs into stupid barking frenzies. And every other dog that starts barking also incites new dogs to bark.

"The second time I tried this problem, I decided to try to organize the problem into a chart. This was far more successful. The first dog barks and causes the other two to bark. The first dog continues barking and causes two more to bark (under the 3rd Set Barkers), then the first dog continues to bark and causes two more to bark (under the 4th Set Barkers), and so on. The first row shows the original dog and the two dogs that he or she inspires every 15 seconds."

1ST BARKER	2ND SET BARKERS	3RD SET BARKERS	4TH SET BARKERS	5TH SET BARKERS
1	2	2	2	2

"Then I had to figure out a way to record the dogs that were inspired to bark by the dogs Rover inspired. See, the first two dogs that Rover inspired are, in turn, going to inspire other dogs to bark every 15 seconds. Those two dogs will each inspire two new dogs every 15 seconds after they start barking. So four new dogs start barking each 15 seconds. I recorded this in the second row. It shows the first two dogs inspired by Rover (circled, with the colon), and the four dogs that take up barking every 15 seconds thereafter, inspired by those same two second-set barkers."

1ST BARKER	2ND SET BARKERS	3RD SET BARKERS	4TH SET BARKERS	5TH SET BARKERS
1	2	2	2	2
	(2:)	4	4	4

"So the chart now shows the original dog, Rover, and the dogs inspired by Rover in the first row. And it shows the set of four dogs that Dot and Spot inspired every 15 seconds. (Dot and Spot are shown circled at the beginning of the second row. Their sets of 'inspired followers' are the 4's that follow them.)

"Now the third row. There were two dogs inspired by Rover and four inspired by Dot and Spot in the third set of barkers. These six dogs will each inspire two dogs every 15 seconds from then on. The third row lists these six dogs (circled, with the colon) and the twelve dogs they inspire every 15 seconds thereafter.

"Similarly, the fourth row starts with 18 dogs (2 + 4 + 12) that inspire 36 dogs thereafter."

1ST BARKER	2ND SET BARKERS	3RD SET BARKERS	4TH SET BARKERS	5TH SET BARKERS
(1:)	2	2	2	2
	(2:)	4	4	4
		(6:)	12	12
			(18:)	36
				(54:)

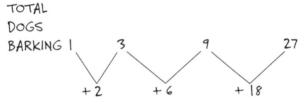

TOTAL DOGS BARKING   1   3   9   27

+2   +6   +18

"The Total Dogs Barking column adds the circled numbers with the colons. At the start, there is just Rover. After one generation, there are Rover, Dot, and Spot, for a total of three dogs barking. After the next generation, there are Rover, Dot, Spot, and six more dogs for a total of nine. Those 9 then get 18 more riled up for a total of 27 barking dogs. Each of them gets 2 more dogs excited apiece, or 54 dogs plus those 27 makes 81.

"Then I looked for a pattern. The sequence of total barking dogs is 1, 3, 9, 27, 81. These were the powers of 3: 3^0, 3^1, 3^2, 3^3, 3^4, and so on.

"After 3 minutes, there are twelve 15-second intervals. So not only do you have to consider 3^0 for the original Rover, but you must also take into account 3^{12} for the 12 intervals. So after 3 minutes, there are $3^{12} = 531,441$ dogs barking.

"By the way, this answer may seem completely unbelievable to you. However, if you've been around my neighborhood, you would probably think the answer was pretty close to reasonable, if not dead-on."

Loc set up a different table to find a pattern for this problem. He organized his table as shown below. The Dogs Barking column refers to the number of dogs that *are* barking at the beginning of each round. The New Dogs Barking column refers to the dogs that *start* barking during each round. And the Total Dogs Barking column shows the number of dogs that are barking at the *end* of each round. The total dogs barking for one round become the dogs barking for the next round.

Time	Round	Dogs Barking	New Dogs Barking	Total Dogs Barking
0	0	0	1	$1 = 3^0$
:15	1	1	2	$3 = 3^1$
:30	2	3	6	$9 = 3^2$
:45	3	9	18	$27 = 3^3$
1:00	4	27	54	$81 = 3^4$

So Loc also concluded that at the end of 3 minutes, which would include 12 rounds, there would be 3^{12} dogs barking.

MILK LOVERS

Alysia and Melissa and Dante and Melody loved milk. They convinced their older brother, Mark, who did all the shopping, to buy each of them their own gallon of milk because they each liked it so much. They all put their names on their gallons. One day, they were all really thirsty and each took ten drinks according to a different system:

Alysia started by drinking half of the milk in her container. Then she drank one-third of what was left. Then she drank one-fourth of what was left, then one-fifth, and so on.

Melissa started by drinking one-eleventh of her milk, then one-tenth of what was left, then one-ninth of what was left, and so on.

Dante started by drinking one-half of his milk, then two-thirds of what was left, then three-fourths of what was left, then four-fifths, and so on.

Melody started by drinking one-half of her milk, then one-half of what was left, then one-half of what was left, and so on.

After each had taken ten drinks, how much milk remained in each container? Work this problem before continuing.

Bimiljit answered the problem in this way:

"This problem seemed a little tough. I examined Melody's usage first because it seemed to be the easiest. I made a chart and looked for a pattern. For example, on the second drink, she drank one-half of the remaining half, which is one-fourth of the whole container. This leaves her with one-fourth of the whole container."

Drink #	Amount drunk	Amount remaining
1	$\frac{1}{2}$	$1 - \frac{1}{2} = \frac{1}{2}$
2	$\frac{1}{2} \times \frac{1}{2} = \frac{1}{4}$	$\frac{1}{2} - \frac{1}{4} = \frac{1}{4}$
3	$\frac{1}{2} \times \frac{1}{4} = \frac{1}{8}$	$\frac{1}{4} - \frac{1}{8} = \frac{1}{8}$

The pattern for the amount remaining was pretty obvious: $\frac{1}{2}$, $\frac{1}{4}$, $\frac{1}{8}$, $\frac{1}{16}$, ... So I looked at each denominator as a power of 2, and it turned out that each power matched up exactly with which drink she was taking. For example, $\frac{1}{8}$ is $\frac{1}{2^3}$ after the third drink. So after ten drinks, Melody would have $\frac{1}{2^{10}} = \frac{1}{1024}$ of her milk left. That's not very much.

"I then tried to make the same kind of chart for Alysia because hers seemed to be the next easiest. On her second drink, she drinks $\frac{1}{3}$ of the remaining half. This is $\frac{1}{6}$ of the whole container. Subtracting $\frac{1}{6}$ from $\frac{1}{2}$ gives $\frac{1}{3}$ left in the container after two drinks."

Drink #	Amount drunk	Amount remaining
1	$\frac{1}{2}$	$1 - \frac{1}{2} = \frac{1}{2}$
2	$\frac{1}{3} \times \frac{1}{2} = \frac{1}{6}$	$\frac{1}{2} - \frac{1}{6} = \frac{1}{3}$
3	$\frac{1}{4} \times \frac{1}{3} = \frac{1}{12}$	$\frac{1}{3} - \frac{1}{12} = \frac{1}{4}$
4	$\frac{1}{5} \times \frac{1}{4} = \frac{1}{20}$	$\frac{1}{4} - \frac{1}{20} = \frac{1}{5}$

"I couldn't believe how easy this pattern was once I saw it. The numerator is 1 and the denominator is 1 more than the drink number. The tenth drink would leave $\frac{1}{11}$ of the milk remaining.

"Next I tried doing Melissa's chart. Hers seemed to be a little harder."

Drink #	Amount drunk	Amount remaining
1	$\frac{1}{11}$	$1 - \frac{1}{11} = \frac{10}{11}$
2	$\frac{1}{10} \times \frac{10}{11} = \frac{1}{11}$	$\frac{10}{11} - \frac{1}{11} = \frac{9}{11}$
3	$\frac{1}{9} \times \frac{9}{11} = \frac{1}{11}$	$\frac{9}{11} - \frac{1}{11} = \frac{8}{11}$
•		
•		
•		
10	$\frac{1}{2} \times \frac{2}{11} = \frac{1}{11}$	$\frac{2}{11} - \frac{1}{11} = \frac{1}{11}$

"The pattern wasn't hard to see: The amount of milk remaining keeps going down by $1/11$. But the end was hard to figure out. I figured out that the pattern for the numerator goes 10, 9, 8, 7, 6, 5, 4, 3, 2, 1. So after ten drinks, she would have $1/11$ of her milk left. The amazing thing was that this final amount was the same as Alysia's.

"Dante's chart seemed like the hardest. But the chart-and-pattern-finding approach was working so well, I just kept at it."

Drink #	Amount drunk	Amount remaining
1	$\frac{1}{2}$	$1 - \frac{1}{2} = \frac{1}{2}$
2	$\frac{2}{3} \times \frac{1}{2} = \frac{1}{3}$	$\frac{1}{2} - \frac{1}{3} = \frac{1}{6}$
3	$\frac{3}{4} \times \frac{1}{6} = \frac{1}{8}$	$\frac{1}{6} - \frac{1}{8} = \frac{1}{24}$
4	$\frac{4}{5} \times \frac{1}{24} = \frac{1}{30}$	$\frac{1}{24} - \frac{1}{30} = \frac{1}{120}$
5	$\frac{5}{6} \times \frac{1}{120} = \frac{1}{144}$	$\frac{1}{120} - \frac{1}{144} = \frac{1}{720}$

"This pattern was much harder to find. I couldn't see any pattern at all in the amount he drank. But the denominators of the remaining amounts looked strangely familiar: 2, 6, 24, 120, 720. Then I remembered where I had seen them. Those are the numbers that show up in factorials. You know, like 5! (5 factorial) is $5 \times 4 \times 3 \times 2 \times 1 = 120$. But the factorial in the denominator of each amount remaining was actually the factorial of the next drink taken. So after three drinks, he had $^1/4! = ^1/24$ of his milk left. And after five drinks, he had $^1/6! = ^1/720$ left. So after ten drinks, he was going to have $^1/11! = ^1/39,916,800$ of his milk left. Wow, that isn't much at all. Those factorial things sure get big fast.

"So the answers are Alysia and Melissa each had $^1/11$ of their milk left; Dante had $^1/39,916,800$ of his left; and Melody had $^1/1024$ of hers left. I can see why Mark bought each of them their own gallon."

Bimiljit was successful with this problem for many reasons, the main reason being that she was unafraid of the problem and persisted in solving it. She found many patterns in the problem. They showed up so easily because she was organized in her thinking and created her charts so that the patterns would be apparent.

Looking for and finding a pattern is a very effective problem-solving strategy. The key to finding most patterns is to organize a problem's information in some sort of chart or table so that the patterns jump out at you. Patterns turn up in many places. Keep your eyes open for them.

Problem Set A

1. **SEQUENCE PATTERNS**

Find the next three terms in each sequence and explain your pattern in a sentence.

a. 2, 5, 10, 17, . . .

b. 64, 32, 16, 8, 4, . . .

c. 5, 10, 9, 18, 17, 34, 33, . . .

d. 1, 3, 7, 13, 21, . . .

e. 2, 3, 5, 9, . . .

f. 1, 5, 13, 26, 45, 71, . . .

g. 1, 2, 6, 24, 120, 720, . . .

MORE SEQUENCE PATTERNS

Find the next four terms in each sequence.

a. 243, 81, 27, 9, 3, _____, _____, _____, _____

b. 4, 9, 8, 13, 12, _____, _____, _____, _____

c. 4, 5, 8, 13, 20, 29, 40, _____, _____, _____, _____

d. 3, 7, 13, 21, 31, 43, _____, _____, _____, _____

e. 8, 11, 16, 23, 32, 43, _____, _____, _____, _____

f. 5, 7, 11, 19, 35, 67, _____, _____, _____, _____

g. 3, 4, 6, 9, 13, 18, _____, _____, _____, _____

h. 8, 11, 17, 26, 38, 53, _____, _____, _____, _____

i. 3, 1, 4, 5, 9, 14, 23, 37, _____, _____, _____, _____

j. 7, −3, 10, −13, 23, −36, 59, _____, _____, _____, _____

3. **AIR SHOW**

To keep the spectators out of the line of flight at an air show, the ushers arranged the show's seats in the shape of an inverted triangle. Kevin, who loves airplanes, arrived very early and was seated in the front row, which contained one seat. The second row contained three seats, and those filled very quickly. The third row contained five seats, which were given to the next five people who came. The next row contained seven seats. This seating pattern continued all the way to the last row, each row containing two more seats than the previous row. All twenty rows were filled. How many people attended the air show?

4. **RECTANGULAR DOTS**

In this chapter you worked with square and triangular numbers. This problem is about rectangular numbers. Find the pattern in the sequence of diagrams shown below, and determine how many dots would be in the thirty-fourth diagram.

```
 o  o        o  o  o        o  o  o  o        o  o  o  o  o
             o  o  o        o  o  o  o        o  o  o  o  o
                           o  o  o  o        o  o  o  o  o
                                            o  o  o  o  o
```

5. PENTAGONAL NUMBERS

This problem is about pentagonal numbers. Find the pattern in the sequence of diagrams shown below, and determine how many dots would be in the seventeenth diagram.

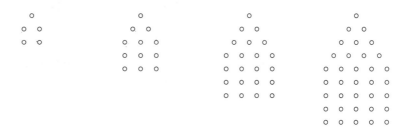

6. LAST DIGIT

What is the digit in the ones place of 2^{57}?

7. BEACH BALL

Kazuko has a beach ball. It is colored with six vertical stripes, in order: white, orange, yellow, blue, red, and green. She spins the beach ball on the surface of the water in her swimming pool, and she notices that the colors whir by very fast. If the first color to go by is white and the ball spins around so that 500 colors go by, what is the 500th color?

8. JUGGLING

Student Cory Craig of Sierra College in Rocklin, California, wrote this problem.

Little Gessop is trying to learn how to juggle. He has scrounged up three balls: two yellow tennis balls and one blue racquetball. He starts his usual juggling procedure by holding the two yellow balls in his left hand and the blue ball in his right hand. Then he throws one yellow ball from his left hand to his right; then he throws the blue ball from right to left just before he catches the first yellow ball; then he throws the second yellow ball from left to right just before he catches the blue ball; then he throws the first yellow ball back to his left hand just before he catches the second yellow ball. (The balls follow a sideways figure-eight pattern.) Gessop considers one catch to be when he throws and catches the first ball, the second catch to be when he catches the second ball, and so on.

(This problem is continued on the next page.)

Gessop has been counting how many catches he can make before dropping a ball—or all three. He can't seem to get past 15 catches before he messes up. He's counted his catches several times, and he's begun to notice a pattern, but because he's becoming only more frustrated rather than a better juggler, he gives up. But he's curious to know which hand the blue ball would end up in if he could make it to 100 catches. Gessop is about as good at math as he is a juggler (that is, not very good), and he's made the assumption that there is a 50-50 chance that the ball would end up in his right hand. Where would the blue ball be on the 100th catch? Is Gessop right about the 50-50 chance?

9. EMAIL VIRUS

In 1999 a computer macro based on a popular suite of programs was launched through the internet. This macro came in the form of an email message that replicated itself via the first 50 email addresses in a recipient's address list. For example, person A sends the message to person B, who inadvertently sends a copy of the message to the first 50 people in his email address book.

Assume that there are no duplicate recipients. If the first email is called the first generation, then how many total emails will have been sent in the first five generations?

10. FUNCTIONS

Determine the rule for each function. Determine the missing outputs.

a.

In	Out
R	–?–
0	−6
1	−5
2	−4
3	−3
4	−2
5	–?–
712	–?–

b.

In	Out
S	–?–
0	−1
1	4
2	9
3	14
4	19
5	–?–
63	–?–

c.

In	Out
T	–?–
0	1
1	2
2	5
3	10
4	17
5	–?–
895	–?–

11. SPREADSHEET

The table shown below is a spreadsheet. You reach the numbers in columns A through G by performing some operation on the numbers in the x and y columns. For example, you reach the numbers in column C by multiplying the numbers in the x column by 3. In row 1, $x = 1$. So multiplying 1 by 3 generates the number 3 that appears in column C. Similarly, in row 4, $x = 5$. So multiplying 5 by 3 generates the number 15 that appears in column C.

The rules for some columns in this table involve only *one* of the numbers x or y. The rules for other columns involve *both* x and y.

	x	y	A –?–	B –?–	C $3x$	D –?–	E –?–	F –?–	G –?–
1.	1	3	4	2	3	5	−1	7	−6
2.	2	1	3	−1	6	5	3	6	−2
3.	3	5	8	2	9	11	1	11	−10
4.	5	−1	4	−6	15	9	11	7	2
5.	−2	0	−2	2	−6	−4	−4	1	0
6.	0	4	4	4	0	4	−4	7	−8
7.	4	5	9	1	12	13	3	12	−10

Determine the rules that generate the numbers in the A, B, D, E, F, and G columns.

12. BEES

A male bee is born from an unfertilized egg, a female bee from a fertilized one. So in other words, a male bee has only a mother, while a female bee has a mother and a father. How many total ancestors does a male bee have going ten generations back? (Try drawing a diagram to help organize this problem's information.)

PASCAL'S TRIANGLE

The triangle shown below is called Pascal's triangle. Find a pattern that will produce the next row. Then copy the triangle and determine the next four rows.

14. **OTHER PATTERNS IN PASCAL'S TRIANGLE**

Look for other patterns in Pascal's triangle. Write down three other patterns.

15. **COIN FLIPS**

Pascal's triangle shows up in the solutions of many problems. Consider how Pascal's triangle may help you solve this problem.

One flipped coin can land in two ways: heads (H) or tails (T). Two coins can be flipped to land in four ways:

| HH | HT | TH | TT |

Make a list of all the ways that three flipped coins can land. Make a list of all the ways that four flipped coins can land. What does this problem have to do with Pascal's triangle? Could Pascal's triangle help you figure out the number of ways five, six, seven, or more flipped coins can land?

16. **FREE INTERNET**

A new internet service has just been announced that gives free internet access for a year if customers agree to receive an email advertisement every 30 seconds while online. In other words, if you were online for five minutes, 10 email ads would show up in your email inbox during that time. Of course, then you'd have to go into your inbox, open the ads, and delete them. But while you were opening and deleting them, you'd still be online, so more ads would come in.

So, let's say you've just been online for one hour. During that time, 120 emails showed up in your inbox. You know that all of these ads are going to be junk, but you still need to open and delete them. Assume it takes 10 seconds to open and delete each ad. During that time, more ads will come in, and you'll have to open and delete *those* ads. And while you're opening and deleting those ads, still *more* ads will come in. You'll finally be able to log off when there are no more ads in your inbox. The ads started coming 30 seconds after you logged on. Including the original hour you were online, how long will you have been logged on when you've deleted the last ad?

Note that the email sends a return receipt that only works when the computer is still online, so you must remain online while opening and deleting the ads.

17. **REFLECTION**

At this time we would like you to reflect on what you have learned so far in this course. Have you learned new problem-solving strategies or become better at strategies you were already familiar with? Have you enjoyed working with other students? What have you liked best about this course so far? What have you liked least? Do you use any of the strategies you've learned so far outside this course?

18. **WRITE YOUR OWN**

Create your own pattern problem. To start with something easy, write a sequence problem. Then try coming up with a situation to go with it.

Problem Set B

1. LEGAL EAGLES

There are exactly five parking spaces along the front side of the law offices of Stetson, Neumann, Ostrom, Savidge, and Schoorl. The colors of the lawyers' cars are blue, tan, black, silver, and burgundy. Match the owners with their car colors and their parking spaces. Then determine whether Neumann is male or female.

1. Ostrom does not own the silver car.

2. The woman who parks in the fifth space owns the burgundy car.

3. Stetson owns the black car.

4. Schoorl parks her car in the middle space.

5. There are cars parked on both sides of Neumann's car.

6. Ostrom parks his car on one end, but the man who owns the blue car does not.

7. A woman parks in the fourth space.

2. RUDY'S CLOTHES RACK

Rudy examined his rack of clothes—five shirts and four ties—trying to decide what combination to wear. His five shirts included three solids and two patterns. His three solid-color shirts were blue, green, and white. One of his two patterned shirts was a blue and green print, and the other was a red and white stripe. He needed to match a shirt with a tie. His solid-color ties were white, blue, and yellow, and his patterned tie was a green and blue stripe. Rudy has two rules of good taste: You don't wear two solids of the same color; and if you wear a pattern, match it with a solid that is the same color as one of the colors of the pattern. Given those conditions, what is the probability that Rudy will pick out a combination that includes blue?

3. ROO AND TIGGER

Roo and Tigger decided to have a jumping race. Their racecourse was 100 feet up and back (200 feet total). Roo could make three jumps of 2 feet each in the same time that Tigger could make two jumps of 1 yard each. Who won the race and by how much?

4.   **GOLF MATCH**

Clark, Chris, Doug, and Diana are standing on the first tee of their favorite golf course, about to begin a best-ball-of-partners match. (A best-ball match pits two golfers against the other two golfers.) They are standing in a square, with two partners standing shoulder to shoulder next to each other on the cart path, directly facing the other two partners standing shoulder to shoulder next to each other on the grass. This standing arrangement is typical of the beginning of a golf match. They shake hands, then throw a tee in the air and let it hit the ground. Whoever it points to will tee off first. Clark is standing diagonally opposite Diana. Chris is facing the person whose name begins with the same letter as that of the name of the person who will tee off first. Partners tee off one after the other. Who will tee off second?

5.   **COMIC OF THE MONTH**

I subscribe to the Comic-of-the-Month Club. Each month I can buy any number of the 48 titles offered by the club. The first month I bought five comics for $3.07. The second month I bought two comics for $1.72. The next month I bought six of the club offerings for $3.52. In May I bought three more for a charge of $2.17. The club charges a handling fee and then a fee for each comic. How much would it have cost to buy all 48 titles at the same time?

A string musician tunes an instrument by checking its pitch, guessing how much to tighten or loosen a string, then checking the pitch again, constantly refining the guesses to zero in on the correct pitch.

6

Guess-and-Check

Guess-and-check: Even the name sounds bad. It sounds like something your math teachers tried for years to get you to stop doing. When you learn the strategy and start to use it, it may even feel like you're cheating. But you won't be. Guess-and-check is a powerful tool for solving problems. In the game of golf, when somebody figured out that using a sand wedge is a great way to escape a sand trap on a golf course, the first people to use this strategy may have felt that they were cheating. (Some people use a hand wedge, which is definitely cheating.) But now sand wedges are an accepted part of the game, and no one feels it is cheating to use them.

The strategy of guess-and-check serves a similar function in mathematics. It isn't cheating, and it really helps! It is tremendously effective in giving you a place to start when you tackle a problem. Guess-and-check helps you understand the problem, and it can quickly lead you to solutions. And, as you will see in Chapter 13: Algebra, this strategy even helps set up an algebraic equation, if that's your goal. (In this chapter you won't use algebra at all.)

Why guess-and-check? Certainly guessing is nothing new to most people. Students have been guessing at answers for years. Some have even gone on to check their answers. So it would seem that the strategy of guess-and-check would arise naturally from most people's educational experience. Unfortunately, this is not the case. While it is true that most people have flirted with the guess-and-check strategy, they probably have not seen its power. The strength of this strategy comes from organizing the problem's information into a useful form. You evaluate your guesses in a systematic way, which enables you to advance to more refined guesses.

Guess-and-check is not only a strategy, it is also an attitude. When guessing and checking, you must first believe that you can solve a problem, even if you don't understand it well at the outset. Then, through your organization and persistence, you will work toward a solution.

The strategy is loose on the one hand and highly structured on the other. With guess-and-check, you guess and then add, multiply, subtract, divide (nothing unusual), and you check your answer. But the heart of guess-and-check is not simply performing operations on numbers. In fact, the heart is not so much a heart as it is a skeleton: a surrounding structure that holds the strategy together. Guess-and-check is all about organizing the way you guess in order to reach an answer. Anybody can guess without being taught. Anybody can check answers without being taught. But not everybody has learned to unite these two activities into a problem-solving tool. And that is simply what guess-and-check is: a tool for organizing information in such a way that the information becomes more useful to you and more powerful in your hands.

In this chapter you'll learn how to use the powerful guess-and-check strategy. Plus, you'll also get a real-world How Guess-and-Check Saved the Day and Changed the Rest of My Life story at the end of the chapter.

SATURDAY AT THE FIVE-AND-DIME GARAGE SALE

Sandy held a garage sale, during which she charged a dime for everything but accepted a nickel if the buyer bargained well. At the end of the day she realized she had sold all twelve items and had raked in a grand total of 95 cents. She had only dimes and nickels. How many of each did she have?

Do this problem before continuing. Even if you think you can write an equation for it, don't. Solve it by guessing a possible answer and checking to see if that answer is correct. Then make another guess, check it, and so on.

The correct answer is seven dimes and five nickels. Let's work through this problem using guess-and-check. The following solution is provided by Kasidra, who gave us a "thought-process" narration of how to solve this problem. As you will see, the method her solution illustrates will not involve just random guesses, but rather will be a very organized procedure.

"First, make a guess. I usually guess five because there are five fingers on my right hand. If I ever end up on an uninhabited island and need to do guess-and-check, I can always check my hand to see what I should guess first. Unless, of course, an alligator bites off one of my fingers.

"Five whats? Five dimes. Or five nickels. It really doesn't matter. I'll make it dimes. Next, set up a chart to keep track of the guesses. This is very important—this is not simply guess-and-guess, it is guess, check, and refine your guess. In order to do this well, you must have an organized chart."

Dimes	
5	

"Not bad for a first guess, but somehow I think this should all be expanded. If she sold 12 items in all, then the number of coins she has must be 12. So if I guess 5 dimes, she must have 7 nickels to make 12 coins."

Dimes	Nickels	
5	7	

"Well, that looks a little better, but there must be more to this problem. I've got to figure out a way to see if this guess is correct. I need to know how much these coins are worth, because the problem says she has 95 cents. Expand the chart again."

Dimes	Nickels	Value of Dimes	Value of Nickels
5	7	$0.50	$0.35

"Looking carefully at the titles here, I see that because the columns of my chart contain numbers, the titles don't have to be so wide. So I'll use two lines for the value titles. That way I'll save space but still use descriptive titles. I always want to have one complete guess fit on one line, but I also like titles that contain a lot of information. The easiest way to accomplish this is to draw narrow columns whose titles may take two or three lines."

Dimes	Nickels	Value of Dimes	Value of Nickels	
5	7	$0.50	$0.35	

"Now this chart is beginning to look like it leads somewhere. This slow process is not devised simply to frustrate people. Part of the point of using guess-and-check is that you often don't know where a solution is heading, even if you have a good approach to solving the problem. I'm developing this chart as I go rather than using a predetermined format. If the chart appears to be working, I'll keep it. If the chart appears to be failing, I'll get rid of it and start again.

"Here's the next improvement to my chart. I need to know the total value of these coins."

Dimes	Nickels	Value of Dimes	Value of Nickels	Total Value	
5	7	$0.50	$0.35	$0.85	

"Now get ready for the mega-action on the chart. I add a rating column to tell me how the guess compares to the right answer of 95 cents. This particular guess has a total of 85 cents, which is less than 95 cents. The answer is low, so I rate the guess as 'low.'"

Dimes	Nickels	Value of Dimes	Value of Nickels	Total Value	Rating
5	7	$0.50	$0.35	$0.85	low

"Now that I appear to have completed the chart, I evaluate my first guess for accuracy. The guess was wrong, and note that the guess gave us a result that was too low. I will continue to guess and will use the previous guess as a guide. I will increase the number of dimes to raise the total value."

Dimes	Nickels	Value of Dimes	Value of Nickels	Total Value	Rating
5	7	$0.50	$0.35	$0.85	low
8	4	$0.80	$0.20	$1.00	high

"The next guess was wrong too, but I did manage to have the results of that guess come out just a little too high. The first guess was too low, the second was too high. Let's try something in-between to see how that comes out. My next guess needs to be between five dimes and eight dimes."

Dimes	Nickels	Value of Dimes	Value of Nickels	Total Value	Rating
5	7	$0.50	$0.35	$0.85	low
8	4	$0.80	$0.20	$1.00	high
7	5	$0.70	$0.25	$0.95	right

"Fortunately, I came up with the right answer on the third guess. The first guess allowed me to make a reasonable second guess, and the first two guesses allowed me to modify and then make what turned out to be a correct guess for the problem.

"Finally I'll check the problem for the question that was asked. The question asked how many dimes and how many nickels Sandy had. I always state my answer in a sentence—I wouldn't want to count on the teacher finding my right answer in the chart. So the answer is that Sandy has seven dimes and five nickels.

"In short, here's what I did:

1. I started by making a guess.

2. I followed my guess through to a reasonable conclusion.

3. I evaluated the guess.

4. I modified and guessed again.

5. When I got a correct guess, I checked to see what the question was and I answered it in a sentence.

"The chart, it is important to note, was nothing sacred. It was made up as I went and was designed to fit the needs of that particular problem. I also didn't clutter the chart with a lot of unnecessary detail. I did my computations in my mind or on scratch paper."

Thank you, Kasidra.

In her solution Kasidra made some excellent points. Another major point is that wrong guesses are just steps on the way to solving a problem. Many people resist guess-and-check at first because they fear being wrong. In some people's school experience, when an answer was wrong, the teacher marked it up with a red pen. When it was right, it was left alone. So many of us became fearful of the red pen that our primary aim when doing schoolwork was to avoid being wrong. Sometimes the best way to avoid being wrong was to skip problems. Let us suggest here that wrong answers just help you find the right answers and are an important part of the journey. So guess. It may take you 50 guesses to reach the right answer, but at least you are on your way. It is far better to guess and be wrong than not to guess at all.

However, we will offer one caution here. Be careful that your arithmetic is correct. Incorrect arithmetic can lead to two difficulties: First, if you make an arithmetic mistake that causes you to rate a high guess as low, or vice versa, you will then be guessing in the wrong direction and you will get very confused. Second, if you make an arithmetic mistake on a guess that would actually turn out to be the right answer, you will *really* be confused because you won't make that guess again and you might think the problem is not solvable.

Here's another problem to guess and check.

FARMER JONES

Farmer Jones raises ducks and cows. She tries not to clutter her mind with too many details, but she does think it's important to remember how many animals she has and how many feet those animals have. She thinks she remembers having 54 animals with 122 feet. How many of each type of animal does Farmer Jones have? Do this problem before continuing.

Here's how Vanessa solved this problem:

Ducks	Duck Feet	Cows	Cow Feet	Total Feet (122)	Check
20	40	34	136	179	high
10	20	44	176	196	high
40	80	14	56	136	high
50	100	4	16	116	low

"At this point, I knew the answer must be somewhere between 40 ducks and 50 ducks, since 40 ducks gave a high result and 50 ducks gave a low result. The other interesting thing was my second guess. My first guess was too high, so I guessed a smaller number the second time. This actually gave me more total feet, so I was guessing in the wrong direction. I thought this was strange, but then I realized that ducks have fewer feet than cows: decreasing the number of ducks would increase the number of cows and add more feet.

"I continued guessing and checking numbers between 40 and 50."

Ducks	Duck Feet	Cows	Cow Feet	Total Feet (122)	Check
20	40	34	136	179	high
10	20	44	176	196	high
40	80	14	56	136	high
50	100	4	16	116	low
45	90	9	36	126	low
47	94	7	28	122	right

"Of course, whenever you work a word problem you should give your answer in words: There are 47 ducks and 7 cows."

There is more than one way to set up a chart. Vanessa set up her chart like this:

Ducks	Duck Feet	Cows	Cow Feet	Total Feet (122)	Check

The chart could also have been set up like this:

Ducks	Cows	Duck feet	Cow feet	Total feet (122)	Check

The Cows and Duck Feet columns have been reversed, which might help you keep in mind that the ducks and cows have to add up to 54. Here's still another way to set up the chart:

Ducks	Duck feet	Cow feet	Cows	Sum of animals (54)	Check
20	40				

Let's follow the guess of "20 ducks" through this chart. We know there is a total of 122 feet, so there must be 82 cow feet because 40 feet are used up on ducks.

Ducks	Duck feet	Cow feet	Cows	Sum of animals (54)	Check
20	40	82			

Because there are 82 cow feet, at 4 feet per cow, we get 20.5 cows (dividing by 4). This gives a total of 40.5 ducks and cows, which is low because there are supposed to be 54 animals.

Ducks	Duck feet	Cow feet	Cows	Sum of animals (54)	Check
20	40	82	20.5	40.5	low

There is nothing sacred about how a chart is set up. Set up your chart in a way that is meaningful to you. If it works, great, but if it doesn't work you have to be willing to scrap it and start again. In any case, using at least *some* kind of chart is very helpful in keeping your work organized and eventually leading you to a solution.

And one more thing: **Note** the arithmetic mistake in the first line of Vanessa's chart. With her first guess (20 ducks), she should have ended up with 176 in the Total Feet column, not 179. This error didn't affect the solution of the problem, because the guess was correctly labeled "high". But suppose 20 ducks had been the right answer—this error would have led Vanessa to believe that the problem was not solvable. Or maybe 20 ducks should have been labeled "low"—but this error caused her to label the guess as "high."

Arithmetic errors like this can be very difficult to catch. (In fact, this error wasn't caught in any of the many reprints of this book's first edition!) Our point is, make sure you do your arithmetic very carefully. If you're having trouble finding a solution to a problem that you seem to understand, it may be that your arithmetic is at fault. Check your arithmetic for all of your guesses before you proceed further.

Here's another problem to hone your newfound skills on.

ALL AROUND THE PLAYING FIELD

The perimeter of a rectangular playing field measures 504 yards. Its length is 6 yards shorter than twice its width. What is its area? Solve this problem before continuing. You might find that a diagram is helpful as well as guess-and-check.

Brad's solution:

"First I drew a picture of a rectangle to represent the field. I figured I had to guess the width and length. It seemed like it was easier to guess the width, because then I could double it and subtract

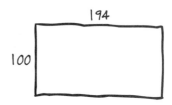

6 for the length. I put my guesses on my diagram as well as in the chart I made."

"This problem essentially breaks down into two subproblems: First find the dimensions and then find the area by using the dimensions. [Breaking a problem down into several subproblems will be the subject of Chapter 7.] I decided to worry about the dimensions first, and after I got them right I would get the area. My diagram helped me realize that the perimeter of a rectangle is twice the width plus twice the length. I had to be sure to go around the whole figure."

Width	Length	Twice Width	Twice Length	Perimeter (504)	Rating
100	194	200	388	588	high
60	114	120	228	348	low
80	154	160	308	468	low
90	174	180	348	528	high
85	164	170	328	498	low
87	168	174	336	510	high
86	166	172	332	504	right

"I couldn't believe how many guesses it took me to get the right answer. My diagram was getting really cluttered with all the eraser marks. I actually ended up drawing new rectangles about every third guess to make it easier on my eraser.

"Finally, after all those guesses, all I had to do was multiply the length times the width (86 yards × 166 yards) to get 14,276 square yards for the area, which answers the question."

Notice in Brad's work that he "bracketed" the right answer. Guessing a width of 60 produced a perimeter that was too low. Guessing a width of 100 produced a perimeter that was too high. He knew that the right answer for the width was between 60 and 100. So he then guessed a number between 60 and 100 to further narrow the range in which the answer lay. His next guess of 80 yards revealed that 80 was too low, and he continued working between 80 and 100 yards.

He also started by guessing the obviously smaller number, the width. Guessing the smaller number generally helps by limiting the range of possible numbers, and allows you to multiply and add to get another number rather than having to divide or subtract.

Note in Brad's work that he drew a diagram and found it helpful. He was also willing to draw several diagrams when his original became too messy. As mentioned in Chapter 1, many people resist drawing a diagram. However, those who go to the extra trouble (about five seconds' worth) find that it pays off in increased understanding.

DAN'S NICKELS AND QUARTERS

Dan has twice as much money in nickels as he does in quarters. He has 33 coins in all (all nickels and quarters). How much money does he have? As usual, work this problem before continuing.

Before reading the solution, make sure you interpreted the problem correctly: Dan does not have twice as many nickels as quarters, but rather has twice as much monetary value in nickels as in quarters. The distinction is huge, and you may need to work the problem again before continuing.

Nathan and Adrian really liked guess-and-check a lot—so much so, in fact, that they nicknamed themselves Gus and Chuck. These nicknames stuck for several years, although most people had to employ a guess-and-check strategy to determine which boy answered to which nickname. Gus and Chuck approached the problem this way:

GUS: Let's set up a chart. These coin problems are all the same. We need a Nickels column, a Quarters column, a Value of Quarters column, a Value of Nickels column, and a Total Value column.

Quarters	Nickels	Value of Quarters	Value of Nickels	Total Value	Rating
5	10	$1.25	$0.50	$1.75	?

CHUCK: Wait a minute, Gus. You've got this all wrong. The problem says that the value of the nickels is twice the value of the quarters. And you left out the bit about 33 coins. If it said that the number of nickels was twice the number of quarters, it would be 11 quarters and 22 nickels. But it doesn't say that. So we need to start over.

GUS: You're right, Chuck. How about this?

Quarters	Value of Quarters	Nickels	Value of Nickels	Total Coins	Rating
20	$5.00	15	$0.75	35	?

CHUCK: That's not bad, but I think it's too inconvenient to check that way. Let's try this:

Quarters	Nickels	Total Coins	Value of Quarters	Value of Nickels	Rating
10	23	33	$2.50	$1.15	too high

GUS: What does "too high" mean?

CHUCK: It means we have too many quarters. The nickels are supposed to be worth twice as much money as the quarters. So we need fewer quarters and more nickels. But we have to keep guessing so that we have 33 coins all the time.

GUS: Okay, so if we guess 5 quarters, we would need 28 nickels to make it 33 coins.

Quarters	Nickels	Total Coins	Value of Quarters	Value of Nickels	Rating
10	23	33	$2.50	$1.15	too high
5	28	33	$1.25	$1.40	too high
2	31	33	$0.50	$1.55	too high
3	30	33	$0.75	$1.50	right

GUS: Wow, that wasn't so bad. So Dan had 3 quarters and 30 nickels. Was that the question?

CHUCK: No, the question was how much money does he have? This adds up to $2.25. So Dan had $2.25.

Again, **note** that Gus and Chuck were willing to start over several times. The magical, wonderfully perfect chart will not necessarily show up the first time you try a problem. Don't be afraid to discard your first approach in favor of a more efficient one. And sometimes you may find you want to go back to your first approach again.

Gus and Chuck were also not afraid to be wrong. Their first few guesses could not have been right because they did not even match some of the conditions of the problem. But those guesses were an important part of the solution process, and without their willingness to be wrong, Gus and Chuck might have just given up and called themselves stuck.

Mewa solved this problem with a diagram. "It occurred to me that if you were going to have twice as much money in nickels as in quarters, then you needed to have 10 nickels for every quarter. I knew this because 10 nickels are 50 cents and 1 quarter is 25 cents, so that would be twice as much money in nickels as in quarters. So I drew a diagram of 10 nickels and 1 quarter."

$$\begin{array}{cccc} N & N & N & N \\ \quad N & \quad N & \quad N & \\ N & N & N & \\ & & Q & \end{array}$$

"That was 11 coins. So for 33 coins I needed to have three of those diagrams. Because I figured that out, I didn't even bother drawing the diagram. So Dan has 30 nickels and 3 quarters, which gives him $2.25."

FERDIE'S ROLLER COASTER

Ferdie was excited. Tonight was the night of the big party, and Ferdie had been practicing his opening lines all week. However, as soon as Ferdie got to the party, 20 of the girls at the party left. There now remained 2 boys for each girl, much to Ferdie's chagrin. A lot of the other boys also thought the party was pathetic, so 20 of the boys also left. There were now 3 times as many girls as boys. This made Ferdie happy. How many boys and girls were at the party when Ferdie got there? Solve this problem before continuing.

This is Robert's contribution to the solution of this problem:

Total	Minus 20 Girls
100	80

This chart is pretty confusing, and one of the reasons for that is the word "total." It's hard to tell what "total" means here.

Here is his second try:

Start (Boys)	(Girls)	Minus 20 Girls (Boys)	(Girls)
50	50	50	30

And now his third try:

End (Boys)	(Girls)	Before 20 Boys Leave (Boys)	(Girls)	Check
1	5	21	5	Nope—has to be a 3:1 boy:girl ratio. This is a 4.2:1 ratio.
10	50	30	50	Nope—this is a 6:1 ratio.
5	20	25	20	Nope—this is a 1.25:1 ratio.

"This problem was getting me totally frustrated. I first started guessing wildly, with no idea of what I should be guessing. This last chart I made looked like it had potential, but it seems like it could take forever because I am guessing two things. I thought by starting at the end and working backwards, it might help. However, even though I am a little less confused, it seems like I'll never be done."

At this point Rickey came over to help Robert. After Robert showed Rickey everything he had tried so far, Rickey came up with a good suggestion: "Why don't you try guessing starting from the middle?"

Robert said, "I don't understand what you mean."

Rickey said, "Let me show you." He drew the following.

Start		Middle		End	
Boys	Girls	Boys	Girls	Boys	Girls
		50	25		

Rickey said, "See? Start guessing in the middle and then work backwards to the beginning (have the 20 girls come back) as well as working forwards to the end (have the 20 boys leave). But make the middle guess have the right ratio of 2 boys for each girl."

Robert said, "Oh, I see. So for 50 boys and 25 girls in the middle, there would be 50 boys and 45 girls at the start, and 30 boys and 25 girls at the end. But how do I check to see if it's right? Oh, wait, don't tell me. I just have to check to see if the ratio of girls to boys at the end is 3:1."

Rickey said, "Right. Go to it."

Start		Middle (Guess Here) 20 Girls Leave		End 20 Boys Leave		End Ratio
Boys	Girls	Boys	Girls	Boys	Girls	Girl:Boy
50	45	50	25	30	25	.833:1
60	50	60	30	40	30	.75:1
30	35	30	15	10	15	1.5:1
20	30	20	10	0	10	10:0
		25	12.5			
26	33	26	13	6	13	2.2:1
24	32	24	12	4	12	3:1

Robert said, "Finally. But at least this way, by always guessing the middle numbers and making sure that the middle boys-to-girls ratio was always 2:1, I saw that I was going to get there eventually. My second guess went the wrong way, since the ratio got further away from 3:1 instead of closer. And I made that other guess of 25 boys to 12.5 girls. That didn't seem like it would help too much, because you couldn't have half of a girl. Actually, if I had carried that guess all the way out, I could still have learned something. This was a pretty tough problem, but guess-and-check really helped a lot. Working backwards part of the way helped too."

"It was also nice to have a second brain working on it. It's funny, even though we've worked together quite a bit in this class, I still feel somewhat resentful when someone comes over to work with me. But working together with someone almost always helps me think more clearly. I hope I get over this attitude of resentment. It's weird that I would feel that way anyway, because I love working in groups."

Note that the guess-and-check system that was finally successful for Robert partially employed the strategy of working backwards. This is a very powerful strategy that will be discussed more fully in Chapter 11. Also **note** that at one point Robert made a guess that was worse than his previous guess. This often happens in guess-and-check. Sometimes it's very difficult to figure out whether a particular guess is too high or too low. When this happens, use your next guess to help you. Consider the direction in which your results are going. If a guess gets you closer to the correct result, you've changed in the right direction. If, on the other hand, you're getting farther from the correct result, make your next guess in the opposite direction.

Robert also made some comments about groups. Some people resent the idea that they might require a second brain to solve a problem. Their perception is that they are somehow not smart enough to reach a solution on their own. But this resentment usually passes quickly as their group works toward a solution. While it is probable that you can eventually solve most problems alone, it is very beneficial to have the input of other people: Solutions are usually achieved more quickly, and it's helpful to see how other people think because doing so makes you a better thinker.

Studies have shown that the number-one reason people are fired from jobs is the inability to work well with other people. Can you think of any job in which you'd work in complete isolation with absolutely no personal contact? Most jobs require lots of contact with people, and those jobs are made a lot easier if you can interact well with people. You will also need to work together with people in other areas of life. A family needs to communicate and cooperate to function smoothly. Successful social organizations need lots of volunteers working together. Good friendships are based on communication. Working with others is a skill that cannot be overemphasized. Seek out opportunities to work with others as much as possible. Problem solving is a good opportunity to practice your cooperative behaviors.

Cloe is two years less than four times as old as Zeke. Cloe is also one year more than three times as old as Zeke. How old is each? Work this problem before reading on.

Bart used guess-and-check to work this problem and came up with the following solution:

CLOE'S AGE	ZEKE'S AGE	
5	?	

Bart remarked: "To find Zeke's age, I would have to add 2 years on to Cloe's age and then divide by 4, giving $1^{3}/_{4}$. So in other words, Zeke isn't even 2 yet. This would be fine, except that the other part of the problem meant I had to add more to the chart."

CLOE'S AGE	ZEKE'S AGE	
5	$1^{3}/_{4}$	

"Computing Zeke's age the other way (Cloe is also 1 year more than 3 times as old as Zeke), I came up with Zeke being $1^{1}/_{3}$ years old. I was encouraged that these two numbers at least came out close to each other, but it wasn't the right answer because they weren't the same.

"I decided to change my chart because it was too hard to calculate Zeke's age if I had Cloe's age. It would be much easier to calculate Cloe's age if I guessed Zeke's age."

ZEKE'S AGE	4 × ZEKE	CLOE'S AGE 4× ZEKE – 2	3× ZEKE	CLOE'S AGE 3× ZEKE + 1	RATING
1	4	2	3	4	WRONG

At this point, Bart said he knew that the numbers in the third and fifth columns of his chart had to be equal because they both represented

Cloe's age. But he didn't know if having a 2 in one column and a 4 in the other meant he needed to guess higher or lower. "However," he noted, "there are a lot more ages higher than Zeke's than there are lower, so I'll start guessing some higher ages."

ZEKE'S AGE	4 × ZEKE	CLOE'S AGE 4× ZEKE − 2	3× ZEKE	CLOE'S AGE 3× ZEKE + 1	RATING
1	4	2	3	4	WRONG
2	8	6	6	7	CLOSER
4	16	14	12	13	HIGH (3RD COL. HIGHER THAN 5TH)
3	12	10	9	10	JUST RIGHT!

"Zeke is 3 years old, and Cloe is 10."

Reconsider some of the things Bart did that made him successful on this problem:

1. He wasn't afraid to guess.

2. When things didn't go quite right, he was willing to back up and start again. He continued using the method of guess-and-check, but changed how he went about making his guesses and organizing his chart. (Originally he guessed Cloe's age, but because this was too hard he changed to guessing Zeke's age.)

3. He guessed smaller numbers and worked up to bigger numbers.

4. He kept working until he found an answer.

Use guess-and-check to work the following problem.

THE MONA AND LISA PAINTING PROBLEM

Working alone, Mona can paint a room in four hours. Working alone, Lisa could paint the same room in three hours. About how long should it take them to paint the room if they work together? Show the answer to the nearest tenth of an hour. Work this problem before reading on.

Aimee approached the problem like this: "The key is knowing that each of them gets a certain part of the room painted in each hour.

"Mona can paint one-fourth of the room in one hour, whereas Lisa can paint one-third of the room. I used my calculator on this, so I set it up as Mona doing 0.25 rooms each hour and Lisa doing 0.33 rooms each hour. I knew 0.33 is a little bit off, but I knew, if I needed to, I could go back and make it more accurate after I got close to the answer. Knowing the work rate, I could calculate the part of the room painted by multiplying. For example, using Mona's work rate, if she works 5 hours she will paint 1.25 rooms (0.25 times 5).

"To check, I wanted the total painted to equal 1, as that represents one room painted."

Her chart looked like this:

Guess (Hours)	Amount Mona Paints	Amount Lisa Paints	Total Painted	Rating
5	1.25	1.65	2.90	high
2	.5	.66	1.16	high
1	.25	.33	.58	low
1.5	.375	.495	.87	low
1.8	.45	.594	1.044	high
1.7	.425	.561	.986	low
1.75	.4375	.5775	1.015	high

"Since we were looking for the answer to the nearest tenth, I figured I was done because 1.7 was too low and 1.75 was too high. Anything in between those two numbers would still round off to 1.7 anyway, so it wasn't important to know the answer to any more decimal places. Who knows, they could have stopped to get a soda, and that makes your answer completely wrong anyway. So, I was done. Mona and Lisa painted for approximately 1.7 hours."

Aimee stated very succinctly the dilemma of producing an exact answer. In a real sense, her answer would probably be wrong anyway because of the inexact nature of the problem as presented.

Carlos also worked the problem and took a slightly different approach:

"I worked on this problem for a little bit using fractions. I saw that if they worked for one hour, Mona painted $1/4$ of the room and Lisa painted $1/3$ of the room. After a few guesses, I realized that I could just add the $1/4$ and $1/3$ together to get how much they painted together in one hour. So I added them and got $7/12$. So they did $7/12$ of the room in one hour. This would mean they would paint $14/12$ of the room in two hours. So it wouldn't take them two hours to paint the whole room."

Hours	Mona Work Rate	Lisa Work Rate	Mona Work Done	Lisa Work Done	Total Work Done
1	$1/4$	$1/3$	$1/4$	$1/3$	$7/12$
2	$1/4$	$1/3$	$2/4$	$2/3$	$14/12$ (or $1\,1/6$)

"It suddenly occurred to me that to make $7/12$ of a painted room come out to one whole room, I had to multiply by the reciprocal of $7/12$. This is where I realized that I didn't have to spend the rest of my life adding fractions to find the answer. I knew that when I multiplied through by $12/7$, the Total Work Done column would have to come out to 1."

Hours	Mona Work Rate	Lisa Work Rate	Mona Work Done	Lisa Work Done	Total Work Done
$12/7$	$1/4$	$1/3$	$3/7$	$4/7$	$7/7 = 1$

"I don't know if I ever would have guessed $1\,5/7$, but that had to be the answer: $1\,5/7$ hours. Or, as the problem asked for, 1.7."

Some people who recognize the next type of problem probably also remember the gut-wrenching feeling of not being able to set up the algebraic equation. Guess-and-check is a useful tool for developing algebraic equations in situations where an equation is desirable. This will be explored more in Chapter 13: Algebra.

NEXT TRAIN EAST

A train leaves Roseville heading east at 6:00 a.m. at 40 miles per hour. Another eastbound train leaves on a parallel track at 7:00 a.m. at 50 miles per hour. What time will it be when the two trains are the same distance away from Roseville? Do not read on until you've worked this problem.

This is a typical problem from an algebra class. In algebra you were probably taught to set up a rate-time-distance chart, then choose a variable and write an equation. This type of problem broke down into three subtypes: same-direction problems, opposite-directions problems, and round-trip problems. You probably had to memorize three different equations for the three different subtypes. Many students get frustrated by these problems because they are unable to master these equations.

Guess-and-check can be a lifesaver in algebra class. Guess-and-check helps you get started with a problem and then, obviously, helps lead to a solution. As you will see in Chapter 13: Algebra, guess-and-check also helps you set up an equation in cases where your teacher requires one or when guessing just becomes too tedious and slow.

Jerel encountered the Next Train East problem in his algebra class. "I hate these rate-time-distance problems. I never could figure out what the equation was, so I just skipped them. When the teacher asked me why, I just said, 'I don't do rate-time-distance problems. Some people don't do windows, I don't do those kind of word problems.' But then one of my friends taught me guess-and-check. What a great method! I'll never fear a word problem again.

"This problem was kind of tough. I knew how fast the trains were going, but I didn't know how long they had been traveling and how far they went. I figured I should guess their times, and then I would be able to figure out how far they went. So I started to set up a chart."

6:00 TRAIN TRAVEL TIME	7:00 TRAIN TRAVEL TIME
10 HOURS	10 HOURS

"I wrote down 10 hours for each train, and then I tried to figure out how to check to see if this was right. After I read the problem again, I realized that the time for the 7:00 train had to be one hour less because it left an hour later. So I changed my guess, and then I figured out how fast they each went."

6:00 TRAIN TRAVEL TIME	7:00 TRAIN TRAVEL TIME	6:00 TRAIN SPEED	7:00 TRAIN SPEED
10 HOURS	9 HOURS	40 MPH	50 MPH

"I then wanted to put the distances on my chart, but I was running out of room. My friend taught me that one guess should fit on one line of my paper. If it carried over into two lines, it was too confusing. He said to make the titles smaller and use more lines for them. So I crossed out my first chart and started over."

6:00 TRAIN TIME	7:00 TRAIN TIME	6:00 TRAIN SPEED	7:00 TRAIN SPEED	6:00 TRAIN DIST.	7:00 TRAIN DIST.	RATING
10 HR	9 HR	40 MPH	50 MPH	400 MI	450 MI	?

"I had no idea if my guess was high or low. That's another thing my friend taught me: Sometimes you can't tell whether your first guess is high or low. So he said to make another guess in one direction, then carefully analyze it and figure out if you are better or worse off than you were before. This is sometimes hard to do, but it is good advice and I try to follow it. I decided that my guess was too low, so I guessed more hours."

6:00 TRAIN TIME	7:00 TRAIN TIME	6:00 TRAIN SPEED	7:00 TRAIN SPEED	6:00 TRAIN DIST.	7:00 TRAIN DIST.	RATING
10 HR	9 HR	40 MPH	50 MPH	400 MI	450 MI	?
14 HR	13 HR	40 MPH	50 MPH	560 MI	650 MI	WORSE

"I decided that this next guess was worse, because the miles between the two trains got further apart. Then it occurred to me why. In my first guess, the early train had gone 400 miles and the later train had gone 450 miles. Since the later train had already passed the early train, the travel time must be less than I was guessing. This was what my friend meant when he said really analyze the guess to see which way it is off. So I made my next guess lower than 10, not just lower than 14, because 10 had been too high in the first place. My next guess turned out too low because the later train hadn't caught up yet. I got it on my fourth guess."

6:00 TRAIN TIME	7:00 TRAIN TIME	6:00 TRAIN SPEED	7:00 TRAIN SPEED	6:00 TRAIN DIST.	7:00 TRAIN DIST.	RATING
10 HR	9 HR	40 MPH	50 MPH	400 MI	450 MI	?
14 HR	13 HR	40 MPH	50 MPH	560 MI	650 MI	WORSE
3 HR	2 HR	40 MPH	50 MPH	120 MI	100 MI	LOW
5 HR	4 HR	40 MPH	50 MPH	200 MI	200 MI	RIGHT

"So it will be 11:00 a.m. when the two trains are the same distance away from Roseville. That's another thing my friend told me: Make sure you answer the question. Like, this question could have been 'How far away are the two trains from Roseville when the later train catches up?' That answer would be 200 miles. My friend told me to watch out for questions like that and make sure I answer them. Boy, I love guess-and-check. It sure has saved my bacon a few times."

Liz solved this problem in a different way: "I drew a diagram of the two trains going in the same direction, one leaving an hour later than the other."

"Then I made a list of possible times and how far away each train was from Roseville at each of those times."

Time	Distance of First Train	Distance of Second Train	Difference Between Distances
7:00	40 mi	0 mi	40 mi
8:00	80 mi	50 mi	30 mi
9:00	120 mi	100 mi	20 mi
10:00	160 mi	150 mi	10 mi
11:00	200 mi	200 mi	0 mi

"I also noticed a pattern here. The difference between the two trains went down by ten miles each hour. That's because the second train goes ten miles per hour faster. 'Eleven o'clock' answers the question."

How Guess-and-Check Saved the Day and Changed the Rest of My Life

Holly works as the office manager and bookkeeper of a law firm in San Francisco, California. One fateful day, she faced a problem she couldn't solve. Now, Holly is no slouch when it comes to mathematics. It's just that she had yet to be exposed to guess-and-check.

The problem she encountered on that day was a tax-payment problem. The law firm's partners used a profit-sharing fund to legally reduce their personal taxes and to provide more money and other benefits for their deserving employees. It was Holly's responsibility to determine the amount of each partner's income to contribute to the profit-sharing fund.

The fund was set up in such a way that the partners reduced their personal taxes based on how much they contributed to the fund. Their contributions were limited by an equation given by the Internal Revenue Service—essentially, to a percentage of the personal income of the highest-paid partner. But the incomes of the partners couldn't be determined until the contributions had been deducted from them. And, of course, one way to figure out how much of a contribution to deduct was to know the personal income of each partner. Yet, again, knowing the amount of personal income could not be determined until the contributions were deducted! Thus, Holly was confronted with a "tax and law" version of the old question "Which came first: the chicken or the egg?" In this case, which came first: the determination of personal income or the declaration of profit-sharing amounts?

Two things Holly considered were her employers' financial well-being and her own financial well-being. She was trying to lawfully maximize the partners' personal income. And she was trying to maximize the size of the profit-sharing fund because she was a direct beneficiary of that fund. These objectives were mutually beneficial: By maximizing the legal contributions to the fund, she not only reduced each of the partners' incomes (and thereby their taxes), she also managed to maximize her own income.

One of the complicating factors was that the social security tax, part of the total tax deducted from earned income, is a tiered type of tax. That is, the social security deduction is not simply a fixed portion of one's income. It's calculated based on what level that income has reached.

Holly worked on the problem all afternoon in the office and spent a few more hours on it at home. She didn't reach an answer, though she had a reasonably good estimate of the percentage of the partners' income to contribute to the fund.

For those familiar with algebra, Holly started with three equations and three unknowns, which boiled down to a very complicated quadratic equation. It appeared that this equation could be solved by using the quadratic formula. But because of the amount of manipulation involved in producing and then solving the equation, she introduced a large amount of error through calculator rounding and limited decimal capacity.

She then called her son. She gave him the information, and after about 45 minutes of fooling with the equations, he called her back to report an answer that he didn't trust. Indeed, *his* calculator answer was sufficiently different from *her* calculator answer to declare a mistrial. They decided neither answer could be trusted.

At this point, they decided to use guess-and-check instead of algebra. They programmed a computer to guess possible solutions and check them. After about 15 minutes of programming and 45 seconds of run time, the computer produced an answer. And the answer also turned out to be readily verifiable, which is something that the previous answers were not, especially because the previous answers were close but wrong.

Using traditional algebraic methods requires you to understand the whole problem much earlier in the solution process than you would using guess-and-check. With the guess-and-check strategy, you can develop a fuller understanding of the problem as you work through the process. But guess-and-check is not always taught in algebra classes, although we think it should be. This strategy often works when algebra doesn't, and it helps builds algebraic concepts when you are learning algebra.

But **remember** to apply this problem-solving strategy when appropriate. Guess-and-check does not perform miracles, but it helps organize information in such a way that you can make that information more useful. It's up to you to take advantage of the strategy. It is like any tool: Used properly, it will help you do the job.

The key points to **remember** about guess-and-check are

1. Start guessing. As you work through a guess, you'll learn more about the problem.

2. Keep your work organized. Guess-and-check helps you organize information. You will defeat this strategy (and yourself) if you don't keep your guesses organized.

3. Be ready to start over. As you learn more by working through guesses, you may discover that your first approach was not productive.

4. Start with smaller numbers and build up to bigger numbers. Let your guesses skip around so you can bracket the right answer.

5. Sometimes you'll misrate a guess, rating a high guess low or a low guess high. It may take two guesses to determine what is high and what is low. Be patient when this happens, and every time you are about to rate a new guess, pay close attention to guesses you made previously.

6. Be very careful to avoid arithmetic mistakes.

    a. If you make a mistake in a rating, you will then make subsequent guesses in the wrong direction.

    b. If you make a mistake with the right answer, you may never guess that number again.

7. Put a lot of information in your column titles so that you know what each column represents. You may have to use several lines to accommodate the long titles, because you want each guess to fit on one line. Generally the contents of your columns will be numbers, so the columns don't have to be wide but they have to be descriptive.

Guess-and-check is a tremendously powerful strategy. Keep the preceding points in mind, and you will enjoy great success.

Problem Set A

1. DIMES AND QUARTERS

Annette has five more dimes than quarters. The total amount of money she has is $3.30. How many of each coin does she have?

2. MARKDOWN

Jenny bought ski gloves that were marked down 30% to $24.01. What was the price of the gloves before the markdown?

3. TAX

The cost of a basketball was $15.54, including 7.25% sales tax. How much of that cost was the price of the basketball, and how much of it was the tax?

4. REFINANCING

The mortgage payments for Covell's home are about $900 per month. He is going to refinance the loan, which will cost him about $2,500 in fees, and the new payments will be $830 per month. How long will it take him before the new loan starts saving him money?

5. NEW CONTRACT

"Bullet Train" Benson was negotiating a new contract with his team. He wanted $700,000 for the year and an additional $1,800 for every game he started. His team was offering $5,000 for every game started but only a $600,000 base salary. How many starts would he need to make in order to earn more with the team's offer?

6. CHECKING ACCOUNT

Recently Javier received a letter from his bank concerning his checking account. Under his current plan, each check he writes costs 15¢ and there is a monthly fee of $1.60. Under the proposed new plan, each check he writes will cost 12¢ and there will be a monthly fee of $2.75. What is the minimum number of checks Javier must write monthly so that the new plan will cost him less than the current plan does?

7. WEIRD NUMBER

If you take a certain two-digit number and reverse its digits to get another two-digit number, then add these two numbers together, their sum is 132. What is the original number?

8. BASEBALL CARDS

Rita has two more than three times the number of baseball cards that Ben has. If Rita gave Ben 12 of her cards, they would each then have the same number of cards. How many cards does Rita have?

9. STAMPS

Charlie put postage worth $1.29 on a package he sent to his sister. He used only 16¢ stamps and 7¢ stamps. How many of each type of stamp did he use?

10. A BUNCH OF CHANGE

Plato has 58 coins in nickels, dimes, and quarters. The number of nickels is three less than twice the number of dimes. The total value of the coins is $7.40. How many of each type of coin does Plato have?

11. BOYS AND GIRLS

There are nine boys to every ten girls in a particular high school. There are 2622 students at the school. How many girls are there?

12. HOW OLD ARE RONNIE AND ALAN?

Ronnie's age plus the square of Alan's age is 2240. Alan's age plus the square of Ronnie's age is 1008. How old are Ronnie and Alan?

13. TRAVELING TO MOM'S HOUSE

Joan got on her bike and went for a ride. She rode at a speed of 16 miles per hour from her house to her sister's house, which is in another city along the way. The two women then got into a car and traveled at a speed of 50 miles per hour to their mother's house. The total distance from Joan's house to her mother's house (via her sister's house) is 315 miles, and Joan traveled for 8 hours. How far is it from Joan's house to her sister's house?

14. RIDING A HORSE

Hilary went riding in the hills. At one point, however, her horse stumbled and was hurt. Hilary left the horse and walked back home to call her vet. Hilary figures the horse walks about twice as fast as she does. If her horse was hurt about 8 miles into her ride and her whole trip took 4 hours total, how fast does Hilary walk?

15. WOMEN'S WORLD CUP SOCCER

The semifinal of the 1999 Women's World Cup Soccer Match is being played at Stanford Stadium on the Fourth of July. Mia Hamm, star of the United States team, has just received the ball on a breakaway. She is 60 yards from Brazil's goal. Brazilian star Sissi is the closest opponent to Hamm and is 10 yards behind her. Mia takes off for Brazil's goal and, while dribbling the ball, is able to run at a speed of 6.8 yards per second. Sissi takes off at the same time that Hamm does and runs at 8.4 yards per second. (She is able to run faster because she isn't dribbling the soccer ball.) Hamm has decided to shoot at the exact moment that Sissi catches up to her, because at that point it will still be difficult for Sissi to block the shot when she is side by side with Hamm. How far away from the goal will Hamm be when she shoots?

16. TELEPHONE SOLICITOR

Keiko is a telephone solicitor. She has been able to convince only 18% of the people she called to donate. If she gets 12 of the next 30 to donate, she'll barely break 25% for the day. She will make about 30 more calls. How many calls has she made so far today?

17. EQUAL VOLUME

A box manufacturing company makes rectangular boxes with a square base. Their most popular box measures 27 inches wide by 27 inches long by 12 inches high. Two employees are experimenting with increasing the volume of the box. Malcolm is experimenting with increasing the measure of the height and leaving the measure of the square base alone. Rosa is experimenting with increasing the measures of both sides of the square base and leaving the measure of the height the same. They were comparing notes one day, when Malcolm said to Rosa, "Wow, what an interesting number. When you increased the measure of the base sides by this number, it gave you a volume increase that was exactly the same as the volume increase I got when I increased the measure of the height by the same number." What was that number?

18. FREE THROWS

Gail's free-throw percentage so far this season is .875. If she makes only 13 of her next 20 free throws, her percentage will drop to .860. How many free throws has Gail made this season?

19. WRITE YOUR OWN

Write your own guess-and-check problem. Start with a situation and an answer, then make up the other necessary information.

Problem Set B

1. DAILY ROUTINE

Aji has an argument with his daughter. She says, "You do the same darn thing every day." Aji does go fishing every day, but contends that every day is different because he does things in a different order each day. Before he leaves shore in his rowboat, he gets fresh bait, checks the weather, and adjusts his seat cushion. Out in the water, he eats his fruit, puts the meat on his sandwich, drinks his apple juice, and eats his sandwich. Back at shore, after tying his boat to the dock, he takes the fishing pole in his right hand and the ice chest in his left hand. Then he finally heads back home to have the same argument with his daughter. For how many days could Aji do things in a different order before he has to repeat the order of some prior day? Is there any easy way he could double the number of days in his cycle?

2. AFTER THE FOOTBALL GAME

A group of students went to their favorite restaurant after the football game one Friday night. They all ordered from the menu and forgot to tell the server to give them separate checks. The bill totaled $27, including the tip. They decided to split the bill evenly, and they figured out how much each of them owed. But then three people said they had no money. The rest of the people each had to chip in 45¢ extra to cover the tab. How many people were in the group?

3. CATS

I hate cats. It seems like cats hate me too. I wonder why. My neighbor Madeleine loves cats. She seems to attract them in bunches, especially alley cats, tabby cats, and Manx cats. She already had three alleys, five tabbies, and two Manx cats when more of each kind of cat began to show up on her doorstep in March. The alley cats showed up first, on the first. That is, one showed up on the first, and one new one showed up every day for the rest of the month. The tabby cats began to show up on the fourth. Two showed up on the fourth, and two new ones showed up every day for the rest of the month. Not to be outdone, the Manx cats showed up on the sixth. Four of them came on the sixth, and four new ones came every day for the rest of the month. How many cats did Madeleine have at the end of the month?

4. STOCK MARKET

Ms. Edwards and three other high school students decided to pretend to invest in the stock market. They all chose one big-name stock to invest in, and each "invested" $1,000 of pretend money. After one month, they checked the stock listings to see how they did. It turned out that three of the girls came out ahead and the other girl lost money. From the clues below, determine the full name of each girl, what stock she "invested" in, and how much each girl made or lost.

1. Two people made more money than the girl who invested in Mokalani Natural Foods.

2. Ms. Kortright did not invest in iscreamuscream.com, but the girl who did made the most money.

3. Denise made $700, which made her the big winner.

4. Ms. McDonald lost $300, and Tina made $200.

5. Nita did not invest in Frisbie Airlines.

6. The girl who invested in Pan Hellenic Shipping was the only one who lost money.

7. Luann, who is neither Ms. Kortright nor Ms. McElhatton, made $300 less than Denise.

5. LARRY LONGWAY AGAIN

Seymour, the census taker, came to Larry Longway's house and asked for the ages of the three children living there. Because Larry does not believe in giving information away easily, he gave Seymour the following clues. The clues were given one at a time. After each clue Seymour really tried to figure it out. If he couldn't figure it out, he then asked for another clue.

Clue 1: The product of their ages is 72.

From this clue, Seymour tried but could not figure out the ages.

Clue 2: The sum of their ages is the same as today's date.

Seymour knew what the date was, but he still could not figure out the ages.

Clue 3: The oldest child loves to eat at Burger Jack.

From this clue, Seymour was able to figure out the ages of the children. What are the children's ages?

Many complex real-world activities, like manufacturing automobiles, are broken down into subproblems, like attaching a door. These subproblems may be divided again into smaller subproblems that must be solved to attain the overall goal.

7

Subproblems

U p to this point, you've learned about two of the three major problem-solving themes of this book, both of which have involved organizing information in some way. When you drew a diagram, you organized information spatially, so diagrams fall under the major theme we call **Spatial Organization**. When you used other strategies, such as making a systematic list or using guess-and-check, you organized information into some sort of a table or a list, which fall under the major theme we call **Organizing Information**.

The strategy you'll learn about in this chapter is different. The strategy of **subproblems** involves organizing your plan of attack. When you use subproblems, you first move your focus away from the main problem you're working with and instead concentrate on achieving a subgoal. When you've achieved your subgoal, you can then solve the main problem, which is your overall goal. Subproblems fit into the third major problem-solving theme, which we call **Changing Focus**.

When a solution method for a problem is not readily apparent, try using the strategy of subproblems. Here is a simple example that will illustrate the concept. The Scholastic Aptitude Test (SAT) is full of problems for which you need to use subproblems, such as this one:

If $3x - 1 = 17$, what is $2x - 4$?

To solve this problem, you must first solve for x in the equation $3x - 1 = 17$. You then substitute the value of x into the expression $2x - 4$. **Note** that you couldn't answer the given question until you'd solved for x first. This "miniproblem" that you solve first is called a subproblem, and it must be solved before you answer the given question.

Some problems involve many subproblems. To attack these types of problems, you'll find it helpful to list the subproblems before starting on the problem's solution: The list becomes your plan of attack. You can then solve each subproblem and in turn reach a solution to the overall problem. And making a list of subproblems can focus your thinking. If you decide you need help with the overall problem, your list of subproblems will help you determine exactly *where* you need help.

According to our friend and mentor Tom Sallee, a professor at the University of California at Davis, solving a problem by using subproblems is much like crossing a river by using stepping stones. If the river is very wide, it isn't possible to jump all the way across it. But by walking through the river on stepping stones, you can make it all the way across. So for problems that are not possible to solve all at once (jumping across the whole river), you can use subproblems (the stepping stones) to achieve your goal of solving the overall problem (getting across the river).

The next problem contains some simple subproblems. List the subproblems and solve them before reading on. (**Hint:** It is helpful to list each subproblem as a question.)

LITTLE GREEN APPLES

How many apples, each of which weighs 2 ounces, are needed to balance three 2-pound weights? Do this problem before continuing.

A typical student-teacher conversation about this problem might go something like this (this student has never heard of the strategy called subproblems, although as you will see, he understands the strategy quite well):

STUDENT:	I need help on this problem.
TEACHER:	Well, what don't you understand?
STUDENT:	I don't understand any of it.
TEACHER:	Well, show me what you've tried.
STUDENT:	I threw it away.
TEACHER:	Why did you throw it away?
STUDENT:	My answer didn't match the one in the back of the book.
TEACHER:	Can you remember anything that you did?
STUDENT:	Yeah. First I figured out the number of apples in 1 pound, and that was 8 because there are 16 ounces in a pound and an apple weighs 2 ounces.
TEACHER:	That's right.
STUDENT:	Then I figured out that the apples had to balance 6 pounds because the problem said there were three weights, each weighing 2 pounds.
TEACHER:	That's right too. I thought you said you didn't understand anything about this problem.
STUDENT:	Well, I didn't get the answer right.
TEACHER:	But so far you have understood the problem completely. Go on, what did you do next?
STUDENT:	Since 8 apples weighed 1 pound and there were 6 pounds to balance, I multiplied 8 times 6 and got 64 apples. But that answer was wrong, so I threw it away.
TEACHER:	You multiplied 8 times 6 and got what?
STUDENT:	I got 64. Oh no, it's 48. Thanks. See ya.

This conversation illustrates two things. First—and probably most important—the student really understood the process of using subproblems to find the solution, but he felt that since he hadn't gotten the "right answer" all his work was meaningless. This reaction couldn't be further from the truth. He made only one minor mistake in one of the many subproblems that he'd found and solved. Second, had the student understood the concept of subproblems, he could have shown the teacher his work, including all the stated subproblems. The teacher would have been able to determine quickly that the student understood the whole process. The teacher would also have been able to quickly tell the student that his only mistake was in multiplication and to assure him that his reasoning was perfect—only his mechanics were flawed.

Debbie solved the Little Green Apples problem like this: First, she listed the subproblems shown below—**note** that Debbie's subproblems are the same ones used by the student in the conversation you just read. The difference is that Debbie knows how helpful it is to write the subproblems down rather than just think about them. Writing them down focuses her thinking and gives her a written plan of attack. Instead of trying to find the answer to the original question all at once, she concentrates on finding and then solving the subproblems that will lead to the final answer.

1. How many ounces are in a pound?

2. How many apples does it take to make 1 pound?

3. How many pounds are in three 2-pound weights?

4. How many apples will balance three 2-pound weights?

After she listed the subproblems, solving them was easy.

1. How many ounces are in a pound?

   There are 16 ounces in 1 pound. Some people don't think this is a subproblem because they already know and can recall how many ounces are in a pound. Other people think this is a subproblem because they need to look up the answer.

2. How many apples does it take to make 1 pound?

   Because there are 16 ounces in 1 pound and an apple weighs 2 ounces, 8 apples will weigh 1 pound.

3. How many pounds are in three 2-pound weights?

   Six pounds. Not much of a subproblem, but you still must consider it.

4. How many apples will balance three 2-pound weights?

   Because 8 apples weigh 1 pound and together the weights equal 6 pounds, 48 apples will weigh 6 pounds and will balance the three weights.

Note that the fourth subproblem is actually a restatement of the original problem. The first three subproblems lead in the direction of solving the original problem.

Guille used a different set of subproblems:

1. How many ounces are in a pound?

2. How many pounds are in three 2-pound weights?

3. How many ounces are in three 2-pound weights?

4. How many apples will balance three 2-pound weights?

The solutions to these subproblems indicate a rather different approach to the problem:

1. How many ounces are in a pound?

   There are 16 ounces in a pound.

2. How many pounds are in three 2-pound weights?

   There are 6 pounds in three 2-pound weights.

3. How many ounces are in three 2-pound weights?

   Because there are 16 ounces in a pound and there are 6 pounds, there are 96 ounces.

4. How many apples will balance three 2-pound weights?

   An apple weighs 2 ounces, so dividing 96 by 2 gives 48 apples in 96 ounces.

Notice that both Debbie and Guille got the same answer, 48 apples, to this problem (isn't it nice when you get the same answer each time you do a problem?), but each approached the problem differently. There is often more than one set of subproblems that will solve a problem.

Problems that appear to be difficult often seem much easier once they're broken into subproblems. In fact, listing the subproblems gives you a plan of action. And your list helps you identify known information and what you need to figure out.

Three quarts of water are needed to water 1 square foot of lawn. How many gallons of water are needed to water a lawn that measures 30 feet by 60 feet? List the subproblems and answer the question before proceeding.

E-Chung wrote the following list of subproblems:

1. How many square feet are in the lawn?

2. How many quarts are needed to water the entire lawn?

3. How many quarts are in a gallon?

4. How many gallons are needed to water the entire lawn?

Note that these could have been listed in a different order, the only requirement being that question 1 must precede question 2, and question 4 must be last.

By listing the subproblems, E-Chung has clearly laid out the plan of attack. Finding the solution to the problem now seems relatively trivial. In fact, the hardest part of using the subproblems strategy is figuring out what the subproblems are. Once you know what you have to solve, the actual solving is usually fairly easy. The subproblems don't all have to appear like magic at the same time, well worded and in the right order. In fact, it's likely that when you come up with your subproblems, they'll be in the wrong order and will reflect a couple of different approaches to the problem. Part of solving a problem is arranging the subproblems in the right order. You may find that this task is almost automatic because a subproblem is in the wrong place only if its solution depends on the answer to another subproblem. And then it should be obvious that you need another answer before you can continue with the subproblem at hand.

This is how E-Chung solved the subproblems he listed:

1. How many square feet are in the lawn?

Because the lawn measures 30 feet by 60 feet, the area of the lawn is $30 \times 60 = 1800$ square feet.

2. How many quarts are needed to water the entire lawn?

   One square foot of lawn requires 3 quarts of water. So 1800 square feet of lawn requires 3 × 1800 = 5400 quarts of water.

3. How many quarts are in a gallon?

   Four quarts are in 1 gallon. (Again, this may not be much of a subproblem.)

4. How many gallons are needed to water the entire lawn?

   The whole lawn needs 5400 quarts. There are 4 quarts in a gallon. So, dividing 5400 quarts by 4 gives 1350 gallons to water the entire lawn.

This problem could also be solved with the set of subproblems that Romina used:

1. How many gallons does it take to water 1 square foot of lawn?

   Three quarts equals three-fourths of a gallon, which is what is needed for 1 square foot of lawn.

2. What is the area of the lawn?

   The area is 1800 square feet.

3. How many gallons does it take to water the entire lawn?

   Because each square foot of lawn requires three-fourths of a gallon and the area of the lawn is 1800 square feet, $3/4$ × 1800 = 1350 gallons.

Note that often you can use more than one set of subproblems to solve a given problem.

THE CAR BARGAIN

Paul went into the local new-car lot to buy a car. He knew the kind of car he wanted, because his friend Barbara (often called Bar) Gain had bought the same car the day before. Barbara received a 30% discount on the car, which listed at $15,000. The salesperson offered Paul the $15,000 car at a 20% discount instead. When Paul protested, the salesperson offered an additional 10% off the 20% discounted price. This offer satisfied Paul and he bought the car, convinced he had paid the same price as Barbara. Had he? Solve this problem before continuing.

Pragnesh wrote this list of subproblems:

1. What is 30% of $15,000?

2. How much did Barbara pay for the car?

3. What is 20% of $15,000?

4. What is the sale price that Paul protested?

5. What is 10% of this new price?

6. What is the final price that Paul paid for the car?

7. Who paid more and by how much?

8. How many subproblems do I have to write before the teacher is satisfied?

Again, listing the subproblems gives Pragnesh a plan of attack. Solving the subproblems does not seem too hard, even though the original problem looked rather formidable.

1. What is 30% of $15,000?

   Thirty percent of $15,000 is $4,500. This represents the amount of money that Barbara saved.

2. How much did Barbara pay for the car?

   Barbara paid $15,000 less her discount of $4,500, for a net price of $10,500.

3. What is 20% of $15,000?

   The first discount that the salesperson offered Paul was 20%. Twenty percent of $15,000 is $3,000.

4. What is the sale price that Paul protested?

   The original sale price that Paul was offered was $15,000 less $3,000, for a net price of $12,000.

5. What is 10% of this new price?

   The new price was $12,000, and 10% of this price is $1,200.

6. What is the final price that Paul paid for the car?

   Paul paid the discounted $12,000 less $1,200, for a final price of $10,800.

7. Who paid more and by how much?

   Barbara paid $10,500 and Paul paid $10,800, so Paul paid $300 more. He shouldn't have been so happy.

8. How many subproblems do I have to write before the teacher is satisfied?

   Eight is probably enough.

Problems about percentages can be very confusing, so listing subproblems for them can help you understand what's going on. **Remember** that a given percentage of *different* amounts is never the same amount. For example, suppose a baseball player gets a hit 40% of the time (this is a .400 batting average). Is this player one of the greatest who ever lived, or is he some fluke? Well, it depends on how many times he has been at bat. Suppose he just came up from the minor leagues and has only 5 at-bats. If he gets a hit 40% of the time, he's made two hits. Big deal. But suppose he has played all season and has 500 at-bats. Now, if he gets a hit 40% of the time, he's made 200 hits. That *is* a big deal, and undoubtedly he will be remembered in the Baseball Hall of Fame if he can get that number of hits consistently every season. Forty percent yields very different results in each of these situations. Percentages serve as comparisons, but you have to be careful with them. Sometimes you end up comparing apples with oranges, so the comparison is worthless.

THE ELEVATOR

The capacity of an elevator is either 20 children or 15 adults. If 12 children are currently on the elevator, how many adults can still get on? List the subproblems and solve this problem before continuing. (This problem can also be solved by drawing a diagram, so you might want to try using that method also.)

You could use many sets of subproblems to solve this problem. To be correct, your set doesn't have to match any of those shown in the following solutions. But, of course, to be correct, your set has to work—some of the following approaches do not.

A class presented this problem on the board. Justin wrote his work on the board as shown:

$$^{15}/_{20} = ^x/_{12}$$
$$20x = 180$$
$$x = 9$$

"I figured this problem out with a proportion. I got $x = 9$, so there are 9 adults."

Renita took a different approach. "I figured that I should use subproblems since that is what we have been working on. They were

1. How many adults are equivalent to one child?

2. How many children can still fit on the elevator?

3. This is equivalent to how many adults?

"This seemed like it would work, so I solved my subproblems.

1. How many adults are equivalent to one child?

    Since 20 children are equivalent to 15 adults, one child is equivalent to $^{15}/_{20}$, or $3/4$, of an adult. That seems to be about right, because kids are smaller than adults.

2. How many children can still fit on the elevator?

    There are 12 children on the elevator right now. Since the elevator can hold 20 children, there is room for 8 more children.

3. This is equivalent to how many adults?

    Since one child is equivalent to $3/4$ of an adult, 8 children are equivalent to $3/4 \times 8 = 6$ adults. So six more adults can get on the elevator.

"I didn't get the same answer that Justin got. I think he messed up, but I'm not sure. I think what I did was right."

Lupe explained who was correct. "Justin is way wrong. I did it the same way he did, but he solved only one of the subproblems. He just figured out that 12 children is equivalent to 9 adults. So you could take the 12 children out of the elevator and replace them with 9 adults. But that means that six more adults can get on. So Renita and I are right, and Justin is wrong."

Tim solved this problem with the drawing shown below. "I didn't see this as subproblems, I saw it as a diagram. The drawing on the left represents the elevator filled with children, and the drawing on the right represents the elevator filled with adults. **Notice** that four children take up the same amount of space as three adults. So if 12 children are already on the elevator (taking up 3/5 of the available space), 6 adults (2/5 of the available space) can still get on."

C	C	C	C	A	A	A
C	C	C	C	A	A	A
C	C	C	C	A	A	A
C	C	C	C	A	A	A
C	C	C	C	A	A	A

Mixture problems can be some of the most confusing problems a person faces in algebra. But when you understand the strategy of subproblems, you find that these problems are actually quite straight-forward. What makes them so confusing in algebra are probably the troublesome equations you are given to solve them with. The origin of a mixture problem's equation can be difficult to make sense of, so instead you try to memorize the equation setup. And this, in turn, can lead to all kinds of mistakes. In this chapter you won't use equations.

The following two problems, Paint and Chocolate Milk, are mixture problems. The Paint problem doesn't require algebra to solve.

PAINT

A mixture is 25% red paint, 30% yellow paint, and 45% water. If 4 quarts of red paint are added to 20 quarts of the mixture, what is the percentage of red paint in the new mixture? List subproblems and solve this problem before reading on.

Were you confused by this problem? Did all of the mixture-problem demons come rushing out of the closet of your mind? After you recovered (did you recover?), were you able to write down some subproblems?

Melanie and Kirk worked on this problem:

MELANIE: Arghh, I've never been able to do mixture problems.

KIRK: Me neither. I get all mixed up. Let's try it with these subproblem things.

MELANIE: Okay, I'm game. What do we need to know?

KIRK: What, er, hmm . . . how about, what is the percentage of red paint in the new mixture?

MELANIE: Good, genius. That's the question. Can we figure that out right now?

KIRK: Well, what do we need to know to figure it out? Boy, this problem is making me see red.

MELANIE: We need the amount of red paint in the final mixture and the total amount of paint in the final mixture. Then we can divide and get the percentage.

KIRK: Yello, that's good. Let's start writing these down. (He wrote down the subproblems shown below.)

1. How many quarts of red paint are in the new mixture?

2. How many quarts of paint are in the new mixture?

3. What percentage of the new mixture is red paint?

MELANIE: Okay, let's figure these out. How much red paint is there in the final mixture? How do we figure that out? We don't even know how many quarts of red paint there are in the original mixture.

KIRK: You're right. That's another subproblem. I'll add it to the list. (He added it at the top of list and renumbered the other subproblems.)

1. How many quarts of red paint are in the original mixture?

2. How many quarts of red paint are in the new mixture?

3. How many quarts of paint are in the new mixture?

4. What percentage of the new mixture is red paint?

KIRK: Okay, I think we're in business now. The original mixture is 25% red. Since there are 20 quarts in the original mixture, 25% of 20 = 5 quarts of red paint in the original mixture.

MELANIE: Great. Okay, so in the new mixture there are the original 5 quarts plus the 4 that were added, and that makes 9.

KIRK: Now we've got things stirred up. Our next subproblem is how many quarts of paint are in the new mixture. Well, that's redily apparent. It's 24. We started with 20, and we just added 4.

MELANIE: And, finally, we just have to divide to find the percentage of red paint in the final mixture. So $^9/_{24} = 0.375$. So that's 37.5% red. We did it. These subproblems made this problem not so bad.

KIRK: Yeah. Let's go paint the town.

Note that you could also figure the new percentages of yellow paint and water in the same way. If you couldn't solve this problem before reading the solution, figure the percentages of yellow paint and water by yourself before continuing on.

~~~~~~

The next problem, Chocolate Milk, may bring up more of those ghosts from algebra. Solve this problem by using a combination of the subproblems and guess-and-check strategies. (You could use algebra, but try solving this problem without it.)

CHOCOLATE MILK

Augustus is trying to make chocolate milk. So far he has made a 10% chocolate milk solution (this means that the solution is 10% chocolate and 90% milk). He has also made a 25% chocolate milk solution. Unfortunately, the 10% solution is too weak and the 25% solution is way too chocolaty. He has a whole lot of the 10% solution, but he has only 30 gallons of the 25% solution. How many gallons of 10% solution should he add to the 25% solution to make a mixture that is 15% chocolate? (Augustus is sure the 15% solution will be absolutely perfect.) Solve this problem before continuing on.

Pak loves guess-and-check. Pak would solve every problem by guess-and-check if he could. So he wanted to guess and check for this problem. His solution is a combination of guess-and-check and subproblems. He started by listing a subproblem:

1. How much chocolate is in the 30 gallons of 25% solution? Twenty-five percent of 30 is 7.5 gallons of chocolate in the 30 gallons of solution. This also means that there are 22.5 gallons of milk in the 30 gallons of solution.

Then Pak was stuck. He couldn't think of any other subproblems to ask. So he decided to try his favorite strategy, guess-and-check. He didn't know what to guess, so he adopted the strategy of guessing the answer to the question that the problem posed: How many gallons of 10% solution should be added? So Pak began to set up his chart.

Gallons of 10% Solution					
5					

But Pak didn't know what to write next. Then he realized that there was another subproblem lurking here. If he guessed 5 gallons of 10% solution, he needed to know how much chocolate these gallons contain. So he added this information to his chart. He also created columns for the other information he already had.

Gallons of 10% Solution	Gallons of Choc in 10% Soln	Gallons of 25% Solution	Gallons of Choc in 25% Soln	
5	0.5	30	7.5	

Now he had to determine how to check his guess. He realized that this problem involved more subproblems.

2. How much chocolate is in the new mixture (for that guess)?

3. How many gallons of solution are in the mixture (for that guess)?

4. What percentage of the new mixture is chocolate (for that guess)?

He added three more columns to his chart to account for the new subproblems. **Note** that Pak computed the Percentage of Chocolate in the Total Mixture column by dividing the total gallons of chocolate by the total gallons of the mixture, then changing to a percentage. For example, in the first guess 8 gallons of chocolate divided by 35 gallons of mixture is $8/35 \approx 0.2286 = 22.9\%$ (he rounded off his percentages to a tenth of a percent). Also **note** that the entries in the third and fourth columns of the chart always remain the same because they indicate information given in the problem or that Pak figured out earlier.

Gallons of 10% Solution	Gallons of Choc in 10% Soln	Gallons of 25% Solution	Gallons of Choc in 25% Soln	Total Gallons of Choc	Total Gallons of Mix	% of Choc in Tot Mix	Rate
5	0.5	30	7.5	8	35	22.9%	high
30	3	30	7.5	10.5	60	17.5%	high
50	5	30	7.5	12.5	80	15.6%	high
100	10	30	7.5	17.5	130	13.5%	low
60	6	30	7.5	13.5	90	15%	right

So the answer is that Augustus needs to add 60 gallons of the 10% solution.

Pak's attempt to bracket his answer didn't succeed very well because his first three guesses were rated too high. But he was very willing to guess much larger numbers, which aided him in reaching the answer quite quickly.

The Chocolate Milk problem is another problem in which strategies overlap. We will revisit this problem in Chapter 13: Algebra and discuss where those algebra equations come from.

Cheryl solved this problem in a completely different way. Her solution involves a different subproblem. "This would have been really easy if Augustus had wanted a 17.5% solution 'cause that would be halfway between the 25% solution and the 10% solution. That would mean you'd need the same amount of each solution. So you would need 30 gallons of the 10% solution. Of course, it's not 17.5%, it's 15%.

"But that brought to mind a needed subproblem: What does the ratio have to be between the 10% solution and the 25% solution?

"I noticed that 15% was one-third of the way from 10 to 25, so I thought I only needed to add in a small amount of the 10% mix to create the 15% mix.

"In terms of how close 10% is to 25%, the 15% mix that's asked for is only one of three parts of the way. Or better yet, if you break down into 10%–15%, 15%–20%, and 20%–25%, then getting 10% up to 15% is one part close to 10% and two parts close to 25%. Here's a diagram to show what I mean."

"Fifteen percent is one of three parts of the way toward 25% from 10%. So there's one part on the left and two on the right. That means you have to keep this 1:2 ratio when you mix the solutions together. At first I thought it had to be one part of the 10% mixed with two parts of the 25%, but that would actually make the blend closer to the 25%, so I knew I had it backwards.

"Therefore, the right answer is a 2:1 ratio of the weak stuff to the strong stuff—he already has 30 gallons of strong chocolate milk. In a 2:1 ratio, you need to add twice as much as you've already got, so twice 30 is 60. So he needs 60 gallons of the 10% solution."

Cheryl looked at this problem from a different perspective and thus found that she needed an unusual subproblem. The ratio of the two liquids was the key to her solution. Her diagram helped her find that ratio and solve the problem.

The strategy of subproblems is very useful for solving complicated problems. Often a problem may look impossible when you first see it, but after you break it down into subproblems it may seem quite easy. Listing your subproblems focuses your thinking and helps you more clearly see what you know, what you don't know, and what you can figure out.

Problem Set A

Solve each problem by first listing all the subproblems and then solving them to answer the given question.

1. COFFEE

How many ounces of coffee can be bought for $1.11 if 2 pounds cost $5.92?

2. SHARING EXPENSES

Five students held a party. They agreed to share the expenses equally. Leroy spent $14 on drinks. Alex spent $3 on paper plates. Kulwinder spent $7 on decorations. Max spent $9 on snacks. Bobbi spent $2 on envelopes and paper to send invitations out, and she also spent $5.80 in postage. Who owes money to whom?

3. AIRPLANE SEATS

On an airplane that is two-thirds full, 20% of the passengers are boys, one-fourth of the passengers are women, one-eighth of the passengers are girls, and there are 68 men. How many seats are on the plane?

4. SIX SQUARES

The picture shows six equal squares. The total area is 54 ft². What is the perimeter?

5. SHADED AREA

Find the shaded area in the figure. The large figure is a square, and each arc is one-fourth of a circle.

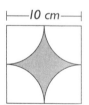

6. SAVINGS PLAN

A woman saves 10% of her salary every month. Her company has fallen on hard times, so her monthly salary has just decreased (what a drag!) from $3,600 to $3,000. The woman decides to save the same dollar amount each month, even though her salary is reduced. What percentage of her new salary will her savings be now?

7. TEST AVERAGE

Mr. Howard's first-period class of 40 students averaged 96% on a recent test. His second-period class of 20 students averaged 90% on the same test. What was the combined average for both classes?

8. CAR TRIP

If Clarence drives 60 miles per hour, it will take him 3 hours to drive to Concordia. How many minutes longer will it take to make the trip if he drives 48 miles per hour?

9. FARGO

Tiffany drove from her home to Fargo, North Dakota, in 2 hours. On the way back home, she drove 54 miles per hour and it took her 14 minutes longer. At what speed did she drive on the way to Fargo?

10. TEST TRACK

A certain car that is being tested by its manufacturer uses its entire fuel supply in about 38 hours when idling. The same car, when driven at 60 miles per hour on a test track, uses about three-and-a-half times as much fuel per hour as it does when idling. If the engine has been idling for 10 hours and the car is then run at 60 miles per hour, how much longer will the car run before it uses up all of its fuel?

11. BOX

The area of the top of a rectangular box is 324 in.², the area of the front of the box is 135 in.², and the area of the end is 60 in.². What is the volume of the box?

12. SWEETENED CEREAL

In her duties as Mom, Denise tries to keep to a minimum the number of empty calories her family consumes. (To Denise, empty calories are calories that don't offer any nutritional value, as opposed to the fructose in an apple.) Her kids love honey-sweetened cereal. She mixes the honey-sweetened cereal with the unsweetened version of the same cereal. Her kids don't notice until she makes it too bland. From experience, she thinks the mixture is too bland when the amount of the honey-sweetened cereal drops to less than 40% of the mix. Her husband, Chris, has just mixed together a 14 oz package of unsweetened cereal with a 32 oz package of sweetened cereal. How much more unsweetened cereal does Denise need to mix in to make the mix 40% sweetened and 60% unsweetened?

13. STYROFOAM CUP

Find the volume of a Styrofoam cup. The diameter of the top is 3 inches. The diameter of the base is 2 inches. The height is 4 inches. **Hint:** The volume of a cone is $V = (1/3)\pi r^2 h$.

14. RED ROAD

In right triangle *RED,* angle *R* is the right angle. Point *O* is on segment *ER* and point *A* is on segment *ED*. Segment *OA* is perpendicular to segment *ED*. *EA* = 6, *AD* = 14, *ER* = 16. Find the area of quadrilateral *ROAD*.

15. WRITE YOUR OWN

Write your own subproblems problem. The easiest types of these problems to make up are those like the Coffee problem in this problem set, or the Little Green Apples and the Watering the Lawn problems in this chapter.

Problem Set B

1. WHO WEIGHS WHAT?

Devon, Frank, Fua, Morris, and Pedro belong to the same workout gym. The gym rules prohibit the staff from giving out personal information about their clients. However, each of the five guys said just enough that you can figure out their exact weights. (Do this problem quickly because after the workout, Morris and Devon are going to an all-you-can-eat buffet.)

Devon: Pedro weighs 18 pounds more than I do. None of us weighs over 200 pounds.

Frank: My weight is divisible by 7. Morris weighs 12 pounds more than I do.

Fua: Three people are heavier than I. Pedro's weight is a prime number.

Morris: I'm heavier than Pedro. Devon is the lightest.

Pedro: Morris's weight is divisible by 10. The five of us together total exactly 840 pounds.

2. FAMILY DAY

Incredibly Huge Motors is planning an employee-and-family day at the baseball park. They have reserved 6000 seats with the ball club. Each section at the ballpark has 15 seats in each row and is 18 rows deep. How many sections does the ball club need to set aside for the IHM employees and family?

3. CARROT JUICE

Bill, a health-food enthusiast, is mixing concoctions in his basement. He's invented a new drink that needs to be 40% carrot juice and 60% other stuff. He has been to the store and has found some concentrated carrot juice (60% carrot juice). His neighbor Clara, who decided one day that she doesn't like carrot juice that much anymore, has contributed 80 quarts of 12% carrot juice. How many quarts of the concentrated carrot juice does he need to add to the 80 quarts of weak juice to produce his perfect drink with 40% carrot juice?

4. HRUNKLA APARTMENT HOUSES

Most Hrunkla lived in giant, 12-story apartment houses, and their homes were large square rooms bounded on four sides by corridors. Each room had a single door which opened halfway along a corridor. On even-numbered floors, the doors opened onto the east corridor; on odd-numbered floors, the doors opened onto the north corridor. At each intersection of corridors, there was something like an elevator which could be ridden up or down. Half of the corridors had moving belts on the floor, and no self-respecting Hrunkla would walk if he could ride one of these belts. The belts were so arranged that those on floors 1, 5, and 9 ran to the east; those on floors 2, 6, and 10 ran to the south; those on floors 3, 7, and 11 ran to the west; and those on floors 4, 8, and 12 ran to the north. Describe how a Hrunkla who lived on floor 10 could use these moving belts and elevators to visit a friend who lived in the room directly below his.*

5. NIGHTMARES

I want to tell you about Elmo and the problem he was having with nightmares. Elmo was having some bad recurring nightmares. Every 19 days he was having a nightmare about 19 ghosts scaring him out of his wits by jumping out of a 1919 Hupmobile and saying "boo" 19 times. (Don't ask me to explain this—it's Elmo's nightmare.) He was also having a nightmare every 13 days about 13 black cats crossing his path in front of his house, located at 1313 Thirteenth Street. He had a bad week in April, when on the night of Friday, April 5, he had the nightmare about the 19 ghosts saying "boo" 19 times. The very next night, he had the nightmare about the 13 black cats. Elmo knows he can handle these nightmares when they occur from time to time, but lately he's been really worried about them both occurring on the same night. Do they ever occur on the same night by the end of the year, and if so, on what date?

*From *Make It Simpler: A Practical Guide to Problem Solving in Mathematics* by Carol Meyer and Tom Sallee. ©1983 by Addison-Wesley Publishing Company. Reprinted by permission of Pearson Learning. Used by permission.

Chemists and physicists often use unit analysis to check that they've set up their calculations correctly.

Unit Analysis

Crane recorded the following conversation on a very bad tape. The recorder ate the tape, and Crane had to wind it back into the cassette manually. When he played the tape back, he could understand only this part of the conversation:

CLERK: Hi! How're you doing?

CUSTOMER: Oh, it feels like I've been going 24-7. Did you hear what happened on 80?

CLERK: Ten-four, buddy! Whew, must be 100.

CUSTOMER: Ain't it! Isn't this two-for-one?

CLERK: Actually it's buy one, get one.

CUSTOMER: Six of one, half dozen of another if you ask me. Isn't it one-fifty?

CLERK: Oh yeah, you're right. Is that 24?

CUSTOMER: No, 18. What's new with you?

CLERK: We're goin' down 85 in 3.

CUSTOMER: That's nothing—we did 75 in 2. Hey, I heard Steve did 285.

CLERK: Naw, that was Laresa. She also got 77 in the afternoon.

CUSTOMER: Wow! Forrest had 17 in 7 the same day.

CLERK: No hits!

Here's a correct interpretation of the same conversation.

CLERK: Hi! How're you doing?

CUSTOMER: Oh, it feels like I've been going 24 [hours per day]-7 [days per week]. Did you hear what happened on Interstate 80?

CLERK: Yes, sir, I did. Whew, must be 100 [degrees] out today.

CUSTOMER: I'll readily agree with that. Isn't this two [donuts] for the price of one [donut]?

CLERK: Actually it's buy one [donut], get one [donut] free.

CUSTOMER: It doesn't seem to matter, either way. Isn't it 1:50 [o'clock]?

CLERK: Oh yeah, you're right. Is that 24 [caret] gold?

CUSTOMER: No, 18 [caret]. What's new with you?

CLERK: We're goin' down Interstate 85 in 3 [days].

CUSTOMER: That's nothing, we biked 75 [miles] in 2 [hours]. Hey, I heard Steve bowled 285 [pins] at Cameranisi's.

CLERK: No, that was Laresa. She also shot 77 [strokes of golf] in the afternoon.

CUSTOMER: Wow! Her brother Forrest had 17 [strikeouts] in 7 [innings] the same day.

CLERK: Gollee!

Although some people might believe that the bad tape made the conversation difficult to understand, it is clear to any mathematician that the lack of units of measure caused the difficulty. In the conversation between the clerk and the customer, all of the following vital units were obscured in the recording: hours per day, days per week, degrees, donuts, hours and minutes in a day, carets, days, miles, hours, pins, strokes of golf, strikeouts, and innings. Think about how many of the phrases were difficult to understand, much less the whole conversation, when the conversation omitted the units. Without them, only a few of the numbers made any sense.

Unit analysis involves dealing with units of measure very carefully in order to produce a correct answer. People often ignore units of measure in everyday computations, but units are a necessary component of a real-world problem and its answer. An answer is not complete without units.

For example, suppose your boss asks you to find out how much fencing you would need to enclose the company parking lot. You do the research and respond by saying you need 145 to do the job. So your boss buys 145 yards of fence material. Unfortunately, you meant she needs 145 feet of fence material. You may end up searching for another job. Here's another example: Suppose you select two cans of tomato paste to buy—at this point "cans" is the unit. Yet when you pay for them at 39¢ each, the total cost may be interpreted as either 78¢ (cents is the unit) or $0.78 (dollars is the unit). When you are solving a problem with numbers, it is extremely important to recognize *what* units are given in the problem, because using the wrong units can result in an incorrect interpretation of the solution.

Unit analysis falls under the major problem-solving theme of Organizing Information. By keeping the units organized, especially in the form of the numerators and denominators of fractions, you can solve many problems simply by manipulating the units to get the answer you're looking for.

The methods used to teach unit analysis (also called *dimensional analysis*) vary greatly. In this book, we will approach the topic of unit analysis by emphasizing the process in every problem. Some of the approach may seem exaggerated, but this book is about really working with a problem, using a process or a variety of processes to reach a solution. Each part of the problem-solving process is important: the problem, the process, and the solution.

This chapter contains three different sections, each discussing how to use units in a different way: in ratios, unit conversions, and compound units.

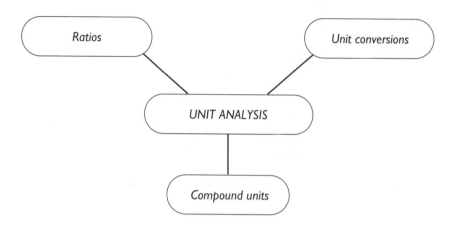

Section 1: Units in Ratios

A **ratio** is a comparison of two numbers. Ratios are often written as fractions, so even the "two-thirds" in the sentence "Bill ate two-thirds of the pizza" represents a ratio (²/₃). Units of measure are often expressed as ratios. A common example is the listing of gas prices in dollars per gallon.

$$\frac{\text{dollars}}{\text{gallon}}$$

A price of $1.20 per gallon can be listed as $1.20/gallon. The ratio even makes sense if listed as $12 for 10 gallons. By looking at the ratio in the form of a fraction and dividing the number in the numerator by the number in the denominator, you simplify the ratio and the units remain.

$$\frac{\$12}{10 \text{ gallons}} = \frac{\$1.20}{1 \text{ gallon}}$$

A 12-ounce can of Rosario's Refried Beans sells for 59 cents, and the 16-ounce size of the same brand sells for 81 cents. Which can is the better buy? Work this problem before continuing.

To work this problem, Amanda arranged the units for both cans into similar ratios. The smaller can is arranged as 59 cents per 12 ounces, and the larger can is arranged as 81 cents per 16 ounces. Both have been arranged in terms of price over weight.

$$\frac{59 \text{ cents}}{12 \text{ ounces}} \quad \text{and} \quad \frac{81 \text{ cents}}{16 \text{ ounces}}$$

Then, by dividing the numerators by the denominators, she got

$$\frac{4.9 \text{ cents}}{1 \text{ ounce}} \quad \text{and} \quad \frac{5.1 \text{ cents}}{1 \text{ ounce}}$$

Amanda discovered that the smaller can is the better buy, because a shopper pays less per ounce for the smaller can than for the larger can.

Many grocery stores feature shelf tags that list something called *unit pricing*. The shelf tags make it easier for shoppers to answer questions like the one posed in the At the Grocery Store problem. Before these shelf tags were a regular fixture in stores, many shoppers spent several minutes doing mental calisthenics with pained expressions on their faces in order to figure out the best buy. The unit-pricing shelf tags resolve the value issue for the customer very quickly. In Amanda's case, the shelf tag for the smaller can would show a unit price of 4.9 cents per ounce and the shelf tag for the larger can would show a unit price of 5.1 cents per ounce. As she found out, the smaller can is clearly the better buy. So the questions shoppers face are no longer about value but about which can will fit their storage and consumption needs.

Occasionally shelf tags give the unit-pricing information in ounces per cent (instead of cents per ounce). So if price were your only concern, you would want to buy the can with the greater number of ounces per cent, because you would be getting more for your money.

Christopher bought a six-pack of soda for $1.50. Each can holds 12 fluid ounces. Identify the total quantity of each unit in the problem.

a. Cans

d. Six-packs

b. Dollars

e. Ounces

c. Cents

f. Cases (a case contains 24 cans)

Solve this problem before continuing.

Here are the answers.

a. 6 cans

d. 1 six-pack

b. 1.5 dollars

e. 72 ounces

c. 150 cents

f. 0.25 case

Most of the units are found in the problem. **Notice** that the quantities of dollars and cents are written slightly differently. This distinction is important. As you'll see, sometimes it will make more sense to work with dollars as the monetary unit when solving a problem and at other times it will make more sense to use cents.

Find each of the following as both a raw ratio and a simplified ratio. Use the $1.50 that Chris spent on a six-pack of soda in the Six for Chris, Part 1 problem for the raw quantities and units. Remember, there are 24 sodas in a case.

a. Cents per six-pack

e. Cents per ounce

b. Dollars per can

f. Ounces per cent

c. Cents per can

g. Cans per dollar

d. Ounces per can

h. Ounces per case

Here are the answers.

a. $\dfrac{150 \text{ cents}}{1 \text{ six-pack}}$

e. $\dfrac{150 \text{ cents}}{72 \text{ ounces}} = \dfrac{2.083 \text{ cents}}{1 \text{ ounce}}$

b. $\dfrac{1.5 \text{ dollars}}{6 \text{ cans}} = \dfrac{0.25 \text{ dollar}}{1 \text{ can}}$

f. $\dfrac{72 \text{ ounces}}{150 \text{ cents}} = \dfrac{0.48 \text{ ounce}}{1 \text{ cent}}$

c. $\dfrac{150 \text{ cents}}{6 \text{ cans}} = \dfrac{25 \text{ cents}}{1 \text{ can}}$

g. $\dfrac{6 \text{ cans}}{1.5 \text{ dollars}} = \dfrac{4 \text{ cans}}{1 \text{ dollar}}$

d. $\dfrac{12 \text{ ounces}}{1 \text{ can}}$

h. $\dfrac{288 \text{ ounces}}{1 \text{ case}}$

Notice that all of the ratios are first written in quantities given or calculated from information in the problem, then simplified (if needed) so that the number associated with the denominator unit becomes 1. Reducing the quantity of the denominator to one unit isn't always necessary but works well when the numbers and units start getting confusing.

Also **notice** that there are a few different types of units found in this problem. First there are monetary units, dollars and cents. There is also a unit of liquid measure, fluid ounces. And there are cans in six-packs and cases, which are units of packaging.

The most difficult ratio in this problem may have been part h, ounces per case. Consider the fractions below.

$$\dfrac{12 \text{ ounces}}{1 \text{ can}} \times \dfrac{24 \text{ cans}}{1 \text{ case}}$$

As shown below, the units of the cans can "cancel," leaving the ounces on top (in the numerator) and the case on the bottom (in the denominator). After you multiply 12 by 24, because there are 12 ounces in one can and 24 cans in one case, the answer to the problem is 288 *ounces per case*.

$$\dfrac{12 \text{ ounces}}{1 \text{ \sout{can}}} \times \dfrac{24 \text{ \sout{cans}}}{1 \text{ case}} = \dfrac{288 \text{ ounces}}{1 \text{ case}}$$

Why does this work? The next problem may help you answer this question.

Toni drove 80 miles in 2 hours and used 5 gallons of gas. **Notice** that there are three different types of units of measure here—miles, hours, and gallons—which measure distance, time, and volume, respectively. From this information, you can calculate six ratios of quantities, considering two units at a time. The six ratios are miles/hour, hours/mile, gallons/hour, hours/gallon, gallons/mile, and miles/gallon. Calculate the value of each of these ratios. Work this problem before continuing.

Using the calculator to simplify, here are the answers.

1. Miles/hour: $\dfrac{80 \text{ mi}}{2 \text{ hr}} = \dfrac{40 \text{ mi}}{1 \text{ hr}} = 40 \dfrac{\text{mi}}{\text{hr}}$

2. Hours/mile: $\dfrac{2 \text{ hr}}{80 \text{ mi}} = \dfrac{0.025 \text{ hr}}{1 \text{ mi}} = 0.025 \dfrac{\text{hr}}{\text{mi}}$

3. Gallons/hour: $\dfrac{5 \text{ gal}}{2 \text{ hr}} = \dfrac{2.5 \text{ gal}}{1 \text{ hr}} = 2.5 \dfrac{\text{gal}}{\text{hr}}$

   This is probably more relevant as a measure of fuel consumption in airplanes.

4. Hours/gallon: $\dfrac{2 \text{ hr}}{5 \text{ gal}} = \dfrac{0.4 \text{ hr}}{1 \text{ gal}} = 0.4 \dfrac{\text{hr}}{\text{gal}}$

   This would be very relevant if you wanted to know what amount of time you could drive before worrying about filling up the gas tank.

5. Gallons/mile: $\dfrac{5 \text{ gal}}{80 \text{ mi}} = \dfrac{0.0625 \text{ gal}}{1 \text{ mi}} = 0.0625 \dfrac{\text{gal}}{\text{mi}}$

   (one-sixteenth of a gallon/mile)

6. Miles/gallon: $\dfrac{80 \text{ mi}}{5 \text{ gal}} = \dfrac{16 \text{ mi}}{1 \text{ gal}} = \dfrac{16 \text{ mi}}{\text{gal}}$

   This is our famous "mpg" (miles per gallon) as a relative measure of fuel economy in cars.

Note that the word *per* means "divide," as you've probably figured out. Writing *mph* or *mpg* might get you into the habit of thinking that mph is a single unit. Instead, you must realize that *mph* stands for "miles per hour," which is actually the ratio miles/hour. Even *miles/hour* is dangerous to write because the slanted fraction bar doesn't call out the distinction of numerator and denominator. So you should get into the habit of writing

$$\frac{\text{miles}}{\text{hour}} \quad \text{and} \quad \frac{\text{miles}}{\text{gallon}}$$

Looking back at the Toni's Trip problem, the answer to part 2 probably does not convey much meaning. You probably do not have a sense of how long 0.025 hour is. So it would be nice if that number of hours were converted into a quantity with a unit that you could conceptualize, like seconds. The problem then becomes, how do we change 0.025 hour into seconds? Or in this case, how do we change 0.025 hour/mile into seconds/mile? You know there are 60 minutes in 1 hour, and 60 seconds in 1 minute, so you could just multiply 0.025 × 60 × 60 to get the correct answer of 90 seconds. However, to be sure you have seconds and to understand how they came about, in this chapter you'll learn how to "cancel" units. Here is a description of that technique applied to this problem.

Start with the quantity 0.025 hour/1 mile and then multiply by the fractions shown below. Multiplying by 60 minutes/1 hour will convert hours into minutes. Multiplying by 60 seconds/1 minute will convert minutes into seconds.

$$\frac{0.025 \text{ hour}}{1 \text{ mile}} \times \frac{60 \text{ minutes}}{1 \text{ hour}} \times \frac{60 \text{ seconds}}{1 \text{ minute}}$$

Because you are multiplying, when the same unit of measure (for example, minute and minute, or hour and hour) appears in a numerator *and* a denominator, it can be "canceled out." (**Remember** to cancel the units in both places!) So "hour" in the numerator of the first fraction cancels "hour" in the denominator of the second fraction. And "minutes" in the numerator of the second fraction cancels "minute" in the denominator of the third fraction.

$$\frac{0.025 \, \cancel{\text{hour}}}{1 \text{ mile}} \times \frac{60 \, \cancel{\text{minutes}}}{1 \, \cancel{\text{hour}}} \times \frac{60 \text{ seconds}}{1 \, \cancel{\text{minute}}} = \frac{90 \text{ seconds}}{1 \text{ mile}}$$

The only unit left in the numerator is seconds, and the only unit left in the denominator is miles. Thus, the answer is in seconds/mile. So, traveling at 40 miles/hour, Toni will travel 1 mile in 90 seconds.

The same technique of canceling units can be used to find the number of minutes it takes to burn 1 gallon of gas. You've already calculated that it takes 0.4 hour to use 1 gallon. Convert this to minutes per gallon.

$$\frac{0.4 \text{ hour}}{1 \text{ gallon}} \times \frac{60 \text{ minutes}}{1 \text{ hour}}$$

Again, the hours cancel out, leaving the answer in minutes per gallon.

$$\frac{0.4 \text{ \cancel{hour}}}{1 \text{ gallon}} \times \frac{60 \text{ minutes}}{1 \text{ \cancel{hour}}} = \frac{24 \text{ minutes}}{1 \text{ gallon}}$$

We know what you are thinking. What exactly is going on here? Why does this method work? Does it always work? Why can't we just multiply 0.4 by 60 to get 24? Why should we do all this fraction work? (If you can't remember how to multiply fractions, see the appendix at the back of the book.)

The answers to all these questions are: Trust us! Unit analysis is a fantastic way to solve any problem involving any kind of units. The fraction technique is *the* way to do it. You may have some success with easy problems without doing unit analysis, but as soon as you come up against a complex problem, you might be overwhelmed.

Let's start again, this time using some really basic conversions.

YARDS TO FEET

How many feet are there in 7 yards? Do this problem before continuing.

The answer is easy unless you don't know that there are 3 feet in every yard. Knowing this gives the answer, 21 feet. But let's solve this problem using the unit analysis technique discussed in the Toni's Trip problem. The key to this method is canceling units. Consider the two fractions below.

$$\frac{3 \text{ feet}}{1 \text{ yard}}$$

$$\frac{1 \text{ yard}}{3 \text{ feet}}$$

Each of these fractions has a value of 1: The numerator is equal to the denominator. But what is so important about 1? Multiplying a number by 1 gives that same number. In other words, when a number is multiplied by 1, the answer is the original number. This concept is key to **unit conversions**.

Consider again the question "How many feet are there in 7 yards?" Another way to solve the problem is to multiply by 1, in this case a very particular form of 1.

$$7 \text{ yards } \times \frac{3 \text{ feet}}{1 \text{ yard}}$$

But in order to solve this problem, 7 yards must be expressed as a fraction with a denominator of 1. (**Remember,** when multiplying a whole number by a fraction, the whole number must be expressed as a fraction with a denominator of 1.)

$$\frac{7 \text{ yards}}{1} \times \frac{3 \text{ feet}}{1 \text{ yard}}$$

By canceling the yards in the problem and multiplying 7 by 3, you get the solution

$$\frac{7 \text{ yards}}{1} \times \frac{3 \text{ feet}}{1 \text{ yard}} = 21 \text{ feet}$$

You may be surprised to see that doing the problem this way gives the correct answer. Throughout this chapter you'll use the concept of multiplying by 1 in various forms.

Now let's do the problem in reverse.

FEET TO YARDS

How many yards are there in 21 feet? Do this problem before continuing.

This time, we have to divide by 3 to get the answer. So in this case we use the **reciprocal** of the fraction we used before. (Recall that if you multiply a fraction and its reciprocal, you'll always get 1.)

$$\frac{21 \text{ feet}}{1} \times \frac{1 \text{ yard}}{3 \text{ feet}}$$

Canceling, we get

$$\frac{21 \cancel{\text{feet}}}{1} \times \frac{1 \text{ yard}}{3 \cancel{\text{feet}}} = 7 \text{ yards}$$

This time the feet cancel. To get the number 7, we have to divide 21 by 3, because 21 is in the numerator of the fraction and 3 is in the denominator.

Note that you should also analyze *what* type of unit is used in each problem, although this may not seem important right now. The last few problems dealt with distances. The next problem deals with time. Also, it applies the concept of multiplying by 1 to a problem with more steps.

DAYS TO MINUTES

How many minutes are there in 5 days? Work this problem before continuing.

Start with 5 days, convert days to hours, then convert hours to minutes. You might think of these conversions as a series of subproblems. (For more about subproblems, see Chapter 7.) The units all conveniently cancel, except for the minutes. Multiplying takes care of converting the units. The solution is 7200 minutes.

$$\frac{5 \cancel{\text{days}}}{1} \times \frac{24 \cancel{\text{hours}}}{1 \cancel{\text{day}}} \times \frac{60 \text{ minutes}}{1 \cancel{\text{hour}}} = 7200 \text{ minutes}$$

This kind of problem can be done rather simply by multiplying, without all of the canceling. The solution is $5 \times 24 \times 60 = 7200$. With such a straightforward example, the answer is obviously correct (though incomplete without the units). However, there are numerous examples that are not so obvious, such as the next one.

RUNNING FOOTBALL FIELDS

Francisco ran 8 miles. Being a football fan, Francisco wondered how many times he had run the equivalent of a full football field (100 yards). How many times had he? Work this problem before continuing.

To solve this problem, you should multiply 8 by 5280, divide by 3, and then divide by 100. Do you believe it? Examine this problem solved by using the canceling-units approach.

$$\frac{8 \ \text{miles}}{1} \times \frac{5280 \ \text{feet}}{1 \ \text{mile}} \times \frac{1 \ \text{yard}}{3 \ \text{feet}} \times \frac{1 \ \text{football field}}{100 \ \text{yards}}$$

After you cancel units, a football field is the unit remaining. To compute the answer, multiply 8 by 5,280 to get 42,240 in the numerator. Multiply 3 by 100 to get 300 in the denominator. To finish the problem, all you need to do is to divide 42,240 by 300. The answer is 140.8 football fields.

$$\frac{42,240 \ \text{football fields}}{300} = 140.8 \ \text{football fields}$$

So Francisco ran the length of a football field about 141 times.

The first approach to solving the problem was to multiply 8 by 5280, divide by 3, and then divide by 100. This approach turns out to be correct. If you still resist the canceling-units technique, ask yourself, "Which of the two solutions can I more readily verify to be correct? Or which solution could I easily explain to another person?"

Manipulatives and One-n-oes

Students often ask, "How do you know which way to set up the fractions?" Suppose you have a problem that involves the ratio 65 miles per hour. Should you set up this ratio as 65 miles over 1 hour, or should you use 1 hour over 65 miles?

$$\frac{65 \ \text{miles}}{1 \ \text{hour}} \quad \text{or} \quad \frac{1 \ \text{hour}}{65 \ \text{miles}}$$

One way to figure out how to set up a fraction is to use **manipulatives**. Manipulatives are objects that can be moved or positioned, in this case small pieces of paper. The strategy of using manipulatives will be explored more fully in Chapter 10: Physical Representations, but here we will use them to solve unit-analysis problems. Consider the next problem.

Lars just arrived at the air base. He came in from Italy and is going to Kuwait next, so he wants to exchange 236,500 Italian lire for Kuwaiti dinars. There is a place at the base where he can exchange money, but he has been able to find out only two exchange rates:

2.1 U.S. dollars = 100 Italian lire

1 U.S. dollar = 0.3065 Kuwaiti dinar

About how many dinars should Lars expect when he exchanges his money? Solve this problem before reading on.

Lars made manipulatives for this problem, one for the 236,500 lire he wants to exchange and one each for the two exchange rates. Then he arranged them in the following order:

$$236,500 \text{ lire} \quad \times \quad \frac{\text{U.S. \$2.1}}{100 \text{ lire}} \quad \times \quad \frac{\text{U.S. \$1}}{0.3065 \text{ dinar}}$$

Lars discovered that he had placed the dollars-to-lire manipulative correctly but that he needed to use the reciprocal of the dollars-to-dinars manipulative. He also wrote in a 1 as the denominator of 236,500 lire so that he could keep the units in this problem straight. His new arrangement of the problem looks like this:

$$\frac{236,500 \text{ lire}}{1} \quad \times \quad \frac{\text{U.S. \$2.1}}{100 \text{ lire}} \quad \times \quad \frac{0.3065 \text{ dinar}}{\text{U.S. \$1}}$$

Now the U.S.-dollars units would cancel. Lars canceled units and multiplied.

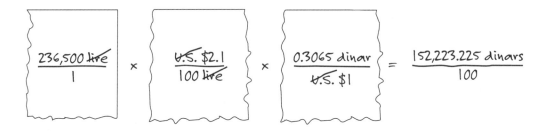

$$\frac{236,500 \text{ lire}}{1} \times \frac{\text{U.S. } \$2.1}{100 \text{ lire}} \times \frac{0.3065 \text{ dinar}}{\text{U.S. } \$1} = \frac{152,223.225 \text{ dinars}}{100}$$

He divided the last fraction to convert it to a fraction with a denominator of 1, giving 1,522.23 dinars. Lars should expect about 1,522 dinars in exchange for his 236,500 lire.

GAS CONSUMPTION

A car is traveling at 65 miles per hour, gets 25 miles per gallon, and travels for 45 minutes. How many gallons does the car use during that time? Read the solution to this problem, making the manipulatives that the solution suggests and setting up the multiplication needed for the solution.

For each piece of information that the problem gives, make a manipulative. On one side of a small piece of paper, write the fraction given. On the opposite side, write the reciprocal of the fraction. For example, for the information about the 45 minutes, write a fraction showing 45 minutes over 1 trip and, on the back, 1 trip over 45 minutes.

$$\frac{45 \text{ minutes}}{1 \text{ trip}} \qquad \text{and on the back} \qquad \frac{1 \text{ trip}}{45 \text{ minutes}}$$

What else do we know here that might be useful? Because the problem involves both hours and minutes, it might be useful to have a manipulative that says 60 minutes equals 1 hour.

We also know that the car can travel 25 miles per 1 gallon.

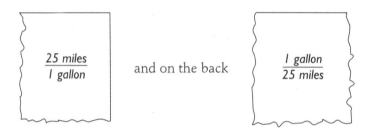

And we know that the car has been traveling at 65 miles per 1 hour.

Now put the manipulatives side by side. The intention is to get everything to cancel out except gallons—we want to know how many gallons were used during the trip. So, the objective is to end up with gallons over trip. Suppose we put the manipulatives together as follows:

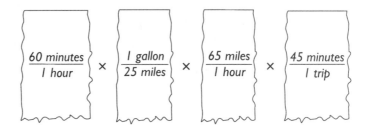

The miles would cancel, the hours would not cancel, and the minutes would not cancel. We could correct this by flipping over the first fraction. Now the hours cancel, the miles cancel, and the minutes cancel. This leaves us with gallons over trip, which is the unit we want. So do the calculation. (**Note,** if you are having trouble, the Leaky Faucet, Part 1 problem later in this chapter thoroughly explains the two possible ways of using your calculator to do the computation.)

$$\frac{1 \text{ hour}}{60 \text{ minutes}} \times \frac{1 \text{ gallon}}{25 \text{ miles}} \times \frac{65 \text{ miles}}{1 \text{ hour}} \times \frac{45 \text{ minutes}}{1 \text{ trip}} = \frac{1.95 \text{ gallons}}{1 \text{ trip}}$$

Note that it is quite easy to get everything to cancel out, even when all of the fractions are upside down. In this problem, the canceling would look like this:

$$\frac{60 \text{ minutes}}{1 \text{ hour}} \times \frac{25 \text{ miles}}{1 \text{ gallon}} \times \frac{1 \text{ hour}}{65 \text{ miles}} \times \frac{1 \text{ trip}}{45 \text{ minutes}} = \frac{1 \text{ trip}}{1.95 \text{ gallons}} = \frac{0.5128 \text{ trip}}{1 \text{ gallon}}$$

Students often think this answer means that the trip used 0.5128 gallon. But because the gallon unit is on the bottom, it actually means that you covered 0.5128 of the trip on 1 gallon of gas. While trips/gallon may be a useful unit, it was not what the problem asked for. So be cautious—make sure that the units in your answer end up where you want them.

The manipulative approach to unit analysis can be very effective. Make manipulatives for all the known information in the problem. These manipulatives will be unique to that particular problem. For example, in the Gas Consumption problem, 25 miles per gallon, 65 miles per hour, and 45 minutes per trip were all quantities unique to that problem.

You also need to have manipulatives for information that will never change, such as the number of minutes in an hour and the number of feet in a mile. Having a stock of manipulatives like these that you use all the time is very helpful. We will call these types of manipulatives one-n-oes (they can be thought of to look like dominoes). A **one-n-o** (pronounced WON-n-oh) is a fraction that equals 1. We will use one-n-oes to convert measurements from one type of measurement unit into another—our friend Carolyn Donohoe-Mather says, "A one-n-o is what gets you to what you wanna know."

An example of a one-n-o is shown below left. Both the denominator and the numerator have the same value, so the value of this fraction is 1. (In layman's terms, anything over itself is 1.) **Notice** that the reciprocal of this fraction, shown below right, is still equal to 1. The reciprocal would appear on the *back* of the one-n-o that is shown below left.

$$\frac{1 \text{ day}}{24 \text{ hours}} \qquad \frac{24 \text{ hours}}{1 \text{ day}}$$

In your stock of one-n-oes, you should have at least all of the following, as well as any others you think you will use all the time.

Remember that each side of a one-n-o is the reciprocal of the other side.

$$\frac{60 \text{ minutes}}{1 \text{ hour}}$$ and on the back $$\frac{1 \text{ hour}}{60 \text{ minutes}}$$

$$\frac{60 \text{ seconds}}{1 \text{ minute}}$$ and on the back $$\frac{1 \text{ minute}}{60 \text{ seconds}}$$

$$\frac{5280 \text{ feet}}{1 \text{ mile}}$$ and on the back $$\frac{1 \text{ mile}}{5280 \text{ feet}}$$

$$\frac{12 \text{ inches}}{1 \text{ foot}}$$ and on the back $$\frac{1 \text{ foot}}{12 \text{ inches}}$$

$$\frac{3.281 \text{ feet}}{1 \text{ meter}}$$ and on the back $$\frac{1 \text{ meter}}{3.281 \text{ feet}}$$

When you make your one-n-oes, be careful. **Note** that it does not make sense to write either

$$\frac{1 \text{ inch}}{12 \text{ feet}} \quad \text{or} \quad \frac{12 \text{ feet}}{1 \text{ inch}}$$

because neither of these fractions has a value of 1. Twelve feet is not the same thing as one inch. If it were, a person who is six feet tall would be really short.

For more of the conversions that you'll use frequently, see the appendix at the back of this book. (Also see the appendix for a list of abbreviations for common units of measure and for information about the metric system, which you'll need as you work through this chapter.)

The trick to using one-n-oes is finding the form (or forms) of 1 that will allow you to solve the problem. Solve the next problem using the one-n-oes that you just made. You will also need to make a new manipulative that reflects the information given in the problem.

LEAKY FAUCET, PART 1

A leaky faucet drips 1 fluid ounce every 30 seconds. How many gallons of water will leak from this faucet in 1 year? Solve this problem before continuing.

Many people would probably be able to solve this problem merely by multiplying $60 \times 60 \times 24 \times 365$, then dividing by $30 \times 8 \times 4 \times 4$. While this method gives the correct numerical answer, it would not be very helpful for making sure that the answer is correct. The key to this problem is unit analysis—remember, unit analysis is an organized way of using the quantities in a problem and other standard unit conversions to produce a verifiably correct answer.

Many students resist the unit-analysis strategy completely. They are much more comfortable just figuring out what numbers to multiply and divide and then doing that. However, they are frustrated with complex problems and they often get simple problems wrong. Demonstrate to yourself that this strategy works. Learn the proper technique, show all of your units and how they cancel, and you will experience great success, not only in this course but in your future chemistry and physics courses.

What units are needed for the Leaky Faucet, Part 1 problem? You need the time units of seconds, minutes, days, and years. You also need to know how many fluid ounces are in a gallon, which you can find by using quarts and cups. Make the following manipulative and one-n-oes. (**Remember** that the reciprocal of the fraction on each one-n-o should be written on the other side of the one-n-o.)

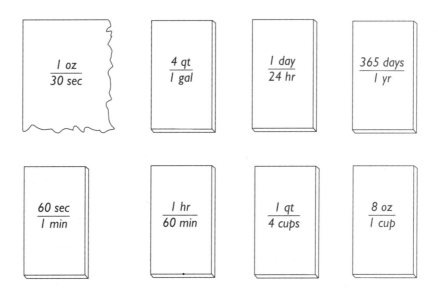

Organize your manipulatives in one long line, making sure that all units cancel except gallons and years. You want to end up with *gallons* on the top and *year* on the bottom. Do this before reading on.

The fractions below work for this problem. **Note** that their order could be rearranged but that none of the fractions could be flipped over. Show all the units that cancel—like units in the numerators and denominators of the fractions can be canceled, such as seconds and seconds, minutes and minutes, and so on.

$$\frac{1 \text{ oz}}{30 \text{ sec}} \times \frac{60 \text{ sec}}{1 \text{ min}} \times \frac{60 \text{ min}}{1 \text{ hr}} \times \frac{24 \text{ hr}}{1 \text{ day}} \times \frac{365 \text{ days}}{1 \text{ yr}} \times \frac{1 \text{ cup}}{8 \text{ oz}} \times \frac{1 \text{ qt}}{4 \text{ cups}} \times \frac{1 \text{ gal}}{4 \text{ qt}}$$

Now just do the arithmetic. You can use one of two methods to do this. The first method is to multiply all the numbers in the tops of the fractions and write down the result. Then multiply all the numbers in the bottoms of the fractions and write down the result. Then divide the resulting top number by the resulting bottom number. For this problem you get the result shown at the top of the next page.

$$\frac{31,536,000 \text{ gal}}{3,840 \text{ yr}} = \frac{8,212.5 \text{ gal}}{1 \text{ yr}}$$

With the second method, simply calculate from left to right, multiplying by each number that appears in a numerator and dividing by each number that appears in a denominator. Other than the first 1 appearing in the numerator of the first fraction (1 oz divided by 30 sec doesn't equal 1), all other 1's can be ignored because they don't affect the calculation. The calculator steps for these calculations go as follows:

$$1 \div 30 \times 60 \times 60 \times 24 \times 365 \div 8 \div 4 \div 4 = 8212.5$$

When you calculate using this technique, the result you get is always in the numerator of the fraction. Thus, the answer to the problem is 8212.5 gal/1 yr. The unit of gallons per year comes from canceling all the other units in the problem.

Notes on rounding: When you use a calculator, don't round any numbers until you finish the problem. Then, and only then, round the answer if you need to.

LEAKY FAUCET, PART 2

You realized that more than 8000 gallons per year was a lot of water to waste with a leaky faucet. You fixed your faucet so that it now takes 11 minutes longer to fill a cup of water than it did when it leaked 1 fluid ounce in 30 seconds. How many gallons will the faucet waste in one year now? Solve this problem before continuing.

The key to this problem is a new ratio, minutes/cup. You must calculate the number of minutes per cup that your sink currently leaks so that you can add 11 more minutes to it and so find the answer to the problem. In the Leaky Faucet, Part 1 problem we used the ratio shown below left. This ratio shows the liquid amount in the numerator and the time amount in the denominator. But the ratio minutes/cup shows the units reversed: time in the numerator and liquid in the denominator. So start with the ratio shown below right.

$$\frac{1 \text{ oz}}{30 \text{ sec}} \qquad \frac{30 \text{ sec}}{1 \text{ oz}}$$

Then convert this to minutes and to cups.

$$\frac{30 \; \cancel{\text{sec}}}{1 \; \cancel{\text{oz}}} \times \frac{1 \; \text{min}}{60 \; \cancel{\text{sec}}} \times \frac{8 \; \cancel{\text{oz}}}{1 \; \text{cup}} = \frac{240 \; \text{min}}{60 \; \text{cups}} = \frac{4 \; \text{min}}{1 \; \text{cup}}$$

So now we know it took 4 minutes to fill 1 cup with our old leaky faucet. Now that the faucet has been fixed, it takes 11 more minutes than that to fill a cup, so it now takes 15 minutes to fill 1 cup.

We are now ready to calculate the number of gallons per year that the faucet wastes. Our answer needs to be expressed in gallons/year, which means liquid in the numerator and time in the denominator. So flip 15 min/1 cup upside down and turn it into 1 cup/15 min. **Note** that this time we don't need to use the 60 sec/1 min one-n-o, because the problem is already expressed in minutes. And we also don't need 1 cup/8 oz, because the problem is already expressed in cups. Show all the units that cancel.

$$\frac{1 \; \cancel{\text{cup}}}{15 \; \cancel{\text{min}}} \times \frac{60 \; \cancel{\text{min}}}{1 \; \cancel{\text{hr}}} \times \frac{24 \; \cancel{\text{hr}}}{1 \; \cancel{\text{day}}} \times \frac{365 \; \cancel{\text{days}}}{1 \; \text{yr}} \times \frac{1 \; \cancel{\text{qt}}}{4 \; \cancel{\text{cups}}} \times \frac{1 \; \text{gal}}{4 \; \cancel{\text{qt}}} = \frac{2190 \; \text{gal}}{1 \; \text{yr}}$$

This is still a fairly sizable leak but much improved upon the earlier leak.

You should have noticed by now that the canceling you can do does not have to be that of units in adjacent fractions. In the set of fractions above, the cups in the numerator of the first fraction canceled with the cups in the denominator of the fifth fraction. However, it is wise to try to arrange your fractions so that the numerators and denominators of adjacent fractions do cancel—arranging your fractions this way will help you make sure you've canceled everything that needs to be canceled. In the example above, the minutes in the first denominator canceled the minutes in the second numerator; the hours in the second denominator canceled the hours in the third numerator, and so on, until the denominator was expressed in years. At that point, because year was the denominator you wanted, you could shift your focus to getting rid of the cups. Cups was changed to quarts and then to gallons so that you could reach the ratio of gallons/year that the problem called for, and so the process was complete. As we mentioned earlier, each one of these intermediary steps can be thought of as a subproblem.

Section 2: Metric and English Unit Conversions

Most people in the United States don't need to worry about converting English units of measure to metric units just yet. However, U.S. companies who manufacture goods outside the United States must know how to convert from English to metric units, and scientists in the United States regularly use the metric system. The importance of metric measurement in the United States is illustrated by the $150 million U.S. spacecraft that crashed into Mars in late 1999 because of scientists' failure to convert crucial measurements from English units to metric units. (For information about metric units of measure, see the appendix at the back of this book.)

CONVERTING WOOD

Raoul had done all of the measurements perfectly. He needed a piece of plywood that measured 122 centimeters by 244 centimeters. The problem was, with all of his traveling, he had gotten used to the notion that if it's Tuesday, this must be Belgium. Unfortunately, it was Thursday and he had jetted to the United States the night before. What size piece of wood should Raoul ask for at the local hardware store, where they don't use the metric system? Solve this problem before continuing.

Raoul needs some conversions, fast. Raoul, along with most of the rest of the world, is using a metric mind to deal with the English measurement system (which even the English won't use anymore). Of course, Raoul remembered to analyze first: The units of measure in this problem are units of distance. Raoul recalled something from his studies of ancient measurement systems: 1 m equals approximately 3.281 ft. So let's help him out with his conversions. Change the meters to feet by using 1 m = 3.281 ft.

$$\frac{122 \text{ cm}}{1} \times \frac{1 \text{ m}}{100 \text{ cm}} \times \frac{3.281 \text{ ft}}{1 \text{ m}} = \frac{4.00282 \text{ ft}}{1}$$

Doing the same series of conversions for Raoul's measurement of 244 cm, we get

$$\frac{244 \text{ cm}}{1} \times \frac{1 \text{ m}}{100 \text{ cm}} \times \frac{3.281 \text{ ft}}{1 \text{ m}} = \frac{8.00564 \text{ ft}}{1}$$

As it turns out, it looks like Raoul needs a 4 ft by 8 ft sheet of plywood.

Pipeline

In this section you will have to solve many conversion problems, converting one type of distance unit to another type of distance unit. For example, in the Converting Wood problem, you needed to convert centimeters to feet, but the only conversion we provided for you that you could use to go from metric distance to English distance was 1 meter = 3.281 feet. For the rest of the problems in this chapter, you can use a diagram we call a **pipeline** to show you how to get from one type of unit to another.

Using the following conversions, you can make a pipeline diagram that shows the paths used to find those conversions:

1 kilometer = 1000 meters	1 foot = 12 inches
1 meter = 100 centimeters	1 yard = 3 feet
1 meter = 3.281 feet	1 mile = 5280 feet

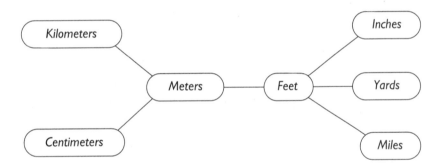

Notice that every conversion in the list is represented exactly once on the pipeline. Each unit of measure is represented in a bubble, and each conversion is represented as a line segment. The actual numbers used in the conversions are not shown in the diagram because they would cause clutter, but it may be possible to include them in a meaningful way. (Can you find a way to do it?)

You can use the pipeline to find paths of conversions. For example, to convert from yards to kilometers, start at yards, convert to feet, convert to meters, and then convert to kilometers. These paths are represented in the next diagram, with one-n-oes set up to convert 7000 yards to kilometers.

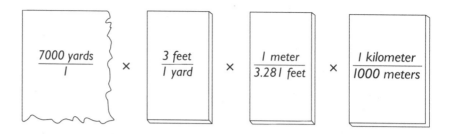

$$\frac{7000 \text{ yards}}{1} \quad \times \quad \frac{3 \text{ feet}}{1 \text{ yard}} \quad \times \quad \frac{1 \text{ meter}}{3.281 \text{ feet}} \quad \times \quad \frac{1 \text{ kilometer}}{1000 \text{ meters}}$$

Doing the arithmetic nets an answer of 6.4 kilometers. So 6.4 kilometers is the same as 7000 yards.

It is also possible to represent more conversions in the pipeline diagram by making connections between more of the diagram's bubbles. For example, you can easily make a connection between inches and yards to show that 1 yard = 36 inches.

CONVERSION PRACTICE

Work the following problems. You may use any English-to-English conversions and any metric-to-metric conversions that you want. However, the only English-to-metric conversions you may use are 1 meter = 3.281 feet and 1 gallon = 3.79 liters.

1. Change 12 feet to meters.

2. Change 5 gallons to liters.

3. Change 85 kilometers to miles.

4. Change 18 inches to centimeters.

Work these problems before continuing. Round answers to the nearest hundredth.

You might **notice** that the strategy of subproblems naturally shows up in these problems, as it does in most unit-analysis problems. Often, you won't be able to go directly from the unit given to the unit asked for, so you must look for intermediate steps along the way. This is the same thought process involved in solving problems with subproblems. The pipeline diagram is a visual representation of such unit-analysis subproblems.

1. Change 12 feet to meters. (distances)

   To change feet to meters, we use 1 meter = 3.281 feet.

   $$\frac{12 \cancel{ft}}{1} \times \frac{1\ m}{3.281 \cancel{ft}} = \frac{12\ m}{3.281} = 3.66\ m$$

2. Change 5 gallons to liters. (volumes)

   5 gal ↓   Change gallons to liters ↙

   $$\frac{5\ gal}{1} \times \frac{3.79\ L}{1\ gal} = \frac{18.95\ L}{1}$$

3. Change 85 kilometers to miles. (distances)

   Tim set up this problem a little differently, with vertical lines rather than multiplication symbols between fractions. He followed the pipeline diagram to take him from kilometers to meters to feet to miles.

85 km	1000 m	3.281 ft	1 mi
1	1 km	1 m	5280 ft

   "Then I just multiplied all the numbers on the top and divided by each of the numbers on the bottom. That gave me 52.82 miles."

4. Change 18 inches to centimeters. (distances)

   Following the pipeline, we need to go from inches to feet to meters to centimeters. We can use the following one-n-oes to solve this problem:

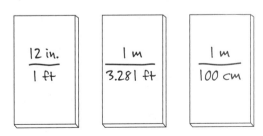

We also need a manipulative for 18 inches.

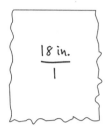

The inches need to cancel, so the inches in the second fraction need to be in the bottom of the fraction. This, in turn, helps set up all the other one-n-oes.

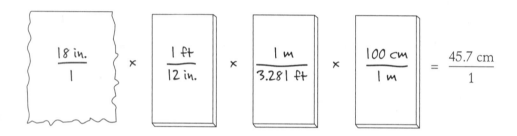

So there are 45.7 centimeters in 18 inches.

The next problem features both English and metric units.

HIDEO NOMO

When the baseball scouts for the Los Angeles Dodgers were looking at bringing Hideo Nomo to this country to pitch for the Dodgers, they must have been interested in knowing the speed of his fastball. In Korea, his fastball was clocked at 43 meters per second. The scouts would have wanted to know the speed in miles per hour. What speed in miles per hour is 43 meters per second? Solve this problem before continuing.

Simone solved this problem. "The problem asks for the answer in miles/hour, which is a measure of distance over time. So I started with meters/second, which is also a measure of distance over time. I used the following manipulative and one-n-oes":

$$\frac{43\ m}{1\ sec} \times \frac{3.281\ ft}{1\ m} \times \frac{1\ mi}{5280\ ft} \times \frac{60\ sec}{1\ min} \times \frac{60\ min}{1\ hr} = \frac{96.2\ mi}{1\ hr}$$

"So Hideo Nomo's fastball would be clocked at 96 miles per hour in the United States."

Note that the fractions in this problem could have been arranged in a different order and the solution would be the same. However, it is very common and simple to systematically convert from one unit to the next. So the numerator unit was converted from meters to feet to miles, the desired numerator. Then the denominator unit was converted from seconds to minutes to hours, the desired denominator.

The next problem involves using unit analysis in a new way. Instead of merely converting from one unit to another, we will use unit analysis to solve an interesting problem. The type of solution for this problem is often used in science classes, such as physics and chemistry. The idea is to take the units that are in the problem and the units that you want in the answer and figure out a way to get all of the other units to cancel, leaving the desired unit.

FASTBALL

Nolan Ryan has been clocked throwing a baseball 100 miles per hour. At that speed, how much time does the batter have to react? (How much time before the ball reaches the plate?) The pitcher's mound is 60 feet 6 inches from home plate. Work this problem before continuing.

This problem involves feet, miles/hour, miles, and seconds. The problem is stated in terms of the unit miles/hour, and the answer must be expressed in terms of time, but the problem doesn't specify whether to give the answer in seconds or in minutes (rather, fractions of a minute). Consider which unit conveys best to another person how little time the batter has to react. For the answer to be in its best form, it should be expressed with a unit that the receiving audience will best relate to.

The unit of speed in the fastball problem is given as the fraction shown below left. This looks wonderful, but miles/hour is a measure of distance over time. The answer needs to be given in terms of the number of seconds it takes to traverse 60 feet 6 inches, or in other words, time over distance. So invert the measure given from miles/hour to hours/mile, as shown in the fraction below right.

$$\frac{100 \text{ mi}}{1 \text{ hr}} \qquad\qquad \frac{1 \text{ hr}}{100 \text{ mi}}$$

Now the units are showing promise as something more helpful. The next thing to do is to make a series of unit conversions. First, change hours/mile to seconds/mile. Start by changing hours to minutes. Again, **note** that subproblems keep popping up.

$$\frac{1 \text{ hr}}{100 \text{ mi}} \times \frac{60 \text{ min}}{1 \text{ hr}} = \frac{60 \text{ min}}{100 \text{ mi}}$$

Next, convert the minutes into seconds, giving seconds/mile.

$$\frac{60 \text{ min}}{100 \text{ mi}} \times \frac{60 \text{ sec}}{1 \text{ min}} = \frac{3600 \text{ sec}}{100 \text{ mi}}$$

Now that the time units are in the form needed, the next thing to consider is the distance units. We'll convert miles into feet, because the distance between the pitcher's mound and home plate is given as 60 feet 6 inches (or 60.5 feet).

$$\frac{3600 \text{ sec}}{100 \text{ mi}} \times \frac{1 \text{ mi}}{5280 \text{ ft}} = \frac{3600 \text{ sec}}{528,000 \text{ ft}}$$

Now our fraction is in the form of seconds/feet. But that's not good enough. We need to know the number of seconds it takes to travel 1 ft (probably not very many) and then multiply by 60.5 to find the total seconds it takes to go all the way to home plate.

$$\frac{3600 \text{ sec}}{528,000 \text{ ft}} = \frac{0.0068181 \text{ sec}}{1 \text{ ft}}$$

$$\frac{0.0068181 \text{ sec}}{1 \text{ ft}} \times \frac{60.5 \text{ ft}}{1} = \frac{0.4125 \text{ sec}}{1}$$

At this point, there are no units in the denominator, because we want to give the answer in seconds, not in seconds/feet. So the ball reaches home plate in slightly less than half of a second. Would you want to bat against Nolan Ryan?

The steps in this problem could have been done all at the same time, as the following set of fractions demonstrates. As you get better at unit analysis, you will be able to carry out all of the steps at once.

$$\frac{1 \text{ hr}}{100 \text{ mi}} \times \frac{60 \text{ min}}{1 \text{ hr}} \times \frac{60 \text{ sec}}{1 \text{ min}} \times \frac{1 \text{ mi}}{5280 \text{ ft}} \times \frac{60.5 \text{ ft}}{1} = 0.4125 \text{ sec}$$

In the Fastball problem we emphasized which units you would use to best express your answer. When considering how to express the answer for a problem that doesn't specify which unit to use, think about how useful the information given in the answer is. Does it tell you what you need to know in a meaningful way? Can you easily use the information or would you need to translate it into another form to be able to really use it? For example, which trip would you rather take: the one for which you travel 2.1 million feet in 28,000 seconds, or the *same* trip for which you travel 400 miles in 8 hours?

Section 3: Compound Units

The units we have dealt with in this chapter so far are solitary units (a single unit by itself, such as feet) or units in a ratio (such as price per gallon). Just as putting units into a ratio is a key use of units, units are also often combined into what are called **compound units**. Compound units are common in physics and chemistry. The next problem provides a simple example of compound units.

AREA

Find the area of a rectangle with length 3 feet and width 2 feet. Solve this problem before continuing.

The area of a rectangle can be found by using the formula Area = length × width.

Area = length × width

= 3 feet × 2 feet

= 6 square feet (which also can be written feet^2 or ft^2)

The unit in the answer to this problem is a compound unit: square feet. The unit started as a measure of linear distance and is now a measure of area. The unit of square feet is an integral part of the problem and answer. A square foot is the area of a square measuring 1 foot on each side.

If we'd used 36 inches (instead of 3 feet) by 24 inches to find the answer, then the area would have been in square inches: 864 square inches. Again, we can show that this measure is equivalent to 6 square feet. (Square inches can also be written as inch • inch.)

$$\frac{864 \; \text{inch} \cdot \text{inch}}{1} \times \frac{1 \; \text{foot}}{12 \; \text{inches}} \times \frac{1 \; \text{foot}}{12 \; \text{inches}} = 6 \; \text{feet}^2$$

Note that to convert square inches to square feet, you don't simply divide by 12 inches. Rather, you must divide by 12 inches squared, or 144 square inches—there are 144 square inches in 1 square foot.

$$\frac{864 \; \text{inches}^2}{1} \times \frac{1 \; \text{foot}^2}{144 \; \text{inches}^2} = 6 \; \text{feet}^2$$

The next problem explores the idea of area combined with unit pricing, which we discussed in the At the Grocery Store Problem earlier in the chapter. Many people who order a pizza assume that the larger the pizza, the better the deal. This is usually the case, but not always. Analyzing pizza prices with unit analysis lets the consumer make an informed purchase. Look at the following problem.

Use the pizza parlor menu shown below to determine which cheese pizza is the best buy. All pizzas are round.

TYPE	DIAMETER	PRICE
Small	10 inches	$6.80
Medium	12 inches	$8.50
Large	14 inches	$12.60
Giant	20 inches	$21.00

Work this problem before continuing.

You first must assume that all these pizzas have the same height, and therefore that their weight is proportional to their area. Second, you must not fall into the trap of comparing price to diameter. The price of a pizza does not go up in proportion to its diameter. In fact, area is the important unit (again, assuming equal heights). So compare price to area and see which is the best buy. You could use either dollars per square inch or square inches per dollar. Let's use square inches per dollar.

A necessary subproblem is then to find the area of each pizza. The formula $A = \pi r^2$ gives the area of a circle. Note that the area comes out in square units because you square the radius unit (in this case, inches) before you multiply it by π (π is unitless). Needing to find the area leads to another subproblem (an easy one), that of finding the radius of each pizza. Then compute the area.

Type	Diameter	Radius	Area
Small	10 inches	5 inches	25π inches²
Medium	12 inches	6 inches	36π inches²
Large	14 inches	7 inches	49π inches²
Giant	20 inches	10 inches	100π inches²

Now compute the value of square inches per dollar, as shown in the next chart. Use 3.14 as an approximation for π. Round off to the nearest hundredths place.

Type	Area	Price	Area/$
Small	25π inches²	$6.80	11.54 inches²/$
Medium	36π inches²	$8.50	13.30 inches²/$
Large	49π inches²	$12.60	12.21 inches²/$
Giant	100π inches²	$21.00	14.95 inches²/$

Clearly the giant pizza is the best buy because it gives the most area per dollar. (If we'd decided instead to find the best buy in dollars per square inch, then we would have wanted to know the lowest price per area.) But the next best deal, which may be rather surprising, is the medium pizza. Understanding how to evaluate best buys gives consumers the opportunity to worry about things other than price, such as how hungry they are and whether there is room in the refrigerator for the leftovers.

Another common type of compound unit—the passenger-mile—shows up in the transportation field, both as a measure of the efficiency of public transportation and in traffic-safety statistics. For example, you might see statistics on deaths per billion passenger-miles, accidents per billion passenger-miles, or even arrests per billion passenger-miles.

Just exactly what is a passenger-mile? It represents 1 passenger traveling 1 mile. For example, a car with 1 passenger traveling 12 miles racks up 12 passenger-miles. A car with 3 passengers traveling 5 miles accounts for 15 passenger-miles (that is, one of the passengers traveled 5 miles, another traveled 5 miles, and the third traveled 5 miles). An airplane that travels 2500 miles with 400 passengers aboard accounts for 1 million passenger-miles.

Cars are quite clearly an inefficient means of transportation because they don't carry very many people and so do not account for very many passenger-miles per car. Many busy freeways have diamond lanes for car pools (two or more passengers) to use during rush hour. But traffic in diamond lanes is often light while the other lanes are congested with cars carrying only one occupant each. In contrast, trains, buses, vans, subways, and trolleys carry many more passengers and are therefore able to accommodate quite a number of passenger-miles per vehicle.

But what about the economics of the situation? Occasionally people drive together and share gas expenses. This type of shared transportation, as well as public transportation, is subject to analysis based on various units. Buses are expensive to buy, and they get only a few miles per gallon in stop-and-go city conditions. A transit district could counter this disadvantage by showing that its buses average over 200 passenger-miles per gallon. When you can pack 40 to 70 people on a bus, it becomes a very fuel-efficient mode of transportation, despite poor gas mileage. When computing the total costs of running the bus, though, you need to consider the driver's wages and the wages of the support personnel. But again, these costs are very low when considered in terms of per passenger-mile (or to study productivity on the basis of an hourly wage, we could calculate per passenger-hour).

The next problem—a problem dealing with a car pool—will serve to illustrate some of these ideas.

LONG COMMUTE

Gerónimo and three friends drove 208 miles. Their car got 35 miles per gallon during the trip. They drove at an average speed of 50 miles per hour, and the gasoline for the trip cost them $8.02. Find each of the following:

1. Gallons of gas used
2. Hours the trip took
3. Average feet per second
4. Dollars per hour
5. Dollars per gallon

6. Dollars per passenger
7. Cents per mile
8. Total number of passenger-miles
9. Passenger-miles per gallon
10. Cents per passenger-mile

Solve this problem before continuing.

Consider the questions one at a time.

1. Gallons of gas used

   To find gallons, consider the given unit, miles per gallon. We want the gallons part, but we need to get rid of the miles part. But miles are also given. Consider multiplying the two quantities together.

   $$\frac{35 \text{ miles}}{1 \text{ gallon}} \times \frac{208 \text{ miles}}{1}$$

This doesn't work because the miles unit will not cancel and the result will be miles²/gallon, which might make sense if you were plowing a field with a tractor but certainly makes no sense here. But if the miles-per-gallon fraction were inverted, miles would cancel, leaving gallons.

$$\frac{1\ gallon}{35\ miles} \times \frac{208\ miles}{1} = 5.94\ gallons$$

Many students might set up the calculation to cancel miles as follows:

$$\frac{35\ miles}{1\ gallon} \times \frac{1}{208\ miles} = \frac{35}{208\ gallons} = \frac{0.168}{gallon}$$

Miles would cancel as needed, but does the answer look reasonable? Does it seem possible that a trip of this length could use less than 1 gallon of gas? Take a close look at the units: They're actually 1/gallons instead of gallons. That is, gallons is in the denominator, not in the numerator. That's why this answer doesn't work.

2. Hours the trip took

   June solved it this way: "This problem looked like it might be similar to the gallons problem because the only way we had hours expressed in the problem was in a ratio."

$$\frac{50\ miles}{1\ hour} \times \frac{208\ miles}{1}$$

"All I did was look, look, look, and then stare at these units. I finally saw that since I wanted hours, I had to flip the miles per hour to make hours per mile and then I could multiply and get the miles to cancel, leaving hours."

$$\frac{1\ hour}{50\ miles} \times \frac{208\ miles}{1} = \frac{4.16\ hours}{1}$$

3. Average feet per second

Terrence said, "This was a piece of cake. First I converted the miles to feet, then I changed the hours to seconds."

$$\frac{50 \text{ miles}}{1 \text{ hour}} \times \frac{5280 \text{ feet}}{1 \text{ mile}} \times \frac{1 \text{ hour}}{60 \text{ minutes}} \times \frac{1 \text{ minute}}{60 \text{ seconds}} =$$

$$\frac{264,000 \text{ feet}}{3,600 \text{ seconds}} = 73.\overline{3} \text{ feet/second}$$

4. Dollars per hour

$$\frac{\$8.02}{4.16 \text{ hours}} = \$1.93/hour$$

5. Dollars per gallon

$$\frac{\$8.02}{5.94 \text{ gallons}} = \$1.35/gallon$$

6. Dollars per passenger

$$\frac{\$8.02}{4 \text{ passengers}} = \$2.005 \ (or \ \$2.01/passenger)$$

7. Cents per mile

$$\frac{\$8.02 \text{ dollars}}{208 \text{ miles}} \times \frac{100 \text{ cents}}{1 \text{ dollar}} = \frac{802 \text{ cents}}{208 \text{ miles}}$$

Which is 3.86 cents per mile, or roughly 4 cents per mile.

8. Total number of passenger-miles

$$4 \text{ passengers} \times 208 \text{ miles} = 832 \text{ passenger-miles}$$

9. Passenger-miles per gallon

$$\frac{832 \text{ passenger-miles}}{5.94 \text{ gallons}} = \frac{140.1 \text{ passenger-miles}}{1 \text{ gallon}}$$

10. Cents per passenger-mile

$$\frac{802 \text{ cents}}{832 \text{ passenger-miles}} = \frac{0.96 \text{ cent}}{1 \text{ passenger-mile}}$$

Or a little less than 1 cent per passenger-mile.

Note that for Gerónimo and his friends, carpooling provided a much more efficient method of transportation than if all four individuals had driven their own cars. In this chapter's Problem Set A, you'll find another problem that illustrates this concept and you will be asked to compare that situation with this one.

Unit analysis can be used to make comparisons between things that may not seem to be similar. For example, which is safer: driving or flying? Well, most people make most trips safely, however they travel. But when there is an airplane accident, the death toll can be very high. The death toll in a single car accident is low, but there are a lot more deaths each year from auto accidents. Consider these statistics from The National Transportation Safety Board: In 1996, 319 people were killed in U.S. commercial airline accidents. Of course this is bad, but how does it compare to the 42,065 people killed in automobile accidents? Is it fair to compare cars and airplanes? People use cars a lot more than they use airplanes. The average car is driven about 15,000 miles per year, but do people fly an average of 15,000 miles per year?

A way to even out the statistics to get a better feel for the relative safety of these modes of transportation is to use the ratio deaths per passenger-mile. Quite bluntly, the more passenger-miles that are created by one mode of transportation, the more accidents and deaths we would expect from that mode. According to the U.S. Department of Transportation during 1996, the commercial airlines accounted for approximately 445.2 billion passenger-miles (445,200,000,000!). Automobiles accounted for 3,630 billion passenger-miles. How do the death statistics compare now?

Write ratios showing deaths per billion passenger-miles for each form of transportation.

Airlines:

$$\frac{319 \text{ deaths}}{434.7 \text{ bill pass-miles}} = \frac{0.73 \text{ death}}{\text{bill pass-miles}}$$

Automobiles:

$$\frac{42,065 \text{ deaths}}{3,630 \text{ bill pass-miles}} = \frac{11.59 \text{ deaths}}{\text{bill pass-miles}}$$

Evidently, automobiles are far more dangerous than airplanes. This is as you might expect. However, how many deaths per year would occur if cars had the same death rate per billion passenger-miles as airplanes?

$$\frac{0.73 \text{ death}}{\text{bill pass-miles}} \times \frac{3,630 \text{ bill pass-miles}}{1 \text{ year}} = \frac{2,649.9 \text{ deaths}}{1 \text{ year}}$$

When you consider that, according to *Accident Facts,* National Safety Council, 1999, every year on Labor Day weekend there will be approximately 500 traffic deaths in the United States, the safety rate of the airlines becomes even more impressive.

The next problem again combines compound units and units in ratios.

MR. ROGERS' NEIGHBORHOOD

Janice, Stephanie, Rose, and Gina are going to be paid $84.70 for cleaning up Mr. Rogers' neighborhood. They each worked 5 hours, except Rose, who was 45 minutes late. How much should each one be paid? Work this problem before continuing.

Rose contributed 4¼ hours of labor. Janice, Stephanie, and Gina contributed 5 hours each (or 15 hours among the three), for a total of 19¼ hours. (**Note** that we could also use 19:15 for 19 hours and 15 minutes. But this is sometimes confused with the decimal 19.15 instead of the correct decimal 19.25 for 19¼ hours.)

Now divide.

$$\frac{\$84.70}{19.25 \text{ hours}} = \$4.40 \text{ per hour}$$

To find the fair share for each worker, multiply her hours by the dollars per hour.

Janice, Gina, and Stephanie:

$$\frac{\$4.40}{1 \text{ hour}} \times \frac{5 \text{ hours}}{1} = \$22.00$$

If you are careful with the units, the hours cancel, leaving dollars as the units.

The computation for Rose is similar.

$$\frac{\$4.40}{1 \text{ hour}} \times \frac{4.25 \text{ hours}}{1} = \$18.70$$

If you attempt to double-check this problem by multiplying the hourly rate by the hours, the hours units cancel, and the unit that is left is dollars.

$$\frac{\$4.40}{1 \text{ hour}} \times \frac{19.25 \text{ hours}}{1} = \frac{\$84.70}{1}$$

Another approach is to set up a chart like you did in algebra classes for solving various word problems. Tom took this approach.

Name	Hours Worked	Pay Rate/Hour	Total Pay
Gina	5		
Stephanie	5		
Janice	5		
Rose	4.25		
Total	19.25		$84.70

"I divided the $84.70 by 19.25 hours, giving $4.40 per hour. Then all I had to do was to multiply each girl's hours times her pay rate to come up with her total pay."

Name	Hours Worked	Pay Rate/Hour	Total Pay
Gina	5	$4.40	$22.00
Stephanie	5	$4.40	$22.00
Janice	5	$4.40	$22.00
Rose	4.25	$4.40	$18.70
Total	19.25	$4.40	$84.70

For more about solving problems with algebra, see Chapter 13: Algebra.

Sometimes, problems from courses such as chemistry and physics are more easily solved if you pay attention to the units involved. One of Ken's students came to him one day with a problem from his chemistry class. Even though Ken is not a chemist, he was able to use unit analysis to assist the student in solving the problem. Using unit analysis does not rely on understanding science, but if you rely strictly on unit analysis and don't understand the science involved, you may make mistakes. Nevertheless, if you keep careful track of units in science problems, an approach to the solution may be more readily apparent. You should use unit analysis in conjunction with your knowledge of science to further enhance your learning and understanding. Ultimately, your goal should be enhanced problem solving in all fields of study, including science. This goal applies not only to textbook problems, but also to problems that come up in research. The ideal is to improve your learning and understanding by tying together all your knowledge and tools.

Real-world problem solving

Rick, a professor of physiology at a leading university, provided this real-world use of unit analysis.

"In our research we are very concerned with the timing of our experiments. The computer can sample data in nanoseconds (1 billionth of a second), microseconds (1 millionth of a second), or milliseconds (1 thousandth of a second). We often have to go back and forth between these different computer sampling rates and match them with the frequency responses of the nerve cells, which are in seconds, milliseconds, and microseconds. The computer sampling rate during the experiment must be configured to maximize the efficacy of the nerve activity that is being sampled.

"There are two types of nerve activity: low-frequency nerve activity and high-frequency nerve activity. To avoid excess computer storage of data, low-frequency nerve activity must be sampled with low computer sampling rates and high-frequency nerve activity must be sampled with fast computer sampling rates. If the nerve activity is occurring every millisecond, we need to set the computer sampling rate to at least 20,000 times per second. So the computer will be sampling every 50 microseconds. In this way, I am sure we will record the necessary data. If the nerve activity occurs every second, and we were to sample 20,000 times per second again, we would waste a lot of computer memory. We would get 1000 times more data points than we would need. Computer storage space is very expensive, so we must be sure that we sample at the right rate. Knowledge of the units involved is very important."

Problem Set A

1. CHRISTINA'S TRIP

Christina drove 116 miles in 2 hours 15 minutes. She used 4 gallons of gas that cost her $4.76. Find the quantities that are expressed with each of these units. (Express a quantity with both the number-amount and the unit.)

a. miles per hour
b. miles per gallon
c. dollars per gallon
d. feet per second

e. dollars per hour
f. quarts per minute
g. cents per minute
h. cents per mile

i. miles per dollar
j. gallons per hour

2. UNIT CONVERSIONS

Convert from metric to English or from English to metric as indicated. The only metric-to-English conversions you are allowed to use are 1 m = 3.281 ft and 1 gal = 3.79 L. Of course, you may use any English-to-English conversions (such as 1 mi = 5280 ft) and any metric-to-metric conversions (such as 1 km = 1000 m).

a. 35 m to feet
b. 170 ft to meters
c. 150 mi to kilometers
d. 47 km to miles
e. 4 ft to centimeters

f. 87 cm to inches
g. 54 in. to millimeters
h. $32 \frac{\text{mi}}{\text{hr}}$ to $\frac{\text{meters}}{\text{second}}$
i. 5 gal to liters
j. 16 L to quarts

3. ANOTHER LONG COMMUTE

Anastoli and two friends drove 87.5 miles and averaged 35 miles per gallon. They drove at an average speed of 50 miles per hour and the trip cost them $3.30 in gasoline. Find the quantities that are expressed with each of these units:

a. gal

b. hrs

c. ft/sec

d. dollars/hr

e. dollars/gal

f. dollars/passenger

g. cents/mi

h. total number of passenger-miles

i. passenger-miles/gal

j. cents/passenger-mile

Comparing this car with Gerónimo's car from the Long Commute problem, which car do you think is being used most efficiently?

4. IN-HOME SODA MACHINES

At the state fair, Bill found a booth where in-home soda machines were being sold. The saleswoman told Bill that if he bought syrup and carbonated it with this machine, it would cost him as little as 11 cents per liter to produce the same soda at home that he'd pay more for in the store. Remember the problem Six for Chris, Part 1? Find the cost per liter of the six-pack if Chris makes it with the in-home soda machine.

5. DRIVING IN ENGLAND

You just arrived in England and hopped into your American car, which was delivered on a boat. You head out onto a country road, where the posted speed limit is 100 kilometers per hour. Your speedometer measures the speed only in miles per hour, so you need to convert from miles to kilometers to know how fast you can drive without exceeding the speed limit. You know that there are 3.281 feet in 1 meter. How fast can you drive?

6. PROJECTILE

A projectile is shot into space at 150 feet per second. How many miles per hour is that? How many kilometers per hour is that?

7. PAINTING CHIPMUNKS

Alvin, Simon, and Theodore went to work helping Dave paint his house. Alvin worked 6 hours, Simon worked $1^{1}/4$ hours fewer than Alvin, and Theodore worked $4^{1}/2$ hours. They were paid $61 for their work. How much did each chipmunk get?

8. READING RATE, PART 1

If you read 15 minutes per day every day and end up reading 12 books of 200 pages each in one year, what is your reading rate in pages per minute?

9. READING RATE, PART 2

If you increase your reading speed so that each page takes you 30 seconds less than it did before, and you begin reading 20 minutes per day, how many 200-page books can you now read in a year?

10. PENALTY KICK

China and the United States are playing each other in the championship match of the 1999 Women's World Cup Soccer Tournament. Brandi Chastain of the United States team is about to take a penalty kick against the Chinese team's goalkeeper, Gao Hong. Chastain will kick the ball from 18 yards away from the goal, at 120 miles per hour. How many seconds does the goalkeeper have to react, dive, and reach the ball before it crosses the goal line?

11. NEW CAR PURCHASE

Sommer wants to buy a new car. She currently drives a car that gets 30 miles per gallon. She is contemplating buying a car that gets 40 miles per gallon. Sommer drives 15,000 miles per year. Assume that gas costs $1.65 per gallon the entire year. How much will Sommer save on gas in one year if she buys the new car?

12. SPEEDING UP

You are driving at 50 miles per hour. If you decrease the time it takes you to travel 1 mile by 8 seconds, what is your new speed?

13. SAILING SHIPS

In the city of San Miguel on the island of Cozumel, Mexico, there is a museum with a room devoted to pirates and sailing ships. One of the displays shows a log chip—a small triangular, weighted device used by fifteenth- and sixteenth-century sailors to measure speed. The log chip was tied to a rope that was wound up on a reel. The sailors tied evenly spaced knots in the rope. They would then throw the rope overboard and the weight of the log chip would allow the rope to unreel as the boat moved along. The sailors would allow it to unreel for 30 seconds, timed with a sand hourglass. They would then haul the rope in and count the number of knots that had been reeled out. This number was the speed of the boat in knots (nautical miles per hour). If one nautical mile is 6076.10333 feet (one minute of arc of the earth's circumference), how many feet apart are the knots?

14. NURSING

Allyson is a nurse in the intensive care unit of a hospital. She works with units daily, administering drugs through intravenous (IV) tubes. A common dosage for the drug dopamine is 2 to 5 micrograms per kilogram of body weight per minute. She will put 400 milligrams of dopamine into 250 cubic centimeters of fluid and administer it to the patient through an IV tube. At what rate, in cubic centimeters per hour, should she set the flow to achieve a dosage of 3 micrograms per kilogram per minute into a patient with a mass of 75 kilograms?

15. **WRITE YOUR OWN**

Write your own unit-analysis problem. A unit-conversion problem is relatively easy to come up with. Consider making up your own system of units, possibly involving funny measures of things, like paper clips or thumbnails.

16. **CONNECTIONS**

Where have you used unit analysis in other courses or in your daily life?

Problem Set B

1. **QUIT WHILE YOU CAN**

Smoking has long been connected with serious diseases, such as lung cancer, emphysema, and heart disease. Let's estimate that for every cigarette a person smokes, he or she loses anywhere from 10 to 15 minutes of his or her life. Assuming the worst (15 minutes of life lost for each cigarette), how much shorter would the life span be of someone who smoked two packs a day for 35 years? (Each pack contains 20 cigarettes.) Answer in years, days, hours, and minutes. (For example, 42 years, 152 days, 7 hours, and 28 minutes.)

2. **SESAME STREET LIVE**

The national touring company of Sesame Street Live visited Seattle, Washington, last year. The producers held a special promotional ticket sale for one hour. During this time, adult tickets sold for $5, junior tickets (ages 8 to 16) sold for $2, and children's tickets (ages 0 to 8) sold for the ridiculously low price of 10¢. During this sale, 120 tickets sold for exactly $120. How many of each kind of ticket were sold during the sale?

3. NO CHAIN LETTERS

Chain letters are illegal. This problem will show you why. Here is a sample.

Dear Friend:

This is a chain letter. Make two copies. Send the two copies and this original to three friends.

Sincerely,
Albin

Albin actually made five originals and sent them out in the first mailing. If the first mailing is considered the first generation, and each set of copies constitutes the next generation, how many letters will be in existence after the tenth generation is produced?

4. WHO WAS SNOOZING?

One of the five members of a company's board of directors was suspected of sleeping during a board meeting. It was known that only one board member had actually slept, but no one (except the five members) knew who it was. The company vice president questioned the members and they made the following statements:

Davis: The snoozer was either Rawls or Charlton.

Rawls: Neither Vongy nor I was asleep.

Charlton: Both Rawls and Davis are lying.

Bobbins: Only one of Rawls or Davis is telling the truth.

Vongy: Bobbins is a liar.

When the board chairperson (she was not questioned) was consulted, she said that three of the board members always tell the truth and two of them always lie. Who slept in the meeting?

Use the league standings for this recreational volleyball league and the schedule for the first three weeks of games to determine which teams won each week. (By the way, the Renegades won their second match.) What happened in each of the three matches that the Buckeyes played?

STANDINGS			SCHEDULE
TEAM	WINS	LOSSES	WEEK 1
Red Skeletons	3	0	Red Skeletons vs Walleyball
Bombay Bicycle	2	1	Bombay Bicycle vs Bill's Thrills
Renegades	2	1	Whine Sox vs Renegades
Sacto Magazine	2	1	Sacto Magazine vs Buckeyes
Walleyball	2	1	WEEK 2
Buckeyes	1	2	Renegades vs Sacto Magazine
Bill's Thrills	0	3	Walleyball vs Whine Sox
Whine Sox	0	3	Buckeyes vs Bombay Bicycle
			Bill's Thrills vs Red Skeletons
			WEEK 3
			Whine Sox vs Sacto Magazine
			Walleyball vs Bill's Thrills
			Red Skeletons vs Buckeyes
			Bombay Bicycle vs Renegades

In a large-scale painting like a mural, solving problems of color and composition can seem impossibly hard, so muralists often create smaller, preliminary studies to give them a sense of how to approach the final work.

Solve an Easier Related Problem

One of the most famous legends in mathematics is that of Carl Friedrich Gauss (1777–1855). The story concerns the young Gauss in fourth grade. One day his teacher was busy and wanted to give the class something to do so that he could get some work done at his desk. He gave the class an assignment: Add up all the numbers from 1 to 100. The teacher believed that this would keep the class occupied for thirty minutes. But after just a short time, Carl Gauss walked up to the teacher's desk with the answer written on his slate. The teacher was very impressed and asked him how he had solved the problem. Before we relate the rest of the story, you should try the problem.

What is the sum of the first one hundred whole numbers? Work this problem before continuing.

There are many ways to approach this problem. One way, the brute-force problem-solving strategy, is to get out a piece of scratch paper or your calculator and just keep adding. A second way is to use your calculator's constant addition feature and its memory and just press the M+ (memory plus) key 100 times. But Carl Gauss didn't have a calculator, so he must have approached the problem in a different way.

Another approach combines the strategies of subproblems and patterns. Tori used this approach.

"I decided to break the problem into subproblems. I split the hundred numbers into groups of ten and computed the sum of each ten. Then I looked for a pattern."

$$1 + 2 + 3 + 4 + 5 + 6 + 7 + 8 + 9 + 10 = 55$$
$$11 + 12 + 13 + 14 + 15 + 16 + 17 + 18 + 19 + 20 = 155$$
$$21 + 22 + 23 + 24 + 25 + 26 + 27 + 28 + 29 + 30 = 255$$

"I quickly saw the pattern, so I added up the sums of the ten groups of ten."

$$55 + 155 + 255 + 355 + 455 + 555 + 655 + 755 + 855 + 955 = 5050$$

"Subproblems and patterns made this problem easy. Of course, I used a calculator and Carl Gauss couldn't have had one two hundred years ago."

So just what did Gauss do anyway? Let's imagine the way he might tell the story.

"When my teacher gave me this problem, I really didn't want to do it. I could tell that he just wanted to give us practice adding. I didn't think I needed practice. I looked around and noticed that all the other kids were busy doing the problem. They kept erasing their slates and everything, but I thought there had to be an easier way. So I thought about the problem for a while. I pretended that the teacher had given us a different problem instead. I thought adding from 1 to 100 would take too long, so I thought about from 1 to 10. I knew I could add that up, no problem."

$$1 + 2 = 3 \quad 3 + 3 = 6 \quad 6 + 4 = 10 \quad 10 + 5 = 15 \quad 15 + 6 = 21 \quad \text{and so on}$$

"I got tired of this real quick. I couldn't imagine going all the way to 100. There had to be an easier way. Then it occurred to me that I didn't have to add up the numbers in that order; I could use any order I wanted. So I started playing around with the numbers. I added 1 and 5 and got 6. Then I added 2 and 4 and got 6 again. I thought that pattern was sort of interesting. I started over again. This time I added 1 and 10. That gave me 11. Then I did 2 + 9 and 3 + 8 and 4 + 7 and 5 + 6, and I got 11 every time. So the sum of the whole numbers from 1 to 10 had to be 5 × 11 since there were five groups of 11."

"From this easy problem, it was immediately obvious how to do the original problem."

$$1 + 100 = 101$$
$$2 + 99 = 101$$
$$3 + 98 = 101$$
$$4 + 97 = 101 \quad \text{and so on}$$

"There were going to be 50 pairs of 101, so the answer was 50 × 101 = 5050. I walked up and told my teacher. Boy, was he impressed."

What Carl Gauss did in the eighteenth century contains a great lesson for today: If a problem seems too hard, make it easier. In this chapter you will see a number of different ways to make a problem easier. Of course, the easier problem has to be related to the harder problem you're trying to solve. That is, it wouldn't have helped Gauss solve the From One to One Hundred problem if he had thought about

"I looked at these numbers and realized that the polling places and the voters had something in common: polling places are locations for voters. The numbers must be connected somehow. Since there were 30,000 voters at 15 polling places last election (by my rounded numbers), that would mean there were 2,000 voters at each polling place.

"The number of households would be important to an elections clerk for deciding the number of information pamphlets to send out, but it probably wouldn't be necessary in calculating the number of polling places needed. Besides, the only information provided for both elections is the numbers of voters for the two elections. So I ignored the information about households.

"I also didn't figure the number of issues mattered a whole bunch. It was probably the same as the last election, but I had no way of knowing because the problem didn't say. It actually would make a difference if there were a whole bunch more issues this time than last time, because it would take someone longer to vote. But I decided to ignore that too.

"Now I needed to know how many polling places were needed for this election. I decided to keep it at 2,000 people per polling place. So I just divided 35,000 by 2,000 and got 17.5. So that's either 17 or 18 polling places for this election.

"Since I now had a plan, I went back to the original problem. In my easier related problem, I came up with $30,000/15$ polling places is 2,000 voters per polling place. So I divided 28,311 by 14 to find out about how many voters there were per polling place in the original problem. The answer was 2,022.2 (rounded). I then divided 34,892 by 2,022.2 and got 17.25 polling places needed. I figured they would try to set up 17 polling places. This would be 34,892 voters divided by 17 polling places, which gives 2,052.5 voters per location, which is probably no problem. And I thought it was interesting that I got basically the same answer with my easier problem."

Janeen's success with this problem can be traced to the following things she did:

1. She organized the information.

2. She simplified the numbers. (Take **note** of this.)

3. She ignored all the irrelevant information.

It's admirable that instead of panicking, Janeen just got started on the problem and worked on it. The problem is complicated because it uses large numbers and there's no direct indication that you need to divide to solve it. Janeen also determined the relevant information and ignored the irrelevant information. And by simplifying the numbers, she was in a better position to analyze the problem. Janeen used the strategy of solving an easier related problem. For her, the easier related problem was essentially:

> The clerk of Easierrelatedtown has the job of getting the materials ready for the next municipal election. In the last election, there were about 30,000 registered voters and they voted at 15 polls. The clerk figures she needs about a proportionate amount of materials for this election. This time there are about 35,000 people registered to vote. How many polling places will be needed?

This problem is nowhere near as complicated as the original problem, yet it is essentially the same problem. An easier related problem can often help you decide how to proceed with a problem that is difficult. Use the strategy of easier related problems to solve the next problem.

HOW MANY SQUARES?

How many squares are there on a checkerboard? (**Hint:** It is more than 64.) Work this problem before continuing.

Angie and Isaac worked on this problem. Isaac is a checker player, so of course he liked this problem. They worked with squares on a piece of graph paper.

ISAAC: This problem is too easy. It's 64—that is, 8-by-8. There are 8 squares on each side, and 8 times 8 is 64.

ANGIE: But that can't be right, because it is too easy. Look, aren't there some other squares on this board? If we divide the square into fourths, we have four more squares that each contain 16 of the little squares. And how about the square that has nine squares in it? (Angie drew the squares shown at the top of the next page.)

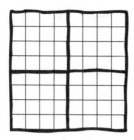 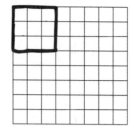

ISAAC: Wow, you're right. This problem is harder than I thought.

ANGIE: Well, let's look at an easier problem. How could we make this one easier?

ISAAC: I know—how about 3 + 5? That's an easier problem, and the answer is 8.

ANGIE: Isaac, the easier problem has to be related to the one we're doing.

ISAAC: Okay, okay. I know, we could use a smaller square. How about 7-by-7 instead of 8-by-8?

ANGIE: Good idea, but that still seems too hard.

ISAAC: Well, this is ridiculous. How about 1-by-1, is that easy enough for you?

ANGIE: Yeah, I think I can handle that. (She drew a 1-by-1 square.) How many squares are here?

ISAAC: Gee, I don't know, one?

ANGIE: Yeah, that was a little easy. Maybe we should try something a little harder. How about a 4-by-4?

ISAAC: Now, wait. Maybe if we go to 2-by-2 and then 3-by-3, we might find a pattern.

ANGIE: Yeah, okay, let's do 2-by-2. (She drew a 2-by-2 square.) Well, I see four squares.

ISAAC: I see five. There are obviously four little squares. But the whole picture is a square, so that makes five.

ANGIE: Oh yeah. Let's try a 3-by-3.

ISAAC: Wow, this is getting harder. Let's see, there are nine little squares and one big square, so there are ten.

ANGIE: Yeah, but wait. There are also some medium-sized squares: squares that contain four squares. They are the same size as the 2-by-2 square we looked at a minute ago.

ISAAC: I see them. They sort of overlap. I think there are four. (He outlined them.)

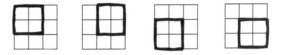

ANGIE: Okay, so there are nine little 1-by-1 squares, four 2-by-2 squares, and one 3-by-3 square. So that is a total of 14. I think I'm seeing a pattern here.

ISAAC: Me too. Can we organize this somehow?

ANGIE: I think so. Let's make a chart.

ISAAC: What are we going to put in the chart?

ANGIE: Good question. Well, let's see. So far we have:

Size of "checkerboard"	Number of squares
1-by-1	1
2-by-2	5
3-by-3	14

ANGIE: Do you see a pattern?

ISAAC: No, I don't. But that last one was interesting. Let's do a 4-by-4.

ANGIE: Okay. (She drew a 4-by-4 square.)

ISAAC: Okay, there are obviously 16 little squares. How many 2-by-2 squares are there?

ANGIE: I don't know. But there is one big square.

ISAAC: Come on, Angie, we've got to do this systematically.

ANGIE: Okay, we're looking for squares that are 2-by-2. I think there are four. We can divide the whole square into fourths, so there are four.

ISAAC: I don't think so. Last time the squares overlapped. I think that happens here too. Let's just look at the top two rows. We can put a square on the left side, one in the middle, and one on the right side. (He outlined them, as shown in the next diagram.)

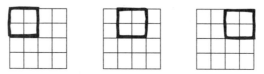

ANGIE: And we can do that in the second and third rows, and in the bottom two rows. So there are nine. I think I see a pattern here.

ISAAC: I do too. I bet there are four 3-by-3 squares.

ANGIE: Yes, there are. (She outlined them.)

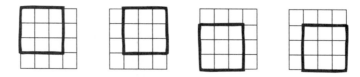

ISAAC: And there is one 4-by-4 square. It seems as though the pattern is the number of squares of each size. We need to organize this.

Size of Board	Number of Squares
1-by-1	1
2-by-2	$4 + 1 = 5$
3-by-3	$9 + 4 + 1 = 14$
4-by-4	$16 + 9 + 4 + 1 = 30$

ISAAC: Oh, hey, look at this. If we reorganize this chart . . .

Size of Board	Size of Squares				Sum
	1×1 Squares	2×2 Squares	3×3 Squares	4×4 Squares	
1-by-1	1				1
2-by-2	4	1			5
3-by-3	9	4	1		14
4-by-4	16	9	4	1	30

ISAAC: I see a ton of patterns.

ANGIE: Yeah, check this out. The first column keeps on increasing; the next row is the next perfect square.

ISAAC: And then it happens again in the second, third, and fourth columns.

ANGIE: And look at the rows: 14 is $1 + 4 + 9$, 30 is $1 + 4 + 9 + 16$, and . . .

ISAAC: I think we're on to something!

ANGIE: Great, so keep going. All we have to do is to add up all the squares up to the size of the checkerboard. So for the original problem, which is 8-by-8, we will add up $8^2 + 7^2 + 6^2 + 5^2 + 4^2 + 3^2 + 2^2 + 1^2$.

ISAAC: And the answer is (using his calculator) 204. Great job. We could do this for any size checkerboard.

ANGIE: Yes, we could. I wonder if there is a formula for this?

ISAAC: I bet there is. Maybe we'll learn it later.

The divisors of 360 add up to 1170. What is the sum of the reciprocals of the divisors of 360? Work this problem before continuing.

Rori approached this problem this way: "I can't even imagine listing all of the divisors of 360, let alone trying to find all of their reciprocals and adding them up. So there has to be an easier way. I'm a little lazy anyway, so it's not hard for me to look for an easier way. I decided to change the number 360 to something smaller. Of course, I wouldn't know what the divisors of my new number added up to, but if I picked a small number, I wouldn't have any problem finding its divisors so I could add them up. I picked the number 24, because it has a fair number of divisors but not so many that my easier problem would be hard to figure out.

"The divisors of 24 are 1, 2, 3, 4, 6, 8, 12, and 24. These added up to 60. The problem asked for the sum of the reciprocals of the divisors. So I added up $1/1 + 1/2 + 1/3 + 1/4 + 1/6 + 1/8 + 1/12 + 1/24$. Yuck. Fractions. Then I needed a common **denominator**. It looked like the least common denominator was going to be 24. Well, that's interesting. So I changed everything to 24ths."

ORIGINAL		NEW
$\frac{1}{1}$	$=$	$\frac{24}{24}$
$\frac{1}{2}$	$=$	$\frac{12}{24}$
$\frac{1}{3}$	$=$	$\frac{8}{24}$
$\frac{1}{4}$	$=$	$\frac{6}{24}$
$\frac{1}{6}$	$=$	$\frac{4}{24}$
$\frac{1}{8}$	$=$	$\frac{3}{24}$
$\frac{1}{12}$	$=$	$\frac{2}{24}$
$\frac{1}{24}$	$=$	$\frac{1}{24}$

"Then I added up all of the new fractions, which amounted to adding up the numerators: 24, 12, 8, 6, 4, 3, 2, 1. I'd added these numbers before. I knew the sum of these numbers was 60, because they were just the factors of 24. So the answer to my easier problem was $60/24$. My prediction was that the answer to the original problem was going to be the sum of the factors over the number. I tested this prediction on another example.

"I tried 10—I picked a smaller number to test my theory quickly. The factors of 10 are 1, 2, 5, 10. Adding up these numbers gives 18. My prediction for the sum of the reciprocals was $18/10$. I tried it."

$$\frac{1}{1} + \frac{1}{2} + \frac{1}{5} + \frac{1}{10} + \frac{10}{10} + \frac{5}{10} + \frac{2}{10} + \frac{1}{10} = \frac{18}{10}$$

"I noticed that again I just added the numerators, which were the factors of the number in reverse order: 10, 5, 2, 1. The sum of the factors was 18 and the denominator was 10, so the answer was $18/10$.

"Therefore, the answer to the original problem was the sum of the divisors over the number, $1170/360$."

Rori did a few specific easier examples, and this led her to an easier process for solving the original problem. She didn't even have to actually work the original problem.

TEN-THOUSAND-DAY WAR

If a ten-thousand-day war starts on a Wednesday, on which day of the week does it end? Work this problem before continuing.

Ms. Warner's class worked this problem.

MS. W: How should we start this problem?

HIREN: I think it's a Friday.

DEMICK: I think it's a Tuesday.

MS. W: Wait a minute, fellas. Let's have a strategy here, not just an argument. Who can suggest a strategy that might work?

BIJAYA: I think we should use a systematic list. We could just write down all the days. So the first day is a Wednesday, the second is a Thursday, the third is a Friday, until we get to 10,000.

MS. W: Don't you think that might take a while?

BIJAYA:	Yeah, maybe about ten minutes.
THERESA:	No way, it would take a lot longer than that. There must be an easier way.
KAPENDA:	What about these easier related problems we've been talking about?
MS. W:	How would you make this problem easier?
KAPENDA:	Well, what about a nine-thousand-day war? Or maybe eight thousand?
THERESA:	Oh, come on. That would still take forever.
SANG:	What if the war were over in one day? Then it would end on a Wednesday, the day it started. Or what about a two-day war? Then it would end on a Thursday.
ERIK:	That's a good idea. I agree with Sang. But I kind of agree with Bijaya too. Let's make a systematic list but with wars that are shorter, not 30 years long like this one— that must be horrible.
MS. W:	Yes, you're right, Eric. And good idea about the list. Who would like to make the list on the board?
KARMEN:	I will. I love to go to the board. What should I write?
DANIELLE:	Write what Sang said. (Karmen writes the list shown below.)

1. Wednesday
2. Thursday
3. Friday
4. Saturday

KARMEN:	This is going to take forever. Maybe we can organize it a little differently.
BRUCE:	How about a calendar?
MS. W:	What do you mean?
BRUCE:	You know, a calendar. We can put the days of the week at the top and the numbers down below. I'll show you. (He goes to the board.)
KARMEN:	Hey, this is my job.

BRUCE: Look, like this. (Bruce draws the following calendar.)

Sun	Mon	Tue	Wed	Thu	Fri	Sat
			1	2	3	4
5	6	7	8	9	10	11
12	13	14	15	16	17	18
19	20	21	22	23	24	25
26	27	28	29	30	31	32
33	34	35	36	37	38	39
40	41	42	43	44	45	46
47	48	49	50	51	52	53
54	55	56	57	58	59	60
61	62	63	64	65	66	67
68	69	70	71	72	73	74

BRUCE: Hey, I'm getting tired of this. Do I need to keep going all the way up to 10,000?

THERESA: No way, that would take forever.

HIREN: See, my answer was right: It's going to be Friday.

DEMICK: No, it's going to be Tuesday.

MS. W: Can anyone suggest something that might help?

CRAIG: I think I see a pattern.

HY: I do too. The numbers in each row are all 7 more than the numbers right above them.

CRAIG: Yeah. And it looks like the Tuesday column is the most significant.

MS. W: What do you mean?

CRAIG: Well, all the numbers in the Tuesday column are multiples of 7. So if 10,000 is a multiple of 7, it will be a Tuesday.

DEMICK: (Punching the buttons on his calculator) I see what Craig is saying. But 10,000 is not a multiple of 7, so it's not a Tuesday and I was wrong.

| | | HY: | What is the closest multiple of 7 to 10,000? |

HY: What is the closest multiple of 7 to 10,000?

DEMICK: Let's see. When I divided 10,000 by 7, I got about 1,428. So if I multiply 1,428 by 7, I get 9,996. So the 9,996th day is a Tuesday because that's where the multiples of 7 fall. (Bruce revises the chart on the board.)

Sun	Mon	Tue	Wed	Thu	Fri	Sat
61	62	63	64	65	66	67
68	69	70	71	72	73	74
...						
		9,996	9,997	9,998	9,999	10,000

BRUCE: The war ends on a Saturday.

HY: You could have also looked at the remainder when you divided 10,000 by 7. The quotient was 1,428 remainder 4. So count four more days from Tuesday: Wednesday is 1, Thursday is 2, Friday is 3, Saturday is 4. So it's a Saturday.

MS. W: Great job, everybody. So the easier related problem helped a lot, and so did making a list and looking for a pattern.

The strategy of solving easier related problems is quite relevant when students are learning traditional math skills. For example, when students are asked to change $12/11$ into a decimal, they often ask, "Which number do you divide by?"

Consider this dialogue between a teacher and a student.

STUDENT: I have to change this to a decimal. How do I punch it into my calculator?

TEACHER: Think back to an easier problem. For this particular type of problem, I like to use $1/2$. How do you punch that in?

STUDENT: I don't know: $1 \div 2$?

TEACHER: Try it!

STUDENT:	No, it's gotta be 2 ÷ 1, because you would've said something.
TEACHER:	I did say something. I said, "Try it." If you think it's 2 ÷ 1, try it. If you think it's 1 ÷ 2, try it.
STUDENT:	But I didn't ask about this problem. I need to know about $^{12}/_{11}$. Anybody knows $^1/_2$ is 0.5.
TEACHER:	Yes, that's why I want you to do the division for $^1/_2$. If you get 0.5 for your answer, then you will have done it correctly and you can use that as a model for doing $^{12}/_{11}$.
STUDENT:	Oh, okay. (A short time later . . .) It works when I punch in 1 ÷ 2. So does that mean I punch in 12 ÷ 11?
TEACHER:	What do you think?
STUDENT:	I think I'm right, because if I'm wrong, you would have told me.
TEACHER:	Okay, do what you want. **Remember** this when you get stuck: Think of a similar problem related to the one you're trying to solve. Pick a problem that you either already know how to do or that you already know the answer to. Do the easier problem, then apply the process you learned to the problem you're really trying to solve. And remember, the more answers you can figure out for yourself, the less you will have to depend on me to help you. That will make you a better student.

The strategy of using simpler problems to learn mathematical skills can be very powerful. Knowing some facts, such as $^1/_2 = 0.5$, can allow a student to extend this easily remembered concept to the general process of changing a fraction to a decimal. In the preceding situation, the student was confused about which number to divide by. By using what he already knew, he worked an easier related problem and applied the knowledge to the more difficult problem.

Another good mathematical topic to use easier related problems with is that of variables and exponents. Many students have difficulty remembering the product rule and the power rule for exponents—they often confuse the two. Work the next problems.

Simplify each expression:

$m^{1/8} \, m^{5/13}$ $(y^{1/3})^{6/7}$

Work this problem before continuing.

If you took algebra just last year, these problems may be very easy for you. However, if your algebra is a bit rusty, problems like these can give you trouble. So consider the following two easier related problems.

Try multiplying variables with whole number exponents.

$x^2 \cdot x^3$ $(x^2)^3$
$(xx)(xxx)$ $(xx)(xx)(xx)$

Work these problems before continuing on to the next paragraph.

The answers to these two problems are x^5 and x^6. Obviously you can get these answers by counting the number of x's in each expression. But look carefully at the problems and the answers. Is there another way to get the answers besides counting x's? To get the answer to the first problem, add the exponents: $2 + 3 = 5$. To get the answer to the second problem, multiply the exponents: $2 \times 3 = 6$.

Now look again at the Exponents problem. To solve the first expression, $m^{1/8} \, m^{5/13}$, you need to realize that this problem looks just like the expression $x^2 \, x^3$ but with exponents that are more complicated. The process to solve both is the same: Add the exponents. To add fractions you need a common denominator, which in this case is 104.

$m^{1/8} \, m^{5/13} = m^{13/104} \, m^{40/104} = m^{53/104}$

Similarly, the second problem, $(y^{1/3})^{6/7}$, looks just like $(x^2)^3$ but with exponents that are more complicated. The process to solve both is the same: Multiply the exponents.

$(y^{1/3})^{6/7} = y^{6/21} = y^{2/7}$

Students often forget the exponent rules when they need to solve problems that involve complicated exponents. Instead of looking up a rule, re-create it for yourself by using easy exponents and then applying the process you learned to the difficult exponents.

The process used in this Exponents problem and in the example about changing the fraction to a decimal is similar to the process used to solve the problems in this chapter. But with this chapter's problems, you probably don't already know the answer to the easier problem you're posing. However, the fact that you're trying to solve an easy problem means that the answer to the easy problem is within your reach. After you solve the easy problem, a way to solve the more difficult problem becomes evident.

GOOD LUCK GOATS

In the mythical land of Kantanu, it was considered good luck to own goats. Barsanta owned some goats at the time of her death and willed them to her children. To her first born, she willed one-half of her goats. (The will was drawn up long before her death and was written in general terms.) To her second born she willed one-third of her goats. And last she gave one-ninth of her goats to her third born (the black sheep among goat owners).

As it turned out, when Barsanta died she had 17 goats. Barring a Solomonic approach, how should the goats be divided?

Work this famous problem before continuing.

This problem involves working an easier related problem. In this case, an even number would probably work better.

Nikki approached it like this: "Since 17 is an odd number, I decided to try a simpler number: 2. Two worked fine for the first born but didn't work for the second born. Since the number had to be divisible by 2 and also divisible by 3, I tried 6. However, 6 didn't work well for the third born. So this time I tried 18, which seemed to work.

$\frac{1}{2}$ of 18 is 9 (1st born)

$\frac{1}{3}$ of 18 is 6 (2nd born)

$\frac{1}{9}$ of 18 is 2 (3rd born)

Total: 17 goats distributed to children; 1 goat left over

"It's weird because there's 1 goat left over, but Barsanta didn't really have 18 goats: she had 17. So there really isn't a goat left over because it doesn't really exist. It's also weird because if you really tried to do half of 17, you'd have to divide a goat. So 17 doesn't work, but 18 does work to make 17 work."

Nikki's solution is an example of changing a condition in the problem to make the problem easier. She changed the number of goats Barsanta had, which enabled her to solve the problem.

This problem is a very strange problem. It contains some "bad" information and an incorrect hidden assumption. The assumption is that all the fractions add up to one whole, as they should because they are a finite set of objects being partitioned. When you were solving the problem, you may not have noticed that it is impossible to divide a group of goats into $1/2$, $1/3$, and $1/9$. If you add $1/2 + 1/3 + 1/9$, the result is $17/18$. This means that Barsanta drew up her will to divvy up only $17/18$ of her estate, not giving instructions about what was to be done with the remaining $1/18$. That is why the additional goat is needed to make the problem work. The extra goat adds the remaining $1/18$, and then the goat is taken away after the other goats are divided up.

Find more combinations of fractions like this and write your own Good Luck Goats problem. To write this type of problem, you need to come up with another set of three unit fractions (fractions with 1 in the numerator) that could work for a different number of goats. For more about this famous problem, read "The Riddle of the Vanishing Camel" by Ian Stewart in the Mathematical Recreations column of the

June 1992 issue of *Scientific American.* (Ian Stewart now writes this column, which was made famous by one of the world's best puzzle makers, Martin Gardner, who wrote for *Scientific American* for many years.)

Another way to make a problem easier is to use numbers in place of variables. Use this technique on the next problem, which deals with the concept of **average**. (Problems like this are quite common on standardized tests.)

AVERAGES

The average of a group of quiz scores is 31.8. There are k quiz scores in the group. The average of 10 of these quiz scores is 24.3. Find the average of the remaining quiz scores in terms of k. Work this problem before continuing.

This problem is complex for many reasons. The given averages are thorny numbers, and the number of quiz scores in the original group is not known. Right off the bat, you can do two things to make the problem easier. You've done this many times before: Make the numbers 31.8 and 24.3 into easier numbers. Use 30 and 25 instead. So now the problem says:

> The average of a group of quiz scores is 30. There are k quiz scores in the group. The average of 10 of these quiz scores is 25. Find the average of the remaining quiz scores in terms of k.

However, you may still have trouble figuring out what to do. If you knew the number of quiz scores, the problem might seem more manageable. So make up an easy number for k. Let's say there are 50 scores. So now the problem says:

> The average of a group of quiz scores is 30. There are 50 quiz scores in the group. The average of 10 of these quiz scores is 25. Find the average of the remaining quiz scores in terms of 50.

It seems a little easier now, although the last sentence may not make a whole lot of sense. For now, pretend that the last sentence of the problem simply says, "Find the average of the remaining quiz scores."

If there are 50 scores with an average of 30, then their total must be 1500. Why is that? To get an average, you take the total of all the scores and divide by the number of scores.

$$\frac{\text{Total scores}}{\text{Number of scores}} = \text{Average}$$

For our easier related problem we have

$$\frac{\text{Total scores}}{50} = 30$$

The total of all the scores must be $30 \times 50 = 1500$. The next part of the problem says that the average of 10 of these quiz scores is 25.

$$\frac{\text{Total of 10 scores}}{10} = 25$$

The total of this group must be $25 \times 10 = 250$. (**Notice** that this is a subproblem.) The remaining scores must add up to $1500 - 250 = 1250$. How many scores are remaining? (More subproblems.) We started with 50 scores and have already considered 10 of them. So there must be 40 scores left that add up to 1250. The average of these scores is

$$\frac{1250}{40} = 31.25$$

Solving this easier related problem gives a clue about how to solve the original problem. Look carefully at the numbers 1250 and 40. Where did they come from? The number 1250 was just $1500 - 250$. But where did we get those numbers? We got 1500 by multiplying 30 (the average of all scores) and 50 (the total number of scores). We got 250 by multiplying 25 (the average of the small group of scores) and 10 (the number of scores in the small group). We got 40 by subtracting 10 (the number of scores in the small group) from 50 (the total number of scores).

$$\frac{1250}{40} = \frac{1500 - 250}{50 - 10} = \frac{30 \times 50 - 25 \times 10}{50 - 10}$$

Now recall the original problem. The average of all scores is really 31.8, not 30. The average of a small group of 10 scores is really 24.3, not 25. And there are really *k* scores in the whole group, not 50. Substitute these numbers into the expression above.

$$\frac{31.8k - 24.3 \times 10}{k - 10} \quad \text{or} \quad \frac{31.8k - 243}{k - 10}$$

In this problem we used two types of easier related problems. We replaced difficult numbers with easier numbers, and we replaced a variable with a number to see what was going on. Both of these substitutions made the problem much more manageable and gave us a plan of attack. After solving the easier problems, the plan for the original problem became clear and it wasn't hard to do anymore. It was just a matter of applying the procedure learned from the easier problem to the hard problem.

The next problem appeared in Chapter 6: Guess-and-Check. This time solve it with an easier related problem by changing some of the conditions in the problem.

NEXT TRAIN EAST

A train leaves Roseville heading east at 6:00 a.m. at 40 miles per hour. Another eastbound train leaves on a parallel track at 7:00 a.m. at 50 miles per hour. What time will it be when the two trains are the same distance away from Roseville? Work this problem before continuing.

Marla solved this with an easier related problem. "It was obvious that the later train was gaining on the slower train 10 miles every hour. So I decided to pretend that the first train had traveled for an hour and then stopped. The second train then left at 10 miles per hour. I thought of this new problem as being the same as the original problem (an example of changing the conditions in the problem). So the second train had to make up 40 miles (the distance the first train traveling at 40 miles per hour covered between 6:00 a.m. and 7:00 a.m.) at 10 miles per hour. Obviously, that meant it would take the second train 4 hours to catch up. So the answer is 4 hours from 7:00 a.m. (when the second train left), which gives 11:00 a.m. I then checked this. The first train goes from 6:00 a.m. to 11:00 a.m., which is 5 hours, and covers 200 miles at 40 miles per hour. The second train goes from 7:00 a.m. to 11:00 a.m. (4 hours) and covers 200 miles at 50 miles per hour. Both trains cover the same distance, so the answer of 11:00 a.m. must be right."

The next problem was first posed by George Pólya, one of the first teachers of problem solving, in his classic book *How to Solve It,* first published in 1945. Pólya said, "If you can't solve a problem, then there is an easier problem you can't solve: find it." Think carefully about what his statement means.

INSCRIBED SQUARE

Given any **triangle**, draw a square inside of it so that all four vertices of the square are on the sides of the triangle. Two of the **vertices** of the square should be on one side of the triangle, and each of the other two sides of the triangle should have one vertex of the square.

Make the problem easier by eliminating one of the conditions. You'll need to draw lots of diagrams. Work this problem before continuing.

Ronaldo and Julie worked on this problem.

RONALDO: This problem seems really tough. How can we make it easier?

JULIE: I'm not sure, let's experiment by drawing triangles and see if we get lucky. (They drew the following triangles and attempted to put the squares inside of them. They were not successful, because the inside figures did not look like squares.)

  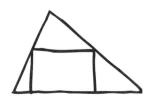

RONALDO: This isn't working at all. We need to make this easier somehow. What did our teacher say about changing the conditions of the problem?

JULIE: She said we could make the problem easier if we changed or fixed or got rid of some conditions.

RONALDO: Well, we can change the conditions and make it a triangle inside of a square. That would be really easy. (He drew the picture below.)

JULIE: I don't think that was what she meant. Maybe we can try putting only three of the vertices of the square on the triangle and let the fourth one float around the inside or outside. (She drew the pictures that follow.)

 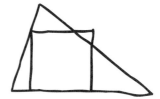

RONALDO: Oh, that must have been what our teacher meant. It's easy to draw just three of the vertices on the triangle. Let's agree to always put the longest side of the triangle on the bottom and to always put two of the vertices on that side.

JULIE: That's a good idea. But wait, I think we should start by picking a point on the left side of the triangle. Then draw a line down to the base. Then measure that distance across the base, and then go up.

RONALDO: That last vertex probably won't be on the triangle. But let's do it anyway. That is relaxing a condition. (They drew the next series of pictures.)

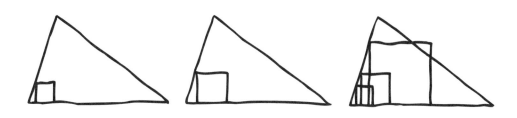

JULIE: I think I see what is going on. All of the fourth vertices form a straight line.

RONALDO: Yes, they do. So all we have to do is draw that line, and where it intersects the third side of the triangle, we have our fourth vertex. Then it's easy to draw the square. (Their final picture is shown below.)

Easier related problems are often used to explain concepts to people who don't understand a particular situation. For example, here's a conversation a father had with his son about traffic. They were driving in rush hour traffic, so cars were moving very slowly.

SON: Why is there so much traffic? Why is everyone driving so slow?

FATHER: Because everyone is going to work right now.

SON: But if everyone just drove 60 miles per hour, then no one would have to slow down.

FATHER: There are too many cars.

SON: I don't understand.

FATHER: Okay, suppose you wanted to leave your classroom at school and go out to the playground. Let's say that it wasn't during recess and that you just went to the door of the classroom and walked out into the hall. How fast could you run to get to the playground?

SON:	Pretty fast.
FATHER:	Right. Now suppose that the bell had just rung for recess. How fast could you go now?
SON:	Not very fast. I'd have a hard time getting out of the room.
FATHER:	Why?
SON:	Because so many kids would be crowding the door.
FATHER:	Right. What would happen when you got out into the hall?
SON:	It would be really crowded because there are a bunch of classrooms on that hall. Kids would be coming out of every single classroom and the hall would be packed.
FATHER:	So how fast could you go?
SON:	Not very fast. If I tried to go fast, I would crash into a bunch of other kids and I'd probably get sent to the office.
FATHER:	Right. Well that's the same thing that happens on the freeway. So many people are going to work that the freeway just can't handle all those cars. So all the cars have to slow down to make sure that they don't crash. And that's why there are traffic jams.
SON:	I get it.

So the next time you are trying to explain a situation to someone who doesn't understand it, try using an easier related problem.

Students often confuse the strategies of subproblems and easier related problems. The strategy of subproblems involves the process of breaking a large problem down into parts. The whole problem is too large to solve all at once, so you must concentrate on solving small manageable parts of the problem. On the other hand, the strategy of easier related problems doesn't involve solving the original problem in any way. You focus instead on easier related problems that are solvable. You then return to the original problem and solve it by using the techniques you learned when you solved the easier problems. Perhaps the following example can shed some light on what can be a difficult topic.

Will recently took a vacation to a theme park. While at the park, he was fortunate enough to see a group of Chinese acrobats, young people who performed amazing feats. One young girl, about 11 years old, performed an impressive stunt.

Will describes her stunt. "This girl was really incredible. She balanced a bowl on her head. Then she placed four bowls in a line on her right foot and going up her leg. Then she kicked her leg into the air, tossing the four bowls up into the air. They all landed stacked in the bowl on her head. She did all this while pedaling a unicycle with her left foot."

Learning to do this stunt was a real problem for this girl. To learn it she had to solve some subproblems and some easier related problems (ERPs). The subproblems were learning how to do the following things:

1. Ride a unicycle by pedaling only with her left foot.

2. Balance a bowl on her head.

3. Balance a bowl on her leg.

4. Kick a bowl up in the air.

5. Catch a bowl on her head.

Each of these subproblem stunts had to be performed flawlessly before she could even attempt the final stunt. (And **note** that to master subproblem 1, the girl actually had to solve the ERP of riding a unicycle with two feet first.)

After she had mastered each subproblem, she was ready to practice the ERPs of the final stunt. She learned to do each of the following ERPs, not proceeding from one problem to the next until she had mastered the current one:

1. Stand on the ground, balance one bowl on her leg, and flip it up and catch it on her head.

2. Stand on the ground, balance two bowls on her leg, and flip them both up and catch them on her head.

3. Then three bowls.

4. Then four bowls.

5. Ride a unicycle, balance one bowl on her leg, and flip it up and catch it on her head.

6. Then two bowls.

7. Then three bowls.

8. Then four bowls. (This is the actual stunt.)

The large diagram shown below illustrates the subproblems and the ERPs in this story:

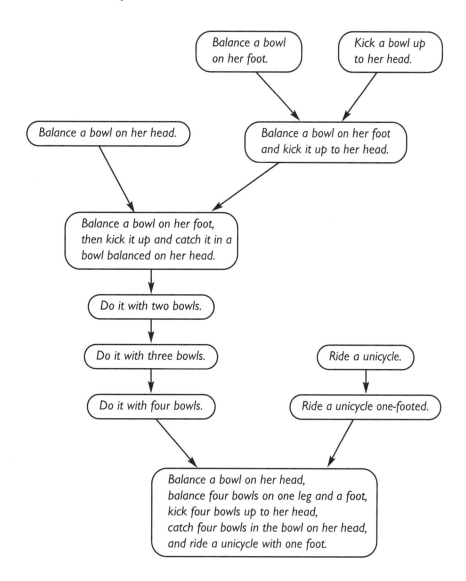

Notice that the places in the diagram where two arrows come together represent two subproblems being solved in order to solve a larger problem (which in turn contributes to the entire problem being solved).

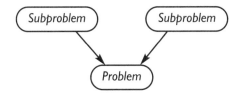

For example, the acrobat balancing a bowl on her foot and kicking a bowl up to her head are two subproblems of the larger problem of balancing a bowl on her foot and kicking it up to her head.

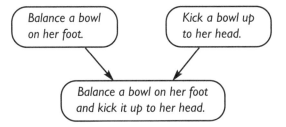

And the larger problem is a subproblem of the problem of balancing a bowl on her foot, then kicking it up and catching it in a bowl balanced on her head. Two arrows directing you from two subproblems to a larger problem appear in the complete acrobat diagram in three places.

ERPs are represented in the diagram by boxes connected serially with arrows. The ERP is found at the unpointy end of the arrow.

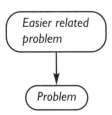

For example, riding a unicycle is an easier problem related to the problem of riding a unicycle with one foot.

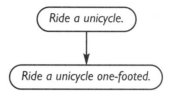

Several ERPs are shown in the large diagram, including the series "do it with two bowls," "do it with three bowls," and "do it with four bowls." Even "do it with four bowls" is an ERP of the final stunt.

The young acrobat had to practice this stunt many, many times. After hours of rehearsal, she was able to perform it flawlessly every time. She topped off her feat by balancing a can and then a spoon on her foot, and tossing them up to her head as well. The crowd applauded wildly. Acrobats and gymnasts use the strategy of easier related problems all the time to learn very complicated tricks. They also must use subproblems to break down difficult tricks into parts.

The following list from Tom Sallee appears at the beginning of this chapter. Next to each method listed below, we've named the problem or problems in the text that used that method. Some problems involved more than one method.

Common ways to make a problem easier:

1. *Use a number instead of a variable.* We used this in Averages.

2. *Use a smaller or easier number in place of a more difficult one in order to develop the process for solving the problem.* We used this in Simpletown Elections, Exponents and the fraction-to-decimal example, and Averages.

3. *Do a set of specific easier examples and look for a pattern.* We used this in From One to One Hundred, How Many Squares? and Ten-Thousand-Day War.

4. *Do a specific easier example and figure out an easier process that will work to solve the problem.* We used this in Divisors and Reciprocals.

5. *Change, fix, or get rid of some conditions.* We used this in Good Luck Goats, Next Train East, and Inscribed Square.

6. *Eliminate unnecessary information.* We used this in Simpletown Elections.

Using an easier related problem takes practice to master. When confronted with a problem that seems too hard or impossible, **remember** to ask yourself the following question: What can I do to make this problem easier?

Problem Set A

1. DIAGONALS

A **diagonal** of a **polygon** is a line segment that connects two nonadjacent vertices of the polygon. A certain convex polygon has 25 sides. How many diagonals can be drawn?

2. SUM OF ODDS

Find the sum of the first 5000 odd numbers.

3. TV TRUCK

Theotis has to load a truck with television sets. The cargo area of the truck is a rectangular **prism** that measures 8 ft by 21 ft by 11 ft. Each television set measures $1^1/_2$ ft by $1^2/_3$ ft by $1^1/_3$ ft. How many sets can be loaded into the truck?

4. POTATOES

To prepare dinner in the army mess hall, Jamie, who is a member of the Fourth Battalion of the Twenty-Third Regiment, generally uses about 85 pounds of potatoes to feed the 358 people in his unit. He usually assigns three soldiers to scrub the potatoes, and it takes them about 2 hours to complete the job. However, last week he needed to feed about 817 people, beginning at 17:30 hours, because of a special army event. When he arrived at the mess hall tent for the field exercises, he discovered that 131 pounds of potatoes had been sent. He'd needed to send for the rest right away. How many pounds did he request, and how many soldiers did he need if he'd planned to have each of them spend about 2 hours scrubbing?

5. **SQUARE AND HEXAGON**

A square has an area of S^2. A regular **hexagon** has a perimeter of T. If p is the perimeter of the square and h is a side of the hexagon, then find $h + p$ in terms of S and T.

6. **TWENTY-FIVE-MAN ROSTER**

The manager of a baseball team received a strange communication from the team's general manager, who told him to select 25 players for his roster according to this formula:

$1/2$ of the team had to be outfielders and infielders

$1/4$ of the team had to be starting pitchers

$1/6$ of the team had to be relief pitchers

$1/8$ of the team had to be catchers

The manager was a bit confused by the general manager's request, yet complied anyway. How did he do it?

7. **ODD AND EVEN**

Find the difference between the sum of the first 500 even numbers and the sum of the first 500 odd numbers.

8. **CHINESE NEW YEAR**

In China each calendar year is given one of 12 names, which rotate year after year. The year 2000 is the year of the Dragon. The year 2001 is the year of the Snake. The subsequent years are, in order, the years of the Horse, Sheep, Monkey, Rooster, Dog, Boar, Rat, Ox, Tiger, and Rabbit. After the year of the Rabbit, the year of the Dragon will occur again and the whole cycle will repeat. What will the year 3000 be?

9. **LAST DIGIT**

What is the last digit in the product $(2^1)(2^2)(2^3)(2^4) \ldots (2^{198})(2^{199})(2^{200})$?

10. FIFTY-TWO CARD PICKUP

A deck of cards was dropped onto the floor. Naoko picked up at least one card. She may have picked up 1, all 52, or any number in between. How many possible combinations are there for what she picked up?

11. ONE-MAN BAND

Simon has decided to be a one-man band, complete with a harmonica, an accordion, and a drum. Draw a diagram and identify the subproblems and the easier related problems Simon must master to be able to play "The Star Spangled Banner" using all three instruments while twirling three hula hoops.

12. WRITE YOUR OWN

Write your own easier-related-problem problem. Stick with it: These problems can be very difficult to make up. The easiest example to follow may be the Ten-Thousand-Day War problem.

Problem Set B

1. COVERING THE GRID

A grid has lines at 90-degree angles. There are 12 lines in one direction and 9 lines in the other direction. Lines that are parallel are 11 inches apart. What is the least number of 12-inch-by-12-inch floor tiles needed to cover all of the line intersections on the grid? The tiles do not have to touch each other. You must keep the tiles intact—don't break or cut them.

2. PLASTICWARE PARTIES

A party host who sold plastic kitchen containers was frustrated by her attempts to get more people to host sales parties for her. She finally offered to pay any host $25 who (a) hosted a party for her and (b) arranged for two other friends to host parties during the next month. To her surprise, it worked! She had 100% success: Every host was able to arrange two more parties. She started with five hosts in the first month. If this continues for the entire year, how many parties will there be during the year?

3. ADDING CHLORINE

I have a small circular swimming pool in my backyard for my kids. Last weekend, I set it up and bought chlorine to put into it. The directions on the bottle said to put in 16 fluid ounces of chlorine per 10,000 gallons of water. Of course, our pool holds a lot less water than 10,000 gallons, so I needed to figure out the correct amount of chlorine to put into it. I measured the pool with my tape measure and found it to have a circumference of 27 feet 3 inches and a water height of 21 inches. I knew that the circumference of a circle was $C = 2\pi r$ and the volume of a cylinder was $V = \pi r^2 h$ (r is the radius of the cylinder, and h is the height). I knew that a milliliter is a cubic centimeter. I also knew that there are 3.79 liters in 1 gallon, and 3.281 feet in 1 meter. How many fluid ounces of chlorine did I need to put into the pool? (I have a measuring spoon capable of measuring to the nearest quarter of a fluid ounce.)

4. JOGGING AROUND A TRACK

Dionne can run around a circular track in 120 seconds. Basha, running in the opposite direction as Dionne, meets Dionne every 48 seconds. Sandra, running in the same direction as Basha, passes Basha every 240 seconds. How often does Sandra meet Dionne?

5. NINE POINTS

There are nine points on a piece of paper. No three of the points are in the same straight line. How many different triangles can be formed by using three of the nine points as vertices?

Rescue workers often perform drills to represent problems physically, allowing them to analyze situations in a hands-on way so that they can be fully prepared in the event of a real emergency.

10
Physical Representations

M any mathematical concepts were developed to solve real-world problems. Other mathematical concepts developed peripheral to real-world problems or were even devoid of apparent real-world applications. This chapter focuses on bringing problems into the real-world arena. Although few of this chapter's problems are actually "true to life," the strategy for solving them and many real-world problems is the same: create a physical representation.

Physical representations fall under the major problem-solving theme of Spatial Organization. **Note** that a physical representation differs from a diagram in that a physical representation lets you touch the problem, not just represent it with a picture. By using objects or people to solve a problem, you gain a new perspective on it.

We begin the chapter with a section about the most basic type of physical representation: people walking through a problem. This process is called **acting it out**. In Section 2 you'll explore the use of physical *models* and *manipulatives*. (As you learned in Chapter 8:

Unit Analysis, a manipulative is an object that can be moved or positioned.) You'll see that the strategies of acting it out and of using models and manipulatives are closely related and overlap one another. They are different ways of physically representing a problem.

Traditionally, physical representations have been left out of the mathematics curriculum of most schools. This is unfortunate because mathematics has become totally abstract to some people. When problems are represented with objects, the problems become concrete and more easily understood.

Section 1: Act It Out

Of all of the strategies presented in this book, the act-it-out strategy is probably the most fun. Acting out a problem gives you a chance to have contact with other people. Other strategies will work to solve the problems in this section, but acting the problems out with a small group of people works very well. There are no written solutions for the problems in this section. The correct solutions should be obvious when you act the problems out.

JACKALS AND COYOTES

Three jackals and three coyotes are on a trek across the Mokalani Plateau when they come to a river filled with carnivorous fish. There is a rowboat in sight, and the party decides to use it. (Both species are known for their cleverness.) However, the boat is too small for any more than two of the group at a time. So they must traverse the river in successive crossings. There is one hitch, though: The jackals must not outnumber the coyotes at any time, in any place. For example, if two jackals and only one coyote are together on the western side of the river, this problem is reduced to simple subtraction: the jackals will overpower, kill, and eat the coyotes. It's okay to have an equal number of each, and it's also okay to have more coyotes than jackals in a given place—neither situation poses a danger to the coyotes, and the coyotes do not pose a threat to the jackals. So, the trick here is to use the one small rowboat, a lot of sweat, and a little brainpower to ensure the coyotes' safety while both groups cross the river.

Close the book and find some people to act this out with. Also, find some object to be physically transported across the room as the boat.

It is usually wise to act out the solution to a problem before actually implementing it. For example, parts of your solution for this problem probably involved some guess-and-check. In real life, you would have to be careful about using guess-and-check, since a wrong guess could lead to an early dinner for the jackals.

When working this problem, you should reach several "major understandings." The first is realizing that there can be only two animals in the boat. The second is dealing with the first move: Sending two coyotes over on the first trip means the end for the third coyote. The next major understanding comes after you get two coyotes and two jackals on the far side. The only thing to do is bring back one of each and then send two more coyotes over. Then finally, you send the solitary jackal back to begin bringing over the other two jackals.

Sometimes the critical elements of acting out a problem are the physical objects you employ. The next problem reflects this notion.

Once upon a time, there was a horse trader. One morning, the horse trader bought a horse for $60. Just after noon, the horse trader sold that same horse back to the original owner for $70. He then bought it back again just before 5:00 for $80. By midnight he managed to sell the horse back to the original owner for $90. How much money did the horse trader make or lose on this horse?

Close the book and act this problem out before continuing. You will need something to represent the horse, some play money in different denominations, and at least two people to act out the roles of the horse trader and the original owner.

Acting this problem out allows several people to act as verifiers, who check for mistakes and make sure that all transactions are done correctly. Part of this problem's trickiness is identifying net financial gain and when it occurs. By having a couple of people acting as the trader and the original owner, you can verify in which direction money flowed and how much.

Problem Set A-1

Solve each problem by acting it out.

1. **THREE ADULTS AND TWO KIDS**

   Three adults and two kids want to cross a river by using a small canoe. The canoe can carry two kids or one adult. How many times must the canoe cross the river to get everyone to the other side?

2. **THE DOG, THE GOOSE, AND THE CORN**

   There was once a farmer who, as part of his route to town, used a rickety old boat to cross a wide river. One day he took his dog and went to town just to buy corn. However, in addition to buying corn, he bought a goose that he intended to take home and use to start raising geese. (This farmer was no fool; he already had another goose.) But he also knew that his boat was not reliable: It could handle only himself and one of the other three things he had with him. He feared that if left alone, the dog would eat the goose or the goose would eat the corn. How could he get himself and everything else across the river safely?

3. HOOP GREETING

A group of ten kids got together at the playground to play basketball. Before the game, every kid shook hands with each of the other kids exactly once. How many handshakes took place?

4. SWITCHING JACKALS AND COYOTES

Three jackals are on one side of a river, and three coyotes are on the other side. They have a boat capable of carrying two animals. At no point can the jackals outnumber the coyotes on one side of the river, or the jackals will eat the coyotes. Each group wishes to change sides of the river. Figure out which side of the river the boat must start from, and how to manage the groups to get each animal safely to its destination.

5. THE HOTEL BILL

Three sales representatives attending a convention decided to share a room to take advantage of some cheap hotel rates. The clerk at the desk charged them $60, which they paid with cash. A little while later, the clerk discovered that he had made an error: The room should have cost only $55. He dispatched a bellhop with a $5 bill to deliver to the women. The bellhop was dishonest, though, and he kept $2 and returned $1 to each of the three women. So each woman thought that her part of the bill was $19 instead of the original $20.

When Franklin heard this story, he did some calculations. Each woman thought she had paid $19, and 3 × $19 is $57. The bellhop kept $2, and $57 + $2 = $59. What happened to the missing dollar? Is Franklin's reasoning right or wrong? Determine what happened to the missing dollar and explain your reasoning.

6. PERSIS'S GIFT SHOP

Persis owns a gift shop. One day while she was opening a shipment of figurines she had just received, a stranger walked in and asked the price of a figurine. The figurines had cost Persis $6 each, but she had not decided on a selling price for them. She finally decided on $13 each, and the stranger promptly said he'd take one. Her new clerk accepted his traveler's check for $40 and gave him change. Persis needed more change for the register and signed the traveler's check over to the pharmacist next door, Dr. Drell. An hour later, though, Dr. Drell came back over and showed her that the traveler's check was actually in French francs, worth about $8 at the time. Persis apologized and wrote the pharmacist a check to cover the difference. Who lost how much in this transaction?

Section 2: Manipulatives and Models

In acting out a problem, people get together and assume roles in order to gain insight into the problem. Several brains work on the problem at once, and physical constraints become more and more apparent and more easily respected by using people in the roles. For example, a coyote (played by a person) can be on only one side of a river at a time. When we use a person in the role of a coyote, we are assured that no laws of physics and biological existence are broken. On the other hand, if we work out the Jackals and Coyotes problem with paper and pencil, a coyote could appear simultaneously on both sides of the river by accident. By having a person act the role of the coyote, we know that normal laws of matter are respected.

Each problem in Section 1 of this chapter was based on re-creating a problem and acting it out. Some of the problems in Section 1 had people in the roles of animals (such as jackals, coyotes, horses, dogs, and geese), and others had people in the roles of inanimate objects (such as corn).

Although the strategy of acting it out is very effective, it can be impractical (there is no one around when you are working on the problem), too time-consuming (there are people around, but it takes a while to round them up), too embarrassing (very few people will want to be the goose, for example), or too expensive (the only way you can get people to be involved in the Horse Trader problem is to use real money—yours—and they get to keep it, and even then you may have to act out the part of the horse).

So now let's abstract the strategy of act-it-out one step. Instead of using actual people to act out the roles of the characters in the problems, we'll simply represent the characters with manipulatives, objects that can be moved or positioned.

Let's look at how we can use manipulatives with the Jackals and Coyotes problem. The advantage of reducing the jackals and the coyotes to little pieces of paper is that you can solve this problem by yourself, without having to hunt up some friends capable of acting like coyotes and jackals. The disadvantage of this method is that you have only one brain working on the problem. However, using a manipulative to solve a problem is only one step away from actually acting it out with people. Keep in mind that you need to design your manipulatives so that they represent the critical elements of the problems and are in a form that will allow you to work the problems out.

JACKALS AND COYOTES REVISITED

 Solve the Jackals and Coyotes problem again, this time using manipulatives. Choose something to represent coyotes and something to represent jackals. Scraps of paper with C written on some and J on others work well. Coins, paper clips, or bottle caps also work. Determine the minimum number of river crossings. Work this problem before continuing.

A disadvantage to using pieces of paper rather than actual people is that paper tends not to contribute any creative thinking to a problem. When acting out the Jackals and Coyotes problem, a person playing the part of a coyote would howl if left alone with two jackals. But a little piece of paper labeled *coyote* will probably not have much to say in its own defense.

Despite such limitations, manipulatives can be useful problem-solving tools. When planning a manipulatives approach, you often have to make a conscious effort to look for a way to do the problem using manipulatives. You must have a little inventiveness in you. The necessary materials are often right around you. For example, dimes and pennies make very good manipulatives. Not only are they different sizes and different colors, but the back side of each can be distinguished from the front side. If you are in the forest, you can always find twigs, leaves, and pebbles (to represent wolves, bears, and campers, for example). If by chance there is a piece of paper nearby (even a burger wrapper or a soda cup), you can tear it up into little pieces and write labels on the pieces. The manipulatives are there; the trick is to think of using them and then to use them effectively. Sometimes the first manipulative doesn't work very well, so it may be effective to create a new one.

So far, none of the problems in this chapter have involved any measurement beyond simple counting (such as counting three coyotes). However, many problems involve an element of magnitude, scale, orientation, quantity, positional relationships, correspondence, dynamic relationships, directional movement, or number combinations. The physical representations you use to solve these types of problems must demonstrate these elements, and you must put more thought into creating the physical representations. We call such representations **models**. A model is a physical representation of a problem that can be used to produce a solution.

The strategy of making a model is used in the real world extensively, though probably not nearly enough. Models are made of airplanes, cars, freeway bridges, buildings, rockets, filing cabinets, and on and on. Models like these can be used to test designs before moving on to more advanced stages of production. Many of the problems in this chapter require you to build some sort of model. In some problems, relative size is one of the critical elements. In other problems, shape is the critical element. In the next problem, orientation is a key ingredient.

FOUR CONTIGUOUS STAMPS

In how many ways can four stamps be attached together? Be sure to pay attention to the thrust of this chapter. Take care to record each configuration. Work this problem before continuing.

The critical elements in this problem are size and shape, so the four items used as manipulatives in the model of this problem have to be relatively similar in size and shape. It's also important to distinguish the tops of the stamps from the bottoms, because stamps are usually printed all in the same direction. You should have found 19 different configurations.

Orientation is also a feature of the next problem.

Build this cube to see what letter is opposite the letter *T*. Pay attention to the orientation of the letters on the faces of the cube.

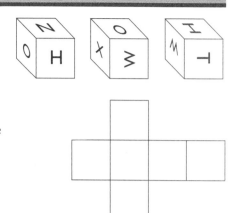

To solve this problem, draw the figure shown at right on a piece of paper (graph paper works well), cut it out, and fold it to make a cube. Then write the letters on its faces. Work this problem before continuing.

Problems of this type often show up on standardized tests. To solve such a problem, you must visualize the cube in your mind and figure out where each letter is. To solve the problem, your spatial visualization skills must be well developed. Many people aren't very good at these problems when they first try solving them. Building a model to solve a problem like the Letter Cube problem is a really helpful way to develop the ability to visualize.

After cutting out and folding up your cube, write the letters on its faces in their correct orientations. The solution for the problem is easily seen to be *O*.

As you read earlier in this chapter, a model is a physical representation of a problem that can be used to produce a solution. Examples of models include architectural models and mock-ups made to scale. These types of models accurately represent magnitude, scale, and orientation, which are all critical elements of design and construction. On the other hand, manipulatives are objects that can be moved around or easily positioned. Some examples of manipulatives you've worked with so far in this book are coins and pieces of paper. Manipulatives are found within a model of a problem. For example, a model of a problem in which jackals and coyotes cross a river will include the river and the two riverbanks. It will also include manipulatives that you can move from riverbank to riverbank to represent the movement of the characters and of the boat. These manipulatives, as well as the land and water that you draw on paper, are all part of the model of the problem.

Creating a model for a problem can make the problem slightly more abstract. For example, a scale model of a car abstracts the car: The inherent qualities of the absolutely real car are only *represented* in the model. And the model car is made from substitute materials that are easy to mold, such as plastic—the materials used to construct the model car do not accurately reflect the way plastic is used in the actual car.

Work the next problem by using a diagram of a volleyball court and manipulatives, pieces of paper with the players' names written on them.

VOLLEYBALL TEAM

The volleyball team has six players: Betty, Martha, Karen, Walt, Guy, and Steve. Using the following clues, put the players into the starting positions that will give the best rotation:

1. The players must alternate by gender.

2. Betty is the team's best server, so she should start in the serving position.

3. Guy and Karen are the team's setters. They must be opposite each other at all times.

4. Walt and Martha communicate well—it helps to put them next to each other.

5. Steve is an effective server. He needs to be positioned so he will rotate into the serving position quickly.

(As this diagram shows, half of a volleyball court has six players (the opposing team plays on the other half of the court.) From the net, there are three players in the front row and three in the back row. The server is in the right back corner. The players rotate in a clockwise manner. Players are considered opposite if they are three positions apart. So server 1 is opposite server 4, server 2 is opposite server 5, and server 3 is opposite server 6.)

Work this problem before continuing.

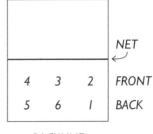

To solve this problem, tear up little pieces of paper and write the names of each of the players on them. You could also solve this problem simply by drawing a diagram, but using manipulatives is faster and requires no erasing. Using manipulatives allows you to try different possibilities quickly, without worrying whether or not they are correct.

The solution to this problem is shown in the figure at right. If you didn't get the correct answer, check two things: (1) Did you use manipulatives, and (2) did you review the clues after you thought you were done to check for compliance?

NET

Walt	*Karen*	*Steve*	*FRONT*
Martha	*Guy*	*Betty*	*BACK*

BACKLINE

When problems are abstract—that is, not real-world situations that have been abstracted with numbers—sometimes it helps to use little pieces of paper with numbers written on them to solve them. Problems like the next one are of great interest to Marcy Cook, a mathematics educator who has created puzzle books and manipulatives used in solving this kind of problem.

NUMBER PUZZLE

Use the digits 0, 1 2, 3, 4, 5, 6, 7, 8, and 9 once each to fill in the blanks of this puzzle:

$$
\begin{array}{c}
4 \\
+ \ \square \\
\hline
\square
\end{array}
\qquad
\begin{array}{c}
\square \\
\times \ \square \\
\hline
2 \ \square
\end{array}
$$

$$\square \times \square = \square \qquad 6 - \square = \square$$

Work this problem by cutting up little pieces of paper and labeling them with the numbers 0 through 9. Then manipulate them around in the puzzle until you find an arrangement that works. There is more than one possible solution.

There are essentially two different solutions to this problem. One of them starts with $4 + 1 = 5$, and the other one starts with $4 + 5 = 9$. We hope you found both solutions. (**Note** that you can change both solutions slightly by reversing the numbers in either of the last two number sentences, but those aren't really different solutions.)

The next problem could possibly be solved with matrix logic, but it could be rather confusing to do so. The key to the problem is the position of each person at the table. Using manipulatives is a good way to attack logic problems that involve positioning.

MEXICAN RESTAURANT

Four friends (one is named Janie) went out to dinner at a Mexican restaurant. The hostess seated them in a booth. Each ordered a different meat (pork, mahimahi, beef, or chicken), and each ordered a different kind of Mexican dish (tostada, burrito, fajita, or chimichanga). Use the clues below to determine what dish each person ordered, the kind of meat it contained, and where each person was sitting.

1. The person who ordered mahimahi sat next to Ted and across from the person who ordered a burrito.

2. Ken sat diagonally across from the person who ate the fajita and across from the person who ordered beef.

3. The person who ordered a chimichanga sat across from the person who ordered chicken and next to Allyson.

Work this problem before continuing.

The first twist to the Mexican Restaurant problem is determining the names of the people. This information is not stated at the beginning of the problem as usual, but instead is hidden in the problem. By reading each clue, you can determine that the names are Janie, Ted, Ken, and Allyson. The meats are pork, mahimahi, beef, and chicken. The dishes are tostada, burrito, fajita, and chimichanga.

We'll use pieces of paper as our manipulatives in this problem, so our first step is to tear a sheet of paper into 12 pieces and write on them the names of the people, the meats, and the dishes. Then read through the clues and arrange the pieces of paper as the clues suggest.

It would be helpful here to make a "booth" manipulative to keep track of position with respect to sides of the table.

The first clue says, "The person who ordered mahimahi sat next to Ted and across from the person who ordered a burrito." So arrange and tape together the Ted, mahimahi, and burrito papers in their relative positions, as shown in the following figure:

	burrito
Ted	mahimahi

There is another possible interpretation for this clue. It is possible for the arrangement to be set up like this:

Ted	mahimahi
	burrito

You can accommodate this second possibility simply by flipping over the three pieces of taped paper and writing the information on their other sides.

Tape the other pieces of paper together in their relative positions as suggested by the clues. Now you can make a set of larger manipulatives by combining two or three of the smaller manipulatives. You can then move these larger manipulatives into a very limited number of positions, especially because some of the clues indicate positions on opposite sides of the table. By arranging the large manipulatives on top of each other, you can find many contradictions, such as two people sitting in the same spot or two types of meat in the same position.

For example, start with the Ted-mahimahi-burrito and the Ken-beef-fajita papers. Place the Ted-mahimahi-burrito paper on your desk and place the Ken-beef-fajita paper on top of it. There are four different ways to do this, three of which require you to turn the paper upside down, over to read the back side, or both.

1.

fajita	beef burrito
Ted	Ken mahimahi

This is possible.

2.

	Ken burrito
fajita Ted	beef *mahimahi*

Impossible because beef and mahimahi are matched with the same person.

3.

Ken	
	burrito
beef Ted	*fajita* *mahimahi*

Possible.

4.

beef	*fajita* burrito
Ken Ted	*mahimahi*

Impossible because Ted and Ken are sitting in the same seat.

So at this point there are only two possible combinations. Now superimpose the third paper (Allyson-chicken-chimichanga) on top of the two possibilities. Again, arrange the paper in four ways for each possible combination so that you see eight arrangements altogether. (If these instructions seem complex, make sure you are [a] using the manipulatives and [b] understanding that this is precisely our point.)

chicken Ken	burrito
chimichanga beef Ted	Allyson *fajita* *mahimahi*

By taping the pieces together in their relative positions, it's been easier to see which combinations have been contradictions and thus haven't worked. For example, it's easy to see that the Allyson-chicken-chimichanga paper doesn't work in any combination with possibility number 1, but does work with possibility number 3, as shown below.

Now you can fill in the remaining information (marked with * below) to solve the problem.

Ken chicken *tostada	*Janie *pork burrito
Ted beef chimichanga	Allyson mahimahi fajita

Using manipulatives allows you to try different solutions very quickly. Sometimes it even helps to attach the manipulatives together, as you did with tape in this problem.

Solving problems by using manipulatives or models is not a common method. In some cases it is warranted, and in others it is not. One of the impediments to working problems with manipulatives is simply that some people are not used to solving problems that way. Thus, an unpracticed skill and strategy fails to become useful.

To become a better problem solver, you must look for opportunities to use manipulatives and models. Very few problems, be they real-world or contrived, are presented in a recognizable manipulatives form. You have to look for ways to use manipulatives to solve the problem.

There are certain types of problems that lend themselves easily to being adapted to manipulatives and models.

Static Arrangements of People

Volleyball rotations, golf foursomes, and starting positions for softball teams are all examples of static arrangements. Also, who is sitting next to whom at a dinner table tends to be a natural manipulatives problem. It is not necessary to have little figurines of people to solve such problems. Usually all you need to do is to tear up little pieces of paper, write the names of the people on them, and draw a representation of the area in which they are to be manipulated.

For example, to arrange the starting positions of a softball team, you want to at least draw a baseball diamond so that you can set the pieces of paper in their relative positions. This is a good way to arrange players of a team that doesn't have fixed positions. That is, some people are strong in any position they play, others are weak in any position, and some can be weak or strong depending on the position. Having weak players on the field may not be an optimal solution, but it is true-to-life, and an acceptable arrangement can often be found.

Dynamic Arrangements of People

You can also use manipulatives to set up transportation to and from various points for a number of people in a few vehicles. You might have to solve this kind of problem if, say, you're responsible for making sure that prior to a wedding, people are picked up from an airport, driven somewhere for shopping, dropped off so they can get their tuxedos fitted, and so on. Many times in such situations there are only a few cars available and many things to be done by various people in various places. Again, by tearing up pieces of paper to represent people, locations, and vehicles and their capacity, you can work out the problem in advance and make sure that everyone is taken care of.

Problems Involving Spatial Relationships

Rearranging furniture is a great problem to work with manipulatives. By making a scale model of the space and using manipulatives to represent the equipment and furniture to set up within that space, you can make a number of changes very quickly without risking anybody's back or toes. With manipulatives you can also determine how to landscape a yard by cutting out paper scaled to a plant's expected size at maturity. By moving around trees, bushes, fountains, or pink flamingos on a scale drawing, you can see where plants may be too crowded or where you can set up a visual focal point.

Problems Involving Logical Connections

In Chapter 4: Matrix Logic, you solved logic problems. Many of these types of problems can also be solved with manipulatives. By writing the names of people and their various characteristics on individual pieces of paper and manipulating the pieces, you can often make the logical connections. Tape even comes in handy in some cases.

Problems Involving Tangible Numbers

Rate-time-distance problems are good examples of problems involving tangible numbers. You can use color rods or money to represent different speeds or different distances or times.

Abstract Problems Involving Numbers

You can tear up little pieces of paper to represent numbers. This technique proves useful with magic squares and other similar problems.

Problems Involving Order

Dilyn manages a record store. Every week she receives the list of a music magazine's top 200 albums, which lists the most popular albums in all musical categories in numerical order from 1 to 200. Dilyn wants the list in alphabetical, rather than numerical, order. So she makes a copy of the list and gives it to one of her employees, who cuts the list up into 200 little strips of paper. He then alphabetizes it by moving the strips around on a large counter. When he's done alphabetizing, he tapes the list back together. Dilyn told me, "We used to have a computer do this. But when the computer did it, the employees wouldn't even notice the new artists that showed up on the list. If a customer came in asking for a new record, my employees probably wouldn't have heard of it. By doing the alphabetizing with the manipulatives every week, they stay current with the most popular artists and records. We actually had to move away from technology for the best results."

Real-World Problem Solving

Models and manipulatives are used often in the real world. The following article, "NASA Fixes Hubble's Antenna," describes a solution to a problem that occurred in outer space. (Article reprinted courtesy of Associated Press.)

> The Hubble Space Telescope, all $1.5 billion of it, was put back into working order Monday because a NASA engineer used a Tinkertoy, a lamp cord, masking tape and glue to help solve a major problem.

The telescope's No. 2 high-gain antenna, wedged in one position since Friday, was free and sending data through relay satellites.

The National Aeronautics and Space Administration expected calibration and other normal start-up work to begin by tonight and to receive its first pictures from the telescope by this weekend. "The moral of the story is that there is no solution that's too humble," said David Skillman, who built a model of the jammed antenna.

"We were faced with a problem on the telescope that involved quite intricate geometry," he said. "A number of us realized we could benefit greatly from a model. Someone suggested that even a Tinkertoy model could be useful."

He drove to a toy store Sunday afternoon and bought two boxes of the construction toy. He got the other items in a drug store and put the model together in 15 minutes with another engineer, John Decker. . . . What they visualized with the model was matched with computer drawings at Lockheed Missiles and Space Co. in California.

Armed with that knowledge, computer commands were sent to the telescope directing exactly the way the dish should move to back out of its jam.

"The antenna moved beautifully and easily out of its problem and back to normal," said Skillman. "Many times a simple solution is the best solution."

Here is another example of the use of models and manipulatives, provided by Sierra College student John Bingham: "When I arrived at the manipulative part of the book, I found myself drifting back to my youthful past. During my high school years I played water polo. Part of each practice involved manipulatives on a whiteboard. During practice we would participate in specific plays with designated positions and so on. After practice we would have a team meeting to review what we had learned. In the team room was a whiteboard that illustrated a water polo pool. On the board were markers in the shape of water polo hats that had our numbers and names on them. Our coach would re-create a specific situation and expect us to move the appropriate hats to the appropriate place on the model of the pool to show that we had a full understanding of what we had participated in during practice. Explaining and justifying helped us to prepare not only our understanding but also our mind in that I could visualize things I had seen on the board and think ahead to what would possibly happen next."

Using models and manipulatives is a very powerful and often underused strategy. Despite the obvious real-world applications of manipulatives, many books and teachers favor a more abstract approach. As a result, many students assume they should be able to visualize a problem in their heads, and get frustrated if they can't. Using manipulatives to create a physical representation of quantities in the problem can simplify an otherwise difficult solution process and relieve that frustration.

So use manipulatives and models when you think they will help you solve a problem. They are extremely helpful. You might even find yourself tearing up little pieces of paper when you take the SAT exam, as one Luther Burbank High School graduate did. It helped him get an 800 on the mathematics section of the exam. Above all else, enjoy this strategy and consciously look for places to use it.

Problem Set A-2

7. **TWO JACKALS LOSE THEIR LICENSES**

Solve the Jackals and Coyotes problem again. All six of them start on the same side of the river. But this time, although all three of the coyotes can operate the boat, only one of the jackals can operate the boat.

8. **JACK-QUEEN-DIAMOND**

Three playing cards from an ordinary deck of 52 cards lie face down in a row. There is a queen to the right of a jack. There is a queen to the left of a queen. There is a diamond to the left of a heart. There is a diamond to the right of a diamond. What are the three cards?

9. **BASEBALL SEATING**

A family of five, consisting of Mom, Dad, and three kids (Alyse, Jeremy, and Kevin) went to a baseball game. They had a little trouble deciding who was to sit where. Alyse would not sit next to either of her brothers. Kevin had to sit next to Dad. Mom wanted to sit on the aisle but not next to any of the children, although she could sit next to her daughter as needed. How was the seating arranged?

10. MAGIC TRIANGLE

Here is a magic triangle. The sum of each side of the triangle is 11. Use the digits 1, 2, 3, 4, 5, and 6 (once each) to find the proper location of each.

11. MAGIC SQUARE

Here is a magic square. The sum of each row is 12. The sum of each column is also 12. And the sum of each diagonal is 12. Use the digits 0, 1, 2, 3, 4, 5, 6, 7, and 8 (once each) to find the proper location of each. (There is more than one correct solution.)

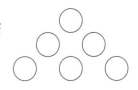

12. TRUE EQUATIONS

Use the digits 0, 1, 2, 3, 4, 5, 6, 7, 8, and 9 to make true equations. Use each digit once.

$$2 + \boxed{} \over \boxed{}$$

$$\boxed{} \times \boxed{} \over \boxed{}\boxed{}$$

$$\boxed{} \div \boxed{} = 2 \qquad \boxed{} - 1 = \boxed{}$$

13. THREE-ON-THREE BASKETBALL

In a recreational basketball league, there were only three players per team. Each team had a center, a forward, and a guard. The tallest on each team was the center; the shortest was the guard. The information below and at the top of the next page refers to three teams.

1. Leon and Weston are guards.

2. Horace and Ingrid play the same position.

3. Kathryn, the shortest, played her best game against Ingrid's team.

4. Horace and Leon are on the same team.

5. Jerome and Taunia are on the same team. On that team, Jerome is not the shortest, and Taunia is not the tallest.

6. Sasha is shorter than both Weston and Horace.

Who is the forward on Kathryn's team? Who plays guard on Sasha's team? What position does Tiffany play and who else is on her team?

14. CUBIST

Three views of a cube are shown below. The cube has the five vowels A, E, I, O, and U on its faces. One letter appears twice. Fill in the blank space in the last cube with the correct letter in the correct orientation.

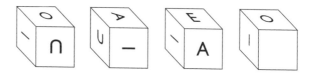

15. FOLDING CUBES

For each figure below, where could you attach a sixth square so that the figure would fold into a cube? (**Note:** This may be impossible for one or more of the figures.)

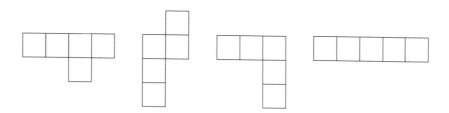

16. MIXED VOLLEYBALL

This volleyball team has eight players: Allyson, Cheryl, Jan, and Sue are the girls; Marty, Ted, Dave, and Harold are the boys. The team will have six players on the court and two players off the court at any time. The two players off the court will rotate into the middle position in the back row. The players must alternate by gender. Set up their starting rotation with the following constraints in mind (for help with volleyball rotation, see the Volleyball Team problem in this chapter).

(This problem is continued on the next page.)

1. Allyson can't be placed next to Dave or Harold because they hog the ball.

2. Sue should be by Harold because she is the best setter and he is the team's best hitter.

3. Dave should probably be next to Sue because he is the team's next best hitter.

4. Allyson prefers to play next to Ted.

5. Harold should get as much time as possible on the front row because he is the team's best front-row player.

6. Dave is the team's best server. He should begin the game serving or be one of the first servers.

7. The weakest players are Jan, Cheryl, and Marty. They should not be placed next to one another.

17. WORCHESTERSHIRE PALACE

At Worchestershire Palace, four guards are pacing back and forth performing maneuvers. Two of the guards (Basil and Barry) are wearing blue uniforms, and the other two guards (Ralph and Randy) are wearing red uniforms. The guards are standing in large tile squares on the floor. The tile arrangement with each guard's present location is shown below.

Basil		Barry
Ralph		Randy

One move for a guard consists of the following: He moves one square from his position in one direction (not diagonal), then turns 90 degrees and moves two squares in that direction. (Or he could move two squares first and then one square.) Each move a guard makes is in this L-shape, and he does not stop until he has finished the complete move.

So, for example, Basil could move one square south and two squares east and end up in the square directly north of Randy's square. No two guards may occupy the same space at the same time. More than one guard may be moving at the same time.

   a. How many moves does it take for the blue guards (Basil and Barry) to change places with the red guards (Ralph and Randy)?

   b. How many moves does it take for Basil to change places with Ralph (ending with Barry and Randy in their original positions)?

18. PROBLEM VATS

In the back room of a scientific supply store, there are two big vats of liquid. The red one contains 10 liters of rubbing alcohol, and the black one contains 10 liters of purified water. Jimmy accidentally pours 3 liters of the alcohol into the water. Then, realizing his mistake and hoping to correct it, he pours 3 liters from the black vat back into the red vat. Each vat again has 10 liters in it. Is there more alcohol in the water, or more water in the alcohol?

19. **WRITE YOUR OWN**

Write your own act-it-out or manipulatives problem. Maybe you've been on a volleyball team. Perhaps you've had the experience of arranging a car pool for lots of people and different days. There is no limit to the ideas here.

Problem Set B

1. **DECREASING NUMBERS**

A number is called a decreasing number if it has two or more digits and each digit is less than the digit to its left. For example 7,421; 964,310; and 52 are decreasing numbers but 3,421; 6,642; 8; and 963,212 are not. How many decreasing numbers are there?

2. **WHITE SALE**

Judy purchased $91 worth of sheets at a sale on Labor Day weekend, when $1.60 was marked off every article. She returned the sheets on Thursday (she really didn't need sheets anyway), when everything was marked at regular prices. Because Judy is a good customer, the sales clerk gave her credit using regular prices and not sale prices, so Judy got more than $91 worth of credit. She was ecstatic about this, so she immediately exchanged the sheets for towels and washcloths. In exchange for one sheet she was able to get a towel and a washcloth. (The towels, washcloths, and sheets were now all marked at regular prices.) She came home with 16 more articles than she'd had before. Because washcloths cost only $2.70, she took six more washcloths than towels. How many washcloths and towels did she buy, and how much would they have cost if Judy had bought them on Saturday at sale prices?

3. **KMRCL TV**

A local TV station, KMRCL, plans its number of commercials based on what type of show is being broadcast. Each commercial is a minute long. On daytime TV, the station runs 18 commercials every hour and then drops the number down to 16 per hour for the news. (Every day there are eight hours of daytime programming and two hours of news.) During KMRCL's prime time, which is three hours per day, the station runs 12 commercials per hour. During the late-night movies, KMRCL sells commercial time really cheap and runs 20 commercials per hour. Late-night movies are shown for six hours each day. The station's "other" programming, which is five hours per day, airs with 8 commercials per hour. For the sake of simplicity, assume that for all seven days of the week, each type of programming airs for the same number of hours just described. Find how many hours per week KMRCL airs commercials.

4. **THUNDER AND LIGHTNING**

In a thunder and lightning storm there is a rule of thumb that many people follow. After seeing the lightning, count seconds to yourself. If it takes 5 seconds for the sound of the thunder to reach you, then the lightning bolt was 1 mile away from you. Sound travels at 331 meters/second. How accurate is the rule of thumb? Express your answer as a percent error.

5. **STATE FAIR**

Dear Wendy,

How's my favorite daughter? How about coming to visit me next week at the state fair? It runs all this week and next, and the way things are going so far, I'm going to be pretty bored.

I'll be at the Hot Spas booth. Let me tell you where it is. But, you know your ol' dad, I can't just tell you straight out. There are seven booths on row 3, and I'm in one of them. On one side of me is Computer Horoscopes—their computers beep all the time. The booth on the other side of me is real quiet. My friend, Ann, works for Encyclopedia Antarctica. She keeps dropping by to visit, as her booth is pretty slow too. She always comes and goes from my right, so her booth must be that way. She told me that the Slice-It-Dice-It-Veggie-Peeler booth is so popular that the vacuum sellers, who were in the booth next to the Slice-It-Dice-It-Veggie-Peeler booth, left the fair because nobody was ever visiting them. So now there are only five booths occupied, because the ladder sellers didn't show up at all. Ann tells me that the other booth on our row is Foot Massage. She says she

(This problem is continued on the next page.)

went to their booth and it is always really noisy with ticklish people laughing hysterically. The last time Ann visited, she was in a real grouchy mood. Seems she was promised an end booth, but they are both presently occupied. She also complained about her neighbor, Computer Horoscopes. After she left, someone actually came to see my stuff. He came from my right and wanted to demonstrate his new Slice-It-Dice-It-Veggie-Peeler on my lunch.

That's it, you have enough information to come directly to my booth. See you next week.

Love,
Dad

Which booth is Wendy's dad's?

Architects and construction workers work backwards from an expected completion date so that they can plan their work.

Work Backwards

Recently, Lucille and her family took a vacation to Hawaii. On the day before they left Hawaii to come home, they planned their activities for the following day. This is Lucille's tale of the problem they faced:

"Our flight was scheduled to leave at 12:40 p.m., and we needed to return our rental car before we left. We also wanted to spend 30 minutes at the pineapple plantation. It was a 45-minute drive to the airport, with about a 10-minute detour to go to the plantation. We also considered going to the sugarcane museum—it was about 10 minutes out of the way, and we planned to stay there about one hour. Based on all this information, we wanted to determine when to leave our condo. We used the strategy of working backwards to solve the problem.

"We started by figuring that we needed to be at the airport 90 minutes before our flight. Since our flight left at 12:40 p.m., we subtracted an hour and a half and decided that we needed to be at the airport at 11:10 a.m. Since we had to return the rental car also, we adjusted that to 11:00 a.m. Ignoring the sugarcane museum for the moment, we figured in the time we needed to visit the plantation. We subtracted the 10-minute drive and the 30 minutes we planned to stay there from 11:00 and got 10:20 a.m. Then we subtracted the 45-minute drive to the airport. This meant we had to leave at 9:35 a.m. If we subtracted the hour and 10 minutes for the sugarcane museum (10-minute detour and an hour to look around) we would need to leave at 8:25 a.m. Since we had to check out of our condominium, and we also had two little kids, we didn't think we could leave that early. So we canceled our plans to go to the sugarcane museum, and we left at about 9:30 a.m.

"We visited the plantation without being rushed (allowing us time to buy some pineapples and a great hat), and we still got to the airport in plenty of time. This was fortunate, since I ended up arguing with the rental car agency for 30 minutes because they were trying to charge me for a minuscule dent in the passenger door. Had we not used working backwards to figure out when we needed to leave, I might have had to rush to the airplane and would not have had enough time to argue. This could have resulted in a large bill when I arrived home."

Working backwards is another strategy that falls under the major theme of Changing Focus. With most other strategies, you work forwards through the information in a problem. To successfully work backwards, you need to change your focus and consider the whole problem in reverse. This is a very useful strategy in certain situations. Much of algebra is based on working backwards, and this strategy is also very useful for planning schedules or agendas, as Lucille's story about her trip to Hawaii demonstrates.

One of the most difficult aspects of working backwards is keeping track of a problem's information and organizing it in a meaningful way. **Note** that although the solutions in this chapter are organized in various formats, we encourage you to experiment with finding new ways to organize the problems so you can solve them.

To begin the chapter, we'll take you through some exercises in working backwards. All of these exercises will prepare you for the rest of the chapter.

At the top of the next page is a map of Wallowville. Mark is exiting the freeway and needs directions to drive to his friend's house. Write the directions and double-check them before you move on.

After visiting his friend, Mark is ready to leave. He needs directions to get back to the freeway. *Without* looking at the map, write the directions.

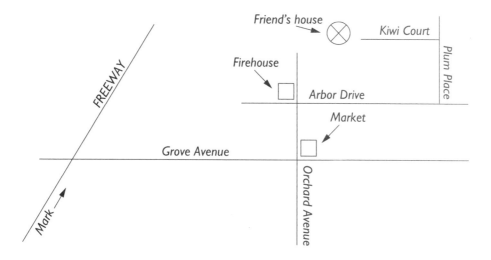

There are at least two basic things you need to do to write the directions for going back to the freeway. The first is to mention the landmarks and the street names in reverse order. The second is to tell Mark to take the opposite action at each juncture (for example, turn left instead of right). Other problems of this nature will involve objects other than landmarks and street names, but the process for solving them will be the same: Reverse the order of the objects and reverse the actions.

The solutions to many mathematics problems involve this process. For example, I am thinking of a whole number between 1 and 10. I double it and come up with 12. What is my number? Obviously, to reach the answer you must take my "doubled" number, 12, and divide it by 2 to get 6. (This is a mathematical example of "reverse the actions": Division reverses multiplication and vice versa, just as subtraction reverses addition and vice versa.)

Now consider an unknown number between 1 and 10. Multiply the number by 3. Then add 5 to the result, giving 32. What is the original number? To find the original number, you must reverse the order of the "objects" in the problem and reverse the actions. The first object is the 3 (as in "multiply by"), and the second object is the 5. Thus, the objects you must work with, in reverse order, are the 5 and the 3. Now reverse each action in the problem. Instead of adding 5, subtract 5 ($32 - 5 = 27$). Reverse multiplying by 3 so that you're dividing by 3 ($27 \div 3 = 9$). Now you have the original number: 9.

Lo and behold, you got the right answer. To check, work the problem forwards: 9 times 3 is 27, and 27 plus 5 gives 32.

Do the next three problems:

1. I'm thinking of a number between 1 and 10. If I multiply by 4 and then subtract 3, my answer is 25. What is my number?

2. I'm thinking of a number between 1 and 30. I add 22. I divide by 3. My answer is 12. What is my number?

3. I'm thinking about a number. Divide it by 2, then subtract 1. The answer is $7\frac{1}{2}$. What is my number?

Note that the answers to these problems can be found on pages 7, 14, and 17, respectively. Now on to more serious endeavors.

POOR CHOICES

The night before their debut in Carnegie Hall, half of the ballet company stayed up late watching tractor pulls on TV. Excuse me, make that half of the company plus one more. There were 13 tired dancers in all, so how many dancers were in the company? Work this problem before continuing.

Here's an example of how to set up the solution. Follow it from line to line:

A. Half of the company

B. And one more

C. Thirteen in all

C.	Thirteen in all	13
B.	And one more (reverse the action to make it 1 less)	12
A.	Half of the company (reverse by multiplying by 2)	24

So there are 24 dancers in the company. To check, work the problem forwards. Start with 24 dancers. Half of the company is tired, which makes 12 dancers. And 1 more makes 13 tired dancers in all. This solution checks with the information in the problem.

THE STOLEN PIGEONS

Bad Bargle sneaked into Homer's pigeon loft one day. He took half of the pigeons. He decided that wasn't bad enough, so he took one more and left. Later, Homer opened the door of the loft to exercise his prize possessions. Half of the remaining flock flew out, leaving six inside the pen. How many pigeons did Homer have before Bad Bargle did his dirty deed? Work this problem before continuing.

First write down the actions in the order in which they appear in the problem.

A. Bargle stole half of the pigeons.

B. Bargle stole one more pigeon.

C. Half of the remaining flock flew out.

D. Six were left.

Whoops. This is only half of the setup for the solution. Before you continue, **note** that you should read the actions on the previous page from top to bottom. In the following solution, read the left-hand column only until specifically instructed otherwise.

Working this forwards we get:

A. Bargle stole half of the pigeons.

B. Bargle stole one more pigeon.

C. Half of the remaining flock flew out.

D. Six were left.

D. Bargle returned half of the original pigeon flock. (Fat chance!)

C. Bargle returned one pigeon.

B. Half of the remaining flock flew back in.

A. Six were left.

Now you can read the right-hand column from bottom to top. These are the reverse actions. And if you read these reverse actions from bottom to top, you also reverse the order of the "objects."

Oops. The numbers are missing. Let's put the numbers in place, using the reverse actions in the reverse order. (All you have to do is read from top to bottom. We've put the reverse actions in reverse order for you.)

A. Six pigeons were left.

There are 6 pigeons.

B. Half of the remaining flock flew back in.

Now there are 12.

C. Bargle returned one pigeon.

Now there are 13.

D. Bargle returned half of the flock. (Fat chance!)

The flock is back to 26 birds.

P.S. Check this solution by working forwards.

Dad was paid on Wednesday. On Thursday morning my brother borrowed half of Dad's money to open a checking account with, because he was always short of money. On Friday I needed some money for a date, so I borrowed half of what remained. Sis came along next and borrowed half of the remaining money. Dad then went to gas up the car and used half of the rest of his money, and he wondered where it all went so fast. He had only $5 left. How much money did he start with in his wallet? Don't forget to reverse the actions and the order. Don't go on until you've worked this problem.

In order, this is what happened to poor Dad:

A. He got his money from the bank.

B. Brother borrowed half of his money.

C. I borrowed half of what remained.

D. Sis borrowed half of what remained.

E. He spent half of the remainder on gas.

Now it's time to reverse the order and reverse the actions (the reverse actions are shown in red text).

E. At the end, the wallet has $5 in it.
Dad spent half on gas.
He gave back the gas and got back the other half of his money.

D. The wallet now has $10 in it.
Sis borrowed half of the remainder.
She gave back what she'd borrowed, which was the same as what she'd left, because she'd borrowed half.

C. The wallet now has $20 in it.
I borrowed half for a date.
I gave back an amount equal to what I left: $20.

B. The wallet now has $40 in it.
Brother borrowed half to start his nest egg.
Brother repaid his loan, half of the money: $40.

A. The wallet now has $80 in it.
So Dad's wallet had $80 in it before all the raids took place.

As you can see, there are different ways to record the information in a problem and use it to solve the problem. You'll see a few other ways to organize the information in later examples. Your organization needs to help, not hinder, the process of working backwards. Be sure to experiment with your own style as you attempt the next problem and the problems that follow.

NUMBER TRICK

Start with a number between 1 and 10.
  Multiply the number by 4.
  Add 6 to the number you have now.
  Divide by 2.
  Subtract 5.
  Tell me the number you end with, and I'll tell you the number you started with.
  Two students, Glenda and Sonia, played this game. Sonia started with a number, did the arithmetic, and told Glenda that she had ended with 12. Glenda then figured out what number Sonia started with. What number did Sonia start with? Work this problem before continuing.

Here's how Glenda found Sonia's number: "I could have tried this problem with guess-and-check, and that definitely would have worked. But I wanted to use working backwards because I thought it would be easier. First I wrote down the given information, and then I worked backwards until I found the original number. I reversed the actions each time. So subtracting 5 became adding 5 as I worked backwards, and so on."

Organizing information is very important for keeping track of what you are doing. Glenda found, as many solvers have, that the most useful way to solve this problem is to work *up* the page. That is, with the information written in its original order, do your work from the bottom of the page to the top. The finished product looks something like the two columns shown at the top of the next page. Read down the right column for the actions. Then read up the left column for the numbers. (In this example, the reverse actions are not written in.)

Start with a number between 1 and 10.

7

Multiply the number by 4.

28

Add 6 to the number you have now.

34

Divide by 2.

17

Subtract 5.

12

The result is 12.

Note that the information and the numbers are staggered every other line so that it's easy to read either down or up. In this form the solution is also easy to check. Start with a number (7). Multiply by 4 to get 28. Add 6 to get 34. Divide by 2 to get 17. Subtract 5 to get 12. It checks. Do this problem again, but this time assume that the final number Sonia reached was 4.

The idea of working up a page may seem strange, but this process is used for real-world problems. For example, airline baggage tags list in reverse order the airports you land in. Your original departure point is sometimes shown at the bottom of the tag, but often it is omitted because, of course, the people working at your point of origin know where the airport is located. Each successive airport you land in is shown on the preceding line, along with your flight numbers. Your final destination is shown at the top of the tag. In the tag shown here, a passenger flew from Sacramento, California (not shown at the bottom), to San Francisco (SFO) on Flight 385. Then the passenger flew from San Francisco to Chicago O'Hare (ORD) on Flight 4689, and then from Chicago to New York's John F. Kennedy Airport (JFK) on Flight 1273.

Work the next problem by writing down and organizing the information, then working backwards up the page.

↑JFK	1273
↑ORD	4689
↑SFO	385

Mr. Phil T. Rich left half of his estate to his wife, $30,000 to his daughter, half of what was left to his butler, half of what remained for the care of his goldfish, and the remaining $8,000 to charity. What was the value of his estate? Work this problem before continuing.

As you did for the Number Trick problem, summarize this problem's information in a column. Then work backwards from the end of the problem. Work up the page. This is Rewa's work on this problem. (It's a good idea to show the way the solution looks and explain it afterwards.)

<table>
<tr><td></td><td>Start</td></tr>
<tr><td>$124,000</td><td></td></tr>
<tr><td></td><td>Half of his estate to his wife</td></tr>
<tr><td>62,000</td><td></td></tr>
<tr><td></td><td>30,000 to his daughter</td></tr>
<tr><td>32,000</td><td></td></tr>
<tr><td></td><td>Half of what was left to his butler</td></tr>
<tr><td>16,000</td><td></td></tr>
<tr><td></td><td>Half of what remained for his goldfish</td></tr>
<tr><td>$8,000</td><td></td></tr>
<tr><td></td><td>The remaining $8,000 to charity</td></tr>
<tr><td>0</td><td></td></tr>
</table>

Rewa explains: "Beginning at the end, he gave his last $8,000 to charity. He must have had $8,000 before that in order to give his last $8,000 to charity. Before that, he gave half of what was left to his goldfish. He must have had $16,000 so that he could give half to the fish and leave $8,000.

"Right before that he gave half of what was left to the butler, leaving $16,000. So the butler got $16,000 also. This means that the value of the estate before paying the butler was $32,000.

"Right before that, he gave $30,000 to his daughter. Since he had $32,000 left after giving money to his daughter, he must have had $62,000 (add $30,000 to $32,000) just before giving money to his daughter.

"Finally (or initially), he gave half of his money to his wife. She must have received $62,000, so there must have been $124,000 to begin with."

The next problem features fractions other than one-half. You might find that a diagram helps you keep track of the information.

MINTS

After dinner, three friends at a restaurant paid their bill and noticed a bowl of mints on the front counter. Sean took one-third of the mints but returned four because he had a momentary pang of guilt. Faizah then took one-fourth of what was left but returned three for similar reasons. Eugene then took half of the remainder but threw two green ones back into the bowl. The bowl had only 17 mints left when the raid was over. How many mints were originally in the bowl? Work this problem before continuing.

Write down all of the events that occurred in their proper order.

Start.

Sean took one-third of the mints.

Sean returned four.

Faizah then took one-fourth of what was left.

Faizah returned three.

Eugene then took half of the remainder.

Eugene threw two back into the bowl.

The bowl had 17 mints left.

This problem can be a little confusing. You may wish to act it out with manipulatives, such as pennies, pieces of paper, or actual mints. Or you might imagine a movie of these events, and then starting from the end, run the movie backwards in your head. Keep in mind, to solve this problem you must reverse the order and the action.

Aniko solved this problem as follows: "I began at the end. There were 17 mints left in the bowl when the raid was over."

> Start.
> Sean took ⅓ of the mints.
> Sean returned 4.
> Faizah then took ¼ of what was left.
> Faizah returned 3.
> Eugene then took ½ of the remainder.
> Eugene threw 2 back into the bowl.
> 17
> The bowl had 17 mints left.

"Right before that, Eugene threw 2 back into the bowl. This means that there must have been 15 mints in the bowl before Eugene threw 2 back. Right before that, Eugene took half of the mints and left 15 in the bowl. This means that there must have been 30 mints in the bowl before Eugene took his greedy turn."

> Start.
> Sean took ⅓ of the mints.
> Sean returned 4.
> Faizah then took ¼ of what was left.
> Faizah returned 3.
> 30
> Eugene then took ½ of the remainder.
> 15
> Eugene threw 2 back into the bowl.
> 17
> The bowl had 17 mints left.

"Right before that, Faizah put 3 mints back into the bowl, leaving 30. So just before she put those 3 back, there must have been 27."

At this point, a common mistake is to add 3 and get 33. But think of watching these events in a movie. If there were 33 mints in the bowl before Faizah put 3 back, then there must have been 36 after she returned the 3. But these actions don't match what the problem says. The reverse action of Faizah putting 3 back is for her to take 3 out. So

when we work backwards, we take 3 away from 30, which leaves 27.
Then going forwards, she will put 3 back, and 27 + 3 = 30.

Start.
Sean took ⅓ of the mints.
Sean returned 4.
Faizah then took ¼ of what was left.

27

Faizah returned 3.

30

Eugene then took ½ of the remainder.

15

Eugene threw 2 back into the bowl.

17

The bowl had 17 mints left.

Aniko continued: "Right before that, Faizah took one-fourth of the mints, leaving 27."

Again, a common mistake here is to multiply 27 by 4. However, this doesn't represent Faizah's actions. A diagram can illustrate what happened. (The following type of diagram, invented by student Hao Ngo, is very helpful.)

Aniko explained, "I drew a rectangle to represent all of the mints before Faizah took any."

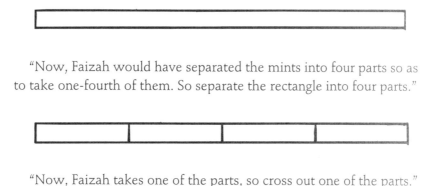

"Now, Faizah would have separated the mints into four parts so as to take one-fourth of them. So separate the rectangle into four parts."

"Now, Faizah takes one of the parts, so cross out one of the parts."

"The three parts that are left total 27 mints. This means, since the parts are all equal, that each part represents 9 mints."

"Therefore, the part that Faizah took, which must be equal to the other three equal parts, must also represent 9 mints."

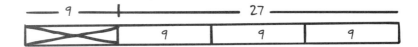

"So with four parts of 9 mints each, there must have been 36 mints in the bowl before Faizah did her dastardly deed.

"Let's see if everything checks at this point. When Faizah arrives at the bowl, she finds 36 mints. She takes one-fourth of them (1/4 of 36 is 9). Now 36 − 9 leaves 27 mints in the bowl. Then she puts 3 back (adds 3), so 27 + 3 = 30 mints in the bowl when Faizah is done. Then Eugene takes half of the mints (1/2 of 30 is 15, and 30 − 15 = 15), which leaves 15 mints in the bowl. Then he puts 2 back, so there are 17 left when he is done. Everything checks thus far."

Start.
Sean took 1/3 of the mints.
Sean returned 4.

36

Faizah then took 1/4 of what was left.

27

Faizah returned 3.

30

Eugene then took 1/2 of the remainder.

15

Eugene threw 2 back into the bowl.

17

The bowl had 17 mints left.

Let's pick up with Rachel's solution. It shows a different way of handling the fractional parts. "Right before Faizah, Sean returned 4 to the bowl. Since there were 36 mints in the bowl when Faizah got there, there must have been 4 fewer mints before Sean put 4 back. So there must have been 32 mints in the bowl before Sean's pangs of guilt."

Start.
Sean took $\frac{1}{3}$ of the mints.

32

Sean returned 4.

36

Faizah then took $\frac{1}{4}$ of what was left.

27

Faizah returned 3.

30

Eugene then took $\frac{1}{2}$ of the remainder.

15

Eugene threw 2 back into the bowl.

17

The bowl had 17 mints left.

"Right before those pangs of guilt, Sean took one-third of the mints. This means he left two-thirds of the mints in the bowl. I used algebra to find how many were in the bowl before that. I used m to represent the number of mints before Sean took one-third of them."

$$(\tfrac{2}{3})m = 32 \qquad \text{Multiply both sides by } \tfrac{3}{2}.$$
$$(\tfrac{3}{2})(\tfrac{2}{3})m = (\tfrac{3}{2})(32)$$
$$m = 48$$

"So there must have been 48 mints in the beginning."

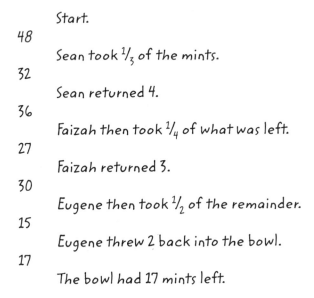

Start.

48

Sean took ⅓ of the mints.

32

Sean returned 4.

36

Faizah then took ¼ of what was left.

27

Faizah returned 3.

30

Eugene then took ½ of the remainder.

15

Eugene threw 2 back into the bowl.

17

The bowl had 17 mints left.

Note that you could also use a diagram like the one shown below to reach the conclusion that Rachel did.

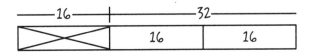

Rachel checked her work as follows: "There were 48 mints to begin with. Sean took one-third (⅓ of 48 = 16, and 48 − 16 = 32), leaving 32. Then he put 4 back, so there were 36 when he was done." With Aniko's check of the rest of the problem, which is shown just before we picked up with Rachel's solution, we are satisfied with this answer. There were 48 mints to start with.

The solution to this problem ends up looking something like the columns shown at the top of the next page.

Start.

48

Sean took ⅓ of the mints.

32

Sean returned 4.

36

Faizah then took ¼ of what was left.

27

Faizah returned 3.

30

Eugene then took ½ of the remainder.

15

Eugene threw 2 back into the bowl.

17

The bowl had 17 mints left.

For this problem, the diagram and the algebraic techniques were both very effective for dealing with the fractional parts that were taken away. But in general, using algebra is not a very efficient way to solve these types of problems. For instance, if m represents the number of mints the bowl contained at the start, an algebraic equation representing the entire problem would look like this:

$$\left\{\left[m - \left(\frac{1}{3}\right)m + 4\right] - \left(\frac{1}{4}\right)\left[m - \left(\frac{1}{3}\right)m + 4\right] + 3\right\}$$

$$- \left(\frac{1}{2}\right)\left\{\left[m - \left(\frac{1}{3}\right)m + 4\right] - \left(\frac{1}{4}\right)\left[m - \left(\frac{1}{3}\right)m + 4\right] + 3\right\} + 2 = 17$$

If you don't believe working backwards is easier, solve this equation.

~~~~~~

For a wonderful article and working-backwards problem involving pirates and pieces of gold, see Ian Stewart's "A Puzzle for Pirates" in the Mathematical Recreations column of *Scientific American,* May 1999.

Guess-and-check can also be used to solve many of these types of problems. However, because the theme of this chapter is working backwards, the solutions focus on that strategy. Getting started with a working-backwards solution is a bit harder than getting started with a guess-and-check solution, but reaching the solution by working backwards is usually easier and quicker.

Problem Set A

1.   LOSING STREAK

A man competing on a game show ran into a losing streak. First, he bet half of his money on one question and lost it. Then he lost half of his remaining money on another question. Then he lost $300 on another question. Then he lost half of his remaining money on another question. Finally, he got a question right and won $200. At this point, the show ended and he had $1,200 left. How much did he have before his losing streak began?

2.   GENEROSITY

Phil Anthropist likes to give away money. One day he was feeling especially generous, so he went to the park with a wad of money. He gave $100 to a man feeding pigeons. He then gave half of his remaining money to a child licking an ice cream cone. He then gave $50 to the balloon seller. He then bought a hot dog and paid for it with a $20 bill. "Keep the extra for a tip," he said to the hot-dog seller. Then he gave half of his remaining money to someone giving a sermon on a soapbox. At this point, he had $3 left and stuck it under the collar of a stray cat. How much money did Phil have when he started his good deeds?

3. COOKIES

This problem was written by David and Eric from Bob Daniel's class at Centaurus High School in Lafayette, Colorado.

Barney had a bag of cookies. He ate 35 in the first 10 minutes. He ate $1/4$ of the remaining cookies during the next 10 minutes. The next day he ate 20, but then he made 10 more. His wife, Louise, ate 15 cookies while Barney was at work. When Barney got home from work, he ate $1/2$ of the remaining cookies. Louise ate 5 more when he went out into the backyard. Barney then ate 15 more and found that he had only 2 left. How many cookies did he start with? How many did he eat? How much weight did he gain if every 10 cookies translates into 1 pound?

4. THE MALL

My sister loves to go shopping. Yesterday she borrowed a wad of money from Mom and went to the mall. She began her excursion by spending $18 on a new compact disc. Then she spent half of her remaining money on a new dress. Then she spent $11 taking herself and her friend out to lunch. Then she spent one-third of her remaining money on a book. On her way home she bought gas for $12 and spent one-fourth of her remaining money on a discount tape at the convenience store. Finally, she slipped me $2 when she got home and gave Mom back $10 in change. Mom was furious and demanded an explanation of where the money went. What did Sis tell her? (List the items and the amount spent on each item.)

5. SNICKERDOODLES

This problem was written by Kendra, Laura, Paul, and Leah from Bob Daniel's class at Centaurus High School in Lafayette, Colorado.

Sandy had some snickerdoodles to give to all her friends as Christmas gifts. She gave 25 to the little elves. She then gave $1/5$ of her remaining snickerdoodles to Santa Claus. She gave 9 to each of the nine reindeer (don't forget them, especially not Rudolph). Sandy gave 71 to Mrs. Claus because poor Mrs. Claus had no idea what to give her friends for Christmas. Then Sandy ate $1/3$ of her remaining snickerdoodles. Next, she gave $1/8$ of her remaining cookies to her best friend in Toronto, and she gave 20 more to Mrs. Claus, who hadn't had enough to give to all her friends. When Sandy was all done giving, she had 15 cookies left, which she gave to Frosty the Snowman. How many snickerdoodles did Sandy have to begin with?

6. USED CAR

A car dealership was trying to sell a used car that no one wanted. First, they tried to sell it for 10% off the marked price. Then they tried to sell it for 20% off the first sale price. Finally, they offered it for 25% off the second sale price, and someone bought it for $3,240. What was the original price of the car?

7. JASMINE'S DANCE TROUPE

Jasmine was the head member of her school's dance group. She and the troupe's choreographer (also a troupe member) decided that they needed to have one more rehearsal before they performed at the school rally. After school she called $1/3$ of the rest of the troupe to let them know about the rehearsal. She then helped prepare dinner and called three more members before sitting down to eat. While her brothers cleaned the kitchen, Jasmine called $2/5$ of the remaining dancers. She did her math homework, then reached one more dancer on the phone. After completing her chemistry homework, Jasmine called $3/4$ of the remaining troupe members. She edited a rough draft of her essay, then called the last two dancers. How many members are there in Jasmine's dance troupe?

8. WHAT'S MY NUMBER?

I am thinking of a number. I multiplied my number by 3, subtracted 8, doubled the result, and added 14. Then I added on 50% of what I had and subtracted 11. Then I divided by 5. After all that, I was left with 8. What number did I start with?

9. LOST HIS MARBLES

This problem was written by student David Lee from Sierra College in Rocklin, California.

Livingston is a marble freak and loves to play at school. During the first break, he doubled the number of marbles he had. During the second break, he lost four marbles (no big deal). During the third break, he increased his stock of marbles by $1/3$. During lunch, however, he lost half of his marbles. After school, Livingston played again and tripled what he had. He went home with 72 marbles. How many did he start with?

10. HOCKEY CARDS

Jack had quite a few hockey cards, and Jill had some of her own. Jack gave Jill as many hockey cards as she already had. Jill then gave Jack back as many cards as he had left. Finally, Jack then gave her back as many cards as she had left. This left poor Jack with no cards and left Jill with 40 cards altogether. How many hockey cards did each of them have just before these exchanges took place? (You might want to try acting this out in conjunction with working backwards.)

11. TWO FOR TENNIS

Scott and Jeremy took a basket of balls with them to tennis practice. Scott took out 2 and threw them at Jeremy. Jeremy chased Scott and accidentally knocked over the basket, dumping out $5/8$ of the remaining balls. Scott threw 3 back in. As they were playing, a hard hit knocked the basket over and $1/5$ of the remaining balls rolled out. Scott put 2 balls back into the basket, but a couple of minutes later a smash hit knocked the basket over again. Half of the remaining balls rolled out, and then there were 7 left in the basket. How many tennis balls did Scott and Jeremy start with in the basket?

12. DONUTS

Four customers came into a bakery. The first one said, "Give me half of all the donuts you have left, plus half a donut more." The second customer said, "Give me half of all the donuts you have left, plus half a donut more." The third customer said, "Give me three donuts." The last customer said, "Give me half of all the donuts you have left, plus half a donut more." This last transaction emptied the display case of donuts. How many donuts were there to start with?

13. GOLF CLUBS

Ken played golf yesterday and shot 107. Considering that he normally shoots in the low 80's or high 70's, this round of golf really frustrated him. It was so frustrating that he decided to buy new golf clubs. But first he had to give his old golf clubs away. He gave half of his golf clubs, plus half a club more, to Daniel. Then he gave half of his remaining golf clubs to Gary. Then he gave half of his remaining golf clubs and half a club more to Will. This left Ken with one club (his putter), which he decided to keep. How many golf clubs did Ken start with before giving them away?

14. WRITE YOUR OWN

Write your own working-backwards problem. Start at the beginning of the problem with your total amount. In other words, start with the number that will be the answer to your problem. Then make up the situation and the steps. By starting with the beginning number (the answer), you will avoid any ugly fractional amounts of things you could get if you started at the end of your problem.

Problem Set B: The Camping Trip

1. HOW MUCH DOG FOOD?

The Family family (Mama, Papa, and the three kids, Ed, Lisa, and Judy) were about to go on a camping vacation. They decided to take their five dogs with them, and they needed to know how many cans of dog food to take. They had received a free sample of dog food in the mail, and all the dogs really liked it. The cans of the sample brand of dog food were on sale for $1.24, and the packaging said that three cans of dog food would feed two dogs for one day. The family was planning on going camping for eight days. How much would the dog food cost them for the eight days?

2. THE LUGGAGE RACK

The Family family was about ready to leave on their camping trip. They loaded up their van with stuff, but it was getting really full with all kinds of equipment, plus five dogs. (Everyone had his or her own dog.) They were trying to decide whether to take the luggage rack for the top of the van to store some of their camping gear, or whether they should just cram it all inside the van. Papa didn't want to take the luggage rack because he said their gas mileage would be worse because of the increased drag. Mama said she didn't want to be crowded inside the van, and she didn't care how much it cost, she wanted to take it. Papa said they got 20 miles per gallon with the luggage rack off, and 17 miles per gallon with it on. Their destination was 3 hours away at 55 miles per hour with the rack off, but with the rack on they could go only 50 miles per hour. Gas cost $1.89 per gallon. How much more would it cost them to take the luggage rack, and how many extra minutes would it take them to get there?

CROSSING THE RIVER WITH DOGS

The five Family family members and their five dogs (each family member owned one of the dogs) were hiking when they encountered a river to cross. They rented a boat that could hold three living things: people or dogs. Unfortunately, the dogs were temperamental. Each was comfortable only with its owner and could not be near another person, not even momentarily, unless its owner was present. Dogs could be with other dogs, however. The crossing would have been impossible except that Lisa's dog had attended a first-rate obedience school and knew how to operate the boat. No other dogs were that well educated. How was the crossing arranged, and how many trips did it take?

4. DON'T FEED THE ANIMALS

For the camping trip, the Family family had brought many bags of peanuts for snacks. Peanuts were everyone's favorite, so they were well stocked. Unfortunately, the campground was quite populated by various animals who also enjoyed an occasional peanut. The first night, after the Family family went to bed, a raccoon visited their camp and ate five of the bags of peanuts they had brought. The next day, the Familys ate one-third of the remaining bags. That night, a beaver came to call and ate two more of the bags. The next day, the Familys consumed one-fourth of the remaining bags for breakfast. Then they took the boat trip described in the Crossing the River with Dogs problem, and they had to feed one bag of peanuts to each dog to get them to quiet down. That night, an elephant from a nearby zoo came to the camp and ate four bags. The next day, each member of the Family family ate one-ninth of the remaining bags. That night, a spotted owl ate half of the remaining bags. The next day, there were only four bags left. The Familys couldn't decide how to split them among the five of them, so they fed them to the ducks. How many bags of peanuts did the Familys bring with them on the camping trip?

5. LOST IN PURSUIT OF PEANUTS

On the fifth day, after the peanuts were all gone, Ed and Judy took a hike to the store to get some more peanuts. On the way back, they got lost in the middle of a big forest. The forested area they were in measured roughly 13 miles from north to south and 14 miles from east to west. When they first discovered they were lost, they were at a point that was 7 miles from the southern border and 7 miles from the eastern border of the forest. (Of course, they didn't know this or they wouldn't have been lost.) In their indecision as to whether they should walk east (toward the morning sun), west (toward the setting sun), south (from which they came), or north (because they might be wrong about the direction from which they came), they decided to walk in all four directions. They devised a plan where they would walk north first for 30 minutes. If they weren't out of the forest yet, they would then turn right and walk east for 60 minutes, then turn right again and walk south for 90 minutes, and so on, adding 30 minutes with each change of direction. (Nobody said this was a good plan.) It turns out that in the forested area, they covered about 1 mile every 30 minutes. They also decided to drop a peanut after every 100 yards so that they would be sure they never doubled back on their tracks. They had 50 bags of peanuts with them, and there were 40 peanuts in each bag. On which side of the forest—north, east, south, or west—did they finally emerge, and how long did it take from the moment they were lost until the moment they got out? How many full bags of peanuts did they have left?

When you recycle, you separate recyclable materials from other trash, then further sort these materials into subsets such as aluminum, glass, and paper. Using Venn diagrams is helpful for problems involving objects that can be sorted into different categories.

12

Venn Diagrams

Mathematics students often use **Venn diagrams** to categorize things, because Venn diagrams can clearly show relationships among different categories. You can also use Venn diagrams to solve problems. Venn diagrams fall into the major theme of Spatial Organization. They organize information in a particular way, which otherwise could be hard to see. When you draw Venn diagrams, you can use loops, closed circles, or rectangles. Two loops can intersect or be entirely disjoint, or one can be completely inside the other. Each of these pairs of loops represents a different type of relationship between two categories.

In certain types of problems, you will often encounter the three words *all, some,* and *no.* For example, the word *all* could be used in a statement such as "All roses are flowers." Using a Venn diagram can help you correctly interpret the meaning of these three important words and of other words in the problems.

(Several words of **caution:** When we talk about correctly interpreting the meanings of words in Venn diagram problems, we are talking about the principal, common understanding of the words. For example, you may know a woman named Rose, but the name Rose is not the principal, common understanding of the word *rose.* Don't waste time looking for obscure meanings or interpretations that will render all the information in a problem false.)

"All roses are flowers." Here is a Venn interpretation of this statement: The diagram at right shows the word *flowers.* Anything inside the rectangle is considered to be a flower. Anything outside the rectangle is considered to be "not a flower." Add the term *roses* to the diagram. Roses is an entirely enclosed subset of the larger set, Flowers. (A **set** is a collection of particular things. Each individual thing in a set is called a **member** or an **element**. A **subset** is a set contained within a set.)

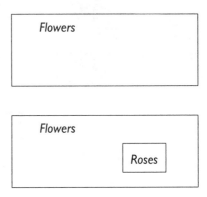

So every member of the group called Roses is also a member of the group called Flowers. Inside the rectangle called Roses are all the individual items that are classified as roses, such as white roses, red roses, damask roses, and rugosas. Anything outside the Roses rectangle is considered "not a rose."

Think of some examples that are not roses: pink carnations, tiger lilies, apricot blossoms, hamburgers, lawn mowers. Not a single one of these items is considered to be a rose. (Unless, of course, the lawn mower is manufactured by a company called Rose Garden Products, Inc. But **remember,** we are using the principal, common understanding of the words in the problem, in which case a rose is a rose is a rose.) But some of these "not rose" items *are* flowers, so they can each be placed in the diagram someplace. Let's call the rectangles *regions* and label them A and B, as shown below.

Region A: Flowers but not roses

Region B: Flowers; in particular, roses

In a Venn diagram, all the characteristics of an outer loop apply to everything within that loop, including other loops. In this case, the characteristics of the large rectangle apply to both regions A and B. The characteristics of a **region** are the same as those of its principal loop minus the characteristics of any smaller, wholly enclosed loop. For example, a pink carnation is a flower, but it is not a rose. These are the characteristics described in the statement for region A, so you would place pink carnations in region A because they lack the characteristic necessary to place them in region B. On the other hand, lawn mowers would be placed *outside* of both regions, because lawn mowers are not flowers. Figure out where you would place each of the other "not rose" items listed previously.

Another example of a Venn diagram is shown below. This example shows two loops: a loop that contains students who take mathematics and a loop that contains students who take chemistry. **Notice** that the word *some* is key in both of the following statements:

1. Some math students are also chemistry students.

2. Some chemistry students are also math students.

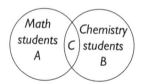

In this diagram, the two loops intersect each other. The math-student loop is labeled A, the chemistry-student loop is labeled B, and the intersection of the two loops is labeled C. What are the characteristics of the regions?

Region A: Math students who are not taking chemistry

Region B: Chemistry students who are not taking math

Region C: Students who are taking both math and chemistry

The **overlapping** section, region C, has the characteristics of both loops and thus of both regions A and B. This was also true in the Venn diagram for the flowers and the roses: The overlap (the inside loop called Roses) had the characteristics of both regions A and B.

With this diagram of math and chemistry students, you can also draw a large rectangle around the two loops to indicate what is called a **universal set**. In this case, the universal set could be assumed to be students. Thus, a student who is taking neither math nor chemistry could be placed in region D, outside of both loops. (You could have put a larger rectangle, called Plants, around the diagram for the flowers and roses. This would have indicated the universal set that includes flowers, roses, and plants that are neither flowers nor roses.) The expanded diagram of all students is shown below.

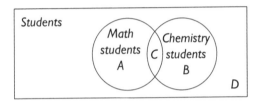

Note that the shapes of the loops is not significant, so shapes may be mixed in a single Venn diagram. In some Venn diagrams, the two regions do not overlap at all. Consider these two statements:

1. No car is a mushroom.

2. No mushroom is a car.

Note that a universal set makes little sense here because cars and mushrooms really couldn't be related with one category, unless one uses a category as general as "things." This car-mushroom diagram shows no overlap either conceptually or in the visual representation. The diagram serves to illustrate and confirm our belief that no cars are mushrooms and no mushrooms are cars.

Let's go back to the overlapping student loops and the following statements:

1. Some math students are also chemistry students.

2. Some chemistry students are also math students.

The key in both of these statements, and in many other statements, is the word *some*. But the word does not automatically indicate overlapping loops. Consider the statement "Some flowers are roses." This statement can be illustrated with the same two loops we showed for the statement "All roses are flowers." Recall that with those two loops, one loop was entirely enclosed within the other.

You need to look carefully at statements that include the word *some*. A Venn diagram may have overlapping loops, or may have one loop inside another. If you are having trouble deciding how to draw the Venn diagram of a statement that includes the word *some,* **remember** that it's safer to draw the loops as **intersecting** and realize that one or more of the regions may be **empty** (contain no elements). (You may not know which regions are empty until the problem is solved.)

BASIC RELATIONSHIPS

Your understanding of creating accurate Venn diagrams is critical to understanding the problems in the rest of this chapter. Draw Venn diagrams that represent each of the following statements.

1. Some birds are pets.

2. All accountants are college graduates.

3. No dogs are sheep.

4. All poodles are dogs.

5. Some dogs are poodles.

Draw these diagrams before continuing.

The correct answers to the problems are shown below. If you haven't drawn the Venn diagrams yet, draw them before reading on.

1. Some birds are pets.

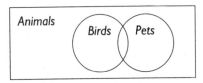

2. All accountants are college graduates.

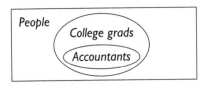

3. No dogs are sheep.

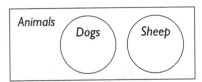

4. All poodles are dogs.

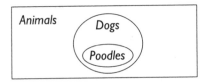

Note that the large rectangle could have been dogs, with only one circle inside it to represent poodles. The large rectangle represents the universal set, and it is up to the person drawing the diagram to decide what that universal set should be.

5. Some dogs are poodles.

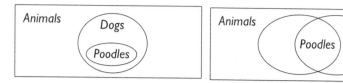

   This problem has been illustrated in two ways. In the left-hand diagram above, the Poodles circle is shown inside the Dogs circle; in the right-hand diagram, the two circles overlap. In the right-hand diagram, the region of the Poodles circle that is outside of the Dogs circle is empty because there are no poodles that are not dogs.

   It is perfectly okay for Venn diagrams to contain empty regions, especially if you're not sure how the members of the different sets are related. For example, if you didn't know what poodles and dogs were, you would have to draw the diagram of the statement "Some dogs are poodles" as two overlapping circles.

THREE LOOPS

In how many ways can three loops be drawn? They can be inside each other, intersect in some way, or not intersect at all. Work this problem before continuing.

   This problem is pretty complex. You have to draw the loops somewhat systematically to avoid leaving any out or repeating yourself. The solution shown on the next page starts with the three possibilities for the two smaller loops: one inside the other, both intersecting, and both **disjoint** (not intersecting at all). Then the third, largest loop is added. It starts out containing the two smaller loops and gradually moves to a position disjoint with both of them. The arrows shown connecting certain pairs of diagrams indicate that the two diagrams are equivalent. (The sizes of loops are not significant except to permit the enclosure of one within another to show a subset-set relationship.)

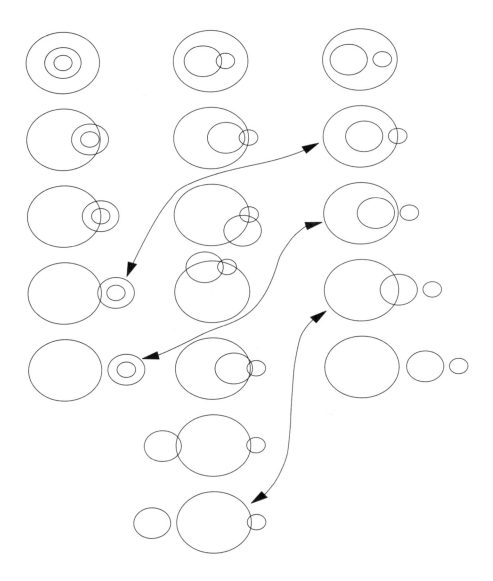

Now that you have drawn the different possible arrangements of three loops, consider the following problems. For each one, draw a Venn diagram that shows the relationships among the given categories. In each problem, one of the categories describes the universal set and the other categories describe the various loops inside the universal set. The universal set is not necessarily listed first.

1. Household pets, dogs, animals, cats

2. Living things, lizards, apes, chimpanzees, reptiles, dogs, mammals, terriers, dachshunds

3. Place of birth, USA, Canada, Miami, Florida, Orlando, Montreal, Missouri

4. Universities, private schools, public schools, Yale, University of Texas at El Paso (UTEP), Notre Dame

5. Trumpets, pianos, musical instruments, clarinets, violins, trombones, brass, woodwinds

6. Water vessels, submarines, war boats, sailboats, battleships, ferries

7. Cows, brown, black, white, dairy, old (these cows can be only one color)

8. Hamburgers, with cheese, double, homemade

Work this problem before continuing.

Are your Venn diagrams equivalent to Takashi's solutions, shown below? If not, how does your interpretation of the relationships differ?

1. Household pets, dogs, animals, cats

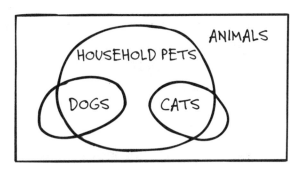

2. Living things, lizards, apes, chimpanzees, reptiles, dogs, mammals, terriers, dachshunds

3. Place of birth, USA, Canada, Miami, Florida, Orlando, Montreal, Missouri

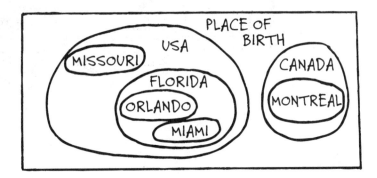

4. Universities, private schools, public schools, Yale, UTEP, Notre Dame

Note that Yale, Notre Dame, and UTEP are shown as points in the diagram, not in circles that represent subsets. These schools are not subsets because each of them is a *single* university, not a set of universities.

5. Trumpets, pianos, musical instruments, clarinets, violins, trombones, brass, woodwinds

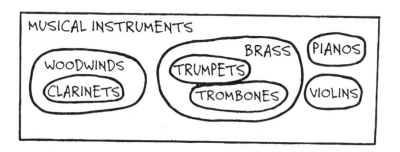

6. Water vessels, submarines, war boats, sailboats, battleships, ferries

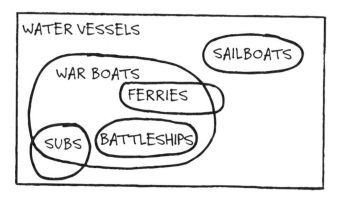

7. Cows, brown, black, white, dairy, old

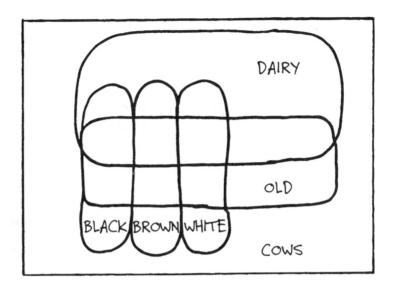

(You might wish to spend a few weeks of your life trying to solve the version of this problem that allows for multicolored cows.)

8. Hamburgers, with cheese, double, homemade

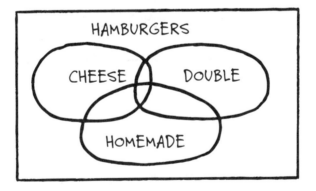

Now you are ready to solve some problems by using Venn diagrams. Draw the diagrams, then fill in the numbers from the problems as they fit.

In a group of students, 12 are taking chemistry, 10 are taking physics, 3 are taking both chemistry and physics, and 5 are taking neither chemistry nor physics. How many students are in the group? Work this problem before continuing.

Bryndyn and Toi worked together on this problem.

BRYN: Man, this problem is so easy. There are 12 in chemistry, 10 in physics, 3 in both, and 5 in neither. So that is a total of $12 + 10 + 3 + 5 = 30$ students in all.

TOI: Yeah, that sounds right. But aren't we supposed to be drawing a Penn diagram to solve these problems, the ones with the circles drawn in pen?

BRYN: A Venn diagram. V-v-v-venn. And we can draw the circles in vencils—I mean pencils—if we want. Let's try that. I guess we need one loop to represent the students that are in chemistry and another loop to represent the students that are in physics.

TOI: Should the circles overlap?

BRYN: I'm not sure. What do you think?

TOI: I think they need to overlap, and the spot where the circles come together, the intersection, will represent the students who are taking both classes. But where do we put the students who aren't taking either class?

BRYN: I guess they should go outside of both circles. Maybe we should draw a big rectangle around the whole thing.

TOI: Yeah, the universal set. That can be students.

BRYN: Okay, let's try drawing this thing. Why don't you draw it.

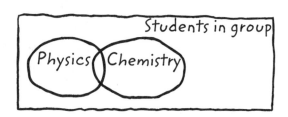

TOI: Okay, there's our Venn diagram. Now what do we do with these numbers?

BRYN: Well, let's see. Let's put the 12 chemistry students in the chemistry-student loop and the 10 physics students in the physics-student loop.

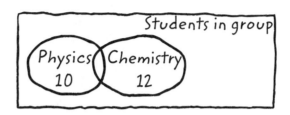

TOI: And put in the 3 students who are in both classes and the 5 that aren't taking either class.

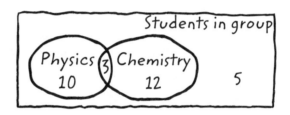

BRYN: Now let's see. That is $10 + 12 + 3 + 5 = 30$ students altogether. And that's what we got before, so it must be right.

TOI: Great. Wait, wait, wait a minute. Something's wrong here.

BRYN: What? It looks fine to me.

TOI: Aren't we counting the people who are taking both classes twice? From the looks of this diagram, there are 13 students taking physics and 15 taking chemistry.

BRYN: How do you figure that?

TOI: Well, look at the physics loop. Those 3 students in the intersection are taking physics, right?

BRYN: Yeah, so what?

TOI: Well, that means we have 3 students in the intersection taking physics and chemistry, and 10 students in the outer portion of the physics circle taking physics and not taking chemistry. That means we have 13 students taking physics.

BRYN: Oh, I see what you mean. And by the same logic, we have 15 students taking chemistry.

TOI: So what can we do about this?

BRYN: Maybe we better start over. I think our original diagram is fine. So let's work with the numbers again.

TOI: Yeah, let's start by putting in the 3 students who are taking both courses in the intersection of the two loops.

BRYN: That sounds like the working-backwards method we just learned.

TOI: Yeah, it does. Okay, of the 12 students taking chemistry, 3 of them are taking both chemistry and physics. This leaves 9 students taking chemistry but not physics.

BRYN: So let's fill in 9 in the section of the chemistry loop that is outside the physics loop.

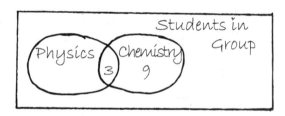

TOI: Yeah, that looks great. Now let's do the same thing for the physics loop.

BRYN: Of the 10 students taking physics, 3 of them are taking both chemistry and physics. This leaves 7 students taking physics but not chemistry. So fill in 7 in the section of the physics loop that represents physics only.

TOI: Great. Now put in the 5 students taking neither course outside of the two loops.

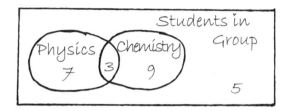

BRYN: Now let's answer the question. The question asks for the number of students in the group. So $7 + 3 + 9 + 5 =$ 24 students.

TOI: So, before, we were counting those students who took both classes three times: once in the physics category, once in the chemistry category, and once in the both category.

BRYN: You're right. It did seem too easy the other way. These Venn diagrams really help.

MUSIC SURVEY

In a poll of 46 students, 23 liked rap music, 24 liked rock music, and 19 liked country music. Of all the students, 12 liked rap and country, 13 liked rap and rock, and 14 liked country and rock. Of those students, 9 liked all three types of music. How many students did not like any of these types? Work this problem before continuing.

There are three categories in this problem, so you need to draw three loops. Because it is possible to like two or three types of music at once, the three loops must intersect as shown in the diagram on the next page.

Tony worked on this problem. He succeeded in drawing the three loops, but after that point he was stuck. Maria joined him.

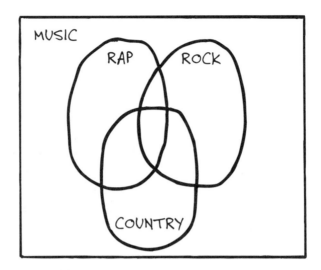

TONY: I can't figure out what to do with this diagram.

MARIA: Well, let's figure out what each section represents. Let's label each section with a letter.

You may not need to label sections, or regions, with letters when you are solving problems, but if you do, be sure you know what each section represents. Before reading on, figure out what type or types of music each section represents in this problem's diagram.

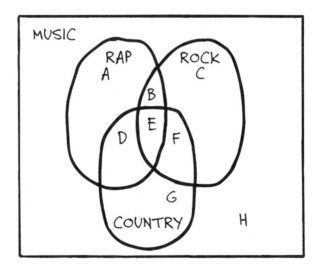

MARIA: The sections represent students who like the following types of music:

$$A = \text{Rap only, not rock nor country}$$
$$B = \text{Rap and rock, not country}$$
$$C = \text{Rock only, not rap nor country}$$
$$D = \text{Rap and country, not rock}$$
$$E = \text{Rap, country, and rock}$$
$$F = \text{Rock and country, not rap}$$
$$G = \text{Country only, not rap nor rock}$$
$$H = \text{None of the three types of music}$$

For this problem we won't show intermediate diagrams. If you haven't been able to solve this problem yet, draw the diagram shown above onto another piece of paper and fill in the numbers as Maria and Tony go through their explanation. We'll show the completed diagram at the end of the solution.

TONY: Okay, I get that. So now what do we do? How do we put the numbers in?

MARIA: Remember the strategy we learned last week?

TONY: You mean working backwards?

MARIA: Yes. So let's work backwards, starting with the last clue. There are 9 students who like all three types of music. This is region E in our Venn diagram, so enter 9 in region E.

TONY: Okay, I get that too. So now we should consider the students who like exactly two types of music. There are 12 students who like rap and country. But how do we put that in the diagram?

MARIA: This encompasses regions D and E, since region D is students who like rap and country and not rock, and region E is students who like all three types of music, which of course includes rap and country. We already have 9 students in region E. This leaves 3 students $(12 - 9)$ in region D.

TONY: This is starting to make sense. Let me do the next one. Thirteen students like rap and rock. This encompasses regions B and E. We already have 9 students in region E, so this leaves 4 students for region B.

MARIA: Great, you're catching on. There are 14 students who like rock and country. This encompasses regions F and E. Since we still have 9 students in region E, this leaves 5 students in region F. But I'm not really sure what to do next. This is as far as I got before I came over to work with you.

TONY: Well, let's keep on working backwards. Now we have to consider the students who like only one type of music. Region G is the students who like country only. We were told that there were 19 students who like country. So far we have 17 students who like country and something else. The country circle encompasses regions D, E, F, and G. Region D has 3 students, region E has 9, and region F has 5. This adds to 17. Since there are 19 students who like country, we have 2 students left who like country but none of the other types. Therefore, put 2 in region G.

MARIA: Okay, I see. Let me do one. The rock circle encompasses regions B, C, E, and F. We already have 4 students in region B, 9 in region E, and 5 in region F. This adds to 18. Since we were told that there are 24 students who like rock music, we have 6 students left over (24 − 18) that just like rock music. So put 6 in region C.

TONY: Great. The rap circle encompasses regions A, B, D, and E. We already have 4 students in region B, 3 in region D, and 9 in region E. This adds to 16. Since we were told that there are 23 students who like rap, this leaves 7 students (23 − 16) who like rap only. So put 7 in region A. And now we're done.

MARIA: No we aren't. We haven't answered the question. How many students didn't like any of the three types of music?

TONY: Maria, Maria, Maria, how are we going to answer that?

MARIA: Let's add up all of the numbers in the regions we have so far: 7 + 4 + 6 + 3 + 9 + 5 + 2 = 36 students.

TONY: But wait, there are supposed to be 46 students because that's what it said. We're off by 10. We messed up.

MARIA: No we didn't. This just leaves 10 students (46 − 36) who don't like any of these three types of music. So put 10 in region H.

TONY: Okay, I see. Now we can answer the question. So, there are 10 students who do not like any of these types of music. Maybe they just like musicals.

Here is the final diagram.

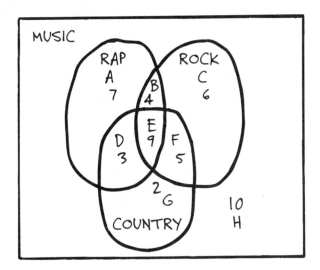

There are 23 students in a homeroom. Eighteen are taking mathematics and 15 are taking science. Six students are taking mathematics but not science. How many are taking neither subject? Work this problem before continuing.

This problem is similar to the Science Courses problem. It also features two circles, one labeled Math and one labeled Science. The circles intersect because it is possible to take both subjects. The region outside of a circle represents those students who are not taking that subject. Debbie's diagram is shown below.

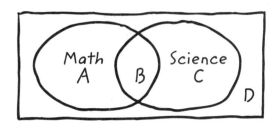

"I sometimes get really confused by these problems, so I decided to label the regions."

A = Students who are taking math but not science
B = Students who are taking both math and science
C = Students who are taking science but not math
D = Students who are taking neither math nor science

As with the Music Survey problem, we will not show intermediate diagrams, so follow along on another sheet of paper. We'll show the complete diagram at the end of the solution.

Debbie went on: "Once I had the regions labeled, it didn't seem that hard. The problem states that there are 6 students who are taking math but not science. So put 6 in region A. The problem states that there are 18 students who are taking math. But I already have 6 in region A, and the students who are taking math are all contained in either A or B. So there must be 12 students (18 − 6) in region B. These 12 students are taking both math and science. There are 15 students who are taking science (and may or may not be taking math), so this leaves 3 students (15 − 12) in region C who are taking only science. There are supposed to be 23 students in the group. I added up the numbers in the diagram so far (6 + 12 + 3) and got 21. This leaves 2 students (23 − 21) for region D. The question asked how many students were taking neither subject. This is region D, so the answer is 2."

The final diagram is shown below.

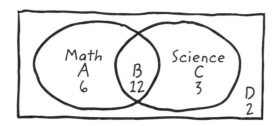

SPRING ROSTER

A manager of a baseball team looked over his roster at the beginning of spring training. He noticed the following facts: Every outfielder is a switch hitter. Half of all infielders are switch hitters. Half of all switch hitters are outfielders. There are 14 infielders and 8 outfielders. No infielder is an outfielder.

How many switch hitters are neither outfielders nor infielders? Work this problem before continuing.

This problem is quite different from those you've been working on so far. It is not obvious from reading the problem what the Venn diagram looks like.

Start with the outfielders and the switch hitters. The problem states that all outfielders are switch hitters. This means that the outfielder loop must be completely contained within the switch-hitter loop. So draw two loops, with the outfielder loop inside the switch-hitter loop as shown in the diagram below. In the diagram, abbreviate switch hitters as SH, outfielders as OF, and infielders as IF. (Abbreviating like this can qualify as an easier related problem, especially if the categories are rather nonsensical. You might **notice** one such problem in the problem set.)

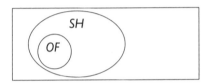

Now consider the infielders. The problem states that half of all infielders are switch hitters. This means that the infielder loop must intersect the switch-hitter loop. The problem also states that no infielder is an outfielder. So although the infielder loop intersects the switch hitter loop, it does not intersect the outfielder loop. The expanded diagram is shown below.

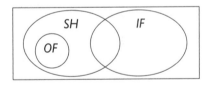

Now consider the numbers given in the problem. It says there are 14 infielders and 8 outfielders. Of the 14 infielders, half of them are switch hitters. Therefore, 7 of the 14 infielders *are* switch hitters, and 7 of the 14 infielders *are not* switch hitters. So put 7 in the intersection of the infielder and switch-hitter loops, and put 7 in the infielders-only part of the infielder loop. Also, put 8 in the outfielder loop, because the problem states there are 8 outfielders.

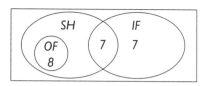

Finally, consider the statement "Half of all switch hitters are outfielders." Because the 8 outfielders represent half of all of the switch hitters, there must be 16 switch hitters. So far, the diagram shows 8 outfielders (all of whom are switch hitters) and 7 infielders who are switch hitters. These add to 15 switch hitters. So there must be one more switch hitter. This switch hitter is neither an outfielder nor an infielder (maybe he is a catcher). So he must go outside of the outfielder and infielder loops, but inside the switch-hitter loop. The final diagram is shown below.

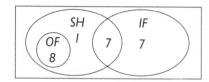

Now answer the question posed by the problem. How many switch hitters are neither outfielders nor infielders? A quick look at the diagram shows the answer to be 1.

You can't use Venn diagrams on very many problems, but they are very effective to use with those problems for which a Venn diagram is appropriate. The diagram organizes information spatially and enables you to consider many different pieces of information at the same time. They are usually quick and easy to use, and can often solve problems that are very confusing when worked with another strategy.

Problem Set A

1. SENIOR CLASS

There are 100 students in the senior class. Twenty-five are on the Mathletes team. Forty students are on the football team. Ten are on both teams. How many are on neither team?

2. HAMBURGERS AND HOT DOGS

Of 900 people interviewed, 254 said they liked only hamburgers, 461 said they liked only hot dogs, and 140 people liked both hamburgers and hot dogs. How many of the people interviewed didn't like either?

3. ROCK BAND

In a third-rate rock band, three play guitar, four sing, and two do both. Six have no talent for singing or guitar, so they do something else. How many members are in the rock band?

4. EATING VEGETABLES

The staff at Tiny Little Cherubs (abbreviated TLC) day-care center observed the eating habits of their 64 students during several lunches. They observed that 59 children ate green beans, 56 ate cauliflower, 60 ate broccoli, 55 ate green beans and cauliflower, 54 ate cauliflower and broccoli, 56 ate green beans and broccoli, and 53 ate all three. How many children did not eat any of these three types of vegetables? How many children ate green beans but not cauliflower? How many children did not eat broccoli? How many children ate only cauliflower? And how many children ate exactly two types of vegetables?

5. **THE FIELD TRIPS**

The Silversnake class, the Jellyfish class, and the Radical Dog-Star class (kindergartners and first- and second-graders) were talking about their favorite field trips during the school year. One of the teachers, Ms. Burke, turned the discussion into a math lesson, and the students conducted a survey. Each child wrote down on paper which trip was his or her favorite. (**Note** that many children named more than one field trip as their favorite.) The survey revealed that 52 wrote down the trip to the river, 50 indicated the trip to the police station, and 44 included the trip to the hardware store. Nineteen papers showed the police station and the river. Thirty-two papers included both the river and the hardware store, and 25 children wrote down the police station and the hardware store on their papers. Seventeen students included all three, and one did not write down any of the three trips. How many children were surveyed?

6. **FAMILY REUNION**

At one family reunion, every niece was a cousin. Half of all aunts were cousins. Half of all cousins were nieces. There were 50 aunts and 30 nieces. No aunt was a niece. How many cousins were neither nieces nor aunts?

7. **JUST WHAT ARE THESE THINGS, ANYWAY?**

All DERFs are ENAJs. One-third of all ENAJs are DERFs. Half of all SIVADs are ENAJs. One SIVAD is a DERF. Eight SIVADs are ENAJs. There are 90 ENAJs. Draw the Venn diagram. How many ENAJs are neither DERFs nor SIVADs?

8. **BLOOD LINES**

Human blood is classified O, A, B, or AB, depending upon whether the blood contains no antigen, an A antigen, a B antigen, or both the A and B antigens. A third antigen, called the Rh antigen, is important to human reproduction. Blood is said to be Rh-positive if it contains this Rh antigen; otherwise, the blood is Rh-negative. So for instance, blood is type A+ if it contains the A antigen and the Rh antigen. Blood is type AB− if it contains the A and B antigens but does not contain the Rh antigen.

(This problem is continued on the next page.)

In a hospital the following data was recorded:

- Twenty-two people were either type A or type AB, sixteen of which had the Rh antigen.

- Twenty-seven were either type B or type AB, eighteen of which had the Rh antigen.

- Eight were type AB, two of which were AB−.

- Thirty-five were type O, five of which were O−.

How many patients are listed here? How many patients have type B+ blood? How many patients have type A− blood? How many have exactly two antigens?

9. WRITE YOUR OWN

Write your own Venn diagram problem. It's easiest to create Venn diagrams that contain just two circles, but if you're feeling ambitious, try a diagram with three circles. Draw the diagrams first and fill in all the numbers. Then create the clues. Here's an example:

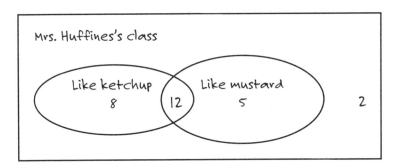

This diagram will serve as the basis for the problem Ben is writing. He notes the following clues:

1. There are 27 students in Mrs. Huffines's class.

2. Eight students like ketchup but do not like mustard.

3. Five students like mustard but do not like ketchup.

4. Twelve students like both ketchup and mustard.

5. Two students like neither ketchup nor mustard.

At this point, Ben can finish the problem by erasing one of the clues. Ben chose to erase clue number 4. He then wrote a question based on the clue he crossed out: "How many students like both ketchup and mustard?"

You don't need to follow Ben's example for creating a Venn diagram problem, but if you're struggling with creating your own problem, give his example some consideration.

Problem Set B: A Family Holiday

1. **HOLIDAY PASTRIES**

Every year, as part of the Family family traditions during the holidays, the whole family bakes something to give to their friends and relatives. This year they decided to make some special pastries. Mama Family was very careful to make sure they baked plenty so there would be plenty to give away. If there was anything the family liked better than baking, it was eating what they baked. So during the night, Papa got up and ate one-third of the pastries. As he started back to bed, he noticed his dog looking very hungry, so he gave one pastry to his dog. Ed was the next to get up. He planned to eat one-fourth of the pastries, but when he separated them into four piles, he found there were three pastries left over. He fed those three pastries to his dog and then ate one-fourth of the remaining pastries. Lisa then got up and ate one-third of the remaining pastries. As she was heading back to bed, her dog whined, so she gave it two pastries. Judy was the last to get up, and she consumed eight pastries but then gave one-eighth of the remaining pastries to her dog. When Mama went into the kitchen the next morning, she found a lot of crumbs, ants, and only 14 pastries. Mama sighed, realizing that again this year they would have no pastries to give away. She ate two, gave two to her dog, and then split the remaining pastries evenly for her whole family, including herself, to have for breakfast. How many pastries did the family bake originally, and how many pastries did each person consume?

2

PRESENTS, OH BOY!

The Family family had two of the kids' cousins, Gail and Randy, over for holiday gift-giving. The Family kids are, of course, named Ed, Lisa, and Judy. The Family parents bought presents for all five kids, but they forgot to buy wrapping paper. Consequently, the gifts were wrapped in strange ways, although every gift was wrapped in something different. One of the gifts was wrapped in a towel.

Interestingly enough, the kids' heights were exactly three inches apart—their heights were 59, 62, 65, 68, and 71 inches.

From the clues that follow, determine the height of each child, the gift received, and the strange way in which it was wrapped.

1. The one who received a set of Legos is three inches shorter than the one who received a gift wrapped in a pillowcase.

2. The child who received shoes is not 59 inches tall but is shorter than the child who received the picture.

3. Randy is shorter than the child who got the belt and one other child, but he is taller than both Gail and the child whose gift was wrapped in a plastic bag.

4. Ed is taller than the one whose present was packaged in a box.

5. The child who received a gift packaged in newspaper is shorter than both Lisa and the child who received candy.

6. The child whose gift was wrapped in a pillowcase is not in the same immediate family as the child who received the belt.

LEGO MY PYRAMID

Of all the presents, the biggest hit was the Legos. None of the kids had played with Legos for years, and they all took turns building things. One of the really great structures built was a sort of pyramid built out of square Legos. It began with a single two-by-two square Lego. Then four squares were attached underneath it, which left a strip one bump wide showing all the way around the outside. This pattern was continued for a total of ten layers. Although the pyramid could have been built by just putting Legos on the perimeter of each layer, they filled in each layer on the underside of the pyramid. How many bumps were showing, and how many Legos were used to make the pyramid?

4. THE HOLIDAY PARTY

After opening up all the presents, the Family family went to Grandma and Grandpa's house for the big Family family holiday party. Judy, who was interested in statistics, went around asking questions of everyone and recording their responses. She collected the following data: Every nephew was a cousin. Half of all uncles were cousins. One-third of all cousins were nephews. There were 30 uncles and 20 nephews. One-sixth of all uncles were nephews. She herself was a cousin but not a nephew or an uncle.

Judy wanted to know two things: She wanted to know how many cousins were neither nephews nor uncles. She also wanted to know how many uncles were also cousins but not nephews. Can you help?

5. HOLIDAY DINNER

The whole Family clan went out to dinner. The menu read as follows:

First course: chicken vegetable soup, shrimp salad, fruit salad

Second course: shrimp, vegetable casserole, beef, chicken

Third course: apple pie, carrot cake, ice cream

Papa wants everyone to order a different meal. (**Note** that soup, beef, and pie would be different from soup, beef, and cake.) Papa wants to know if there are enough different meals available that consist of one item from each course. However, he does not want any of the meals to include the same kind of food more than once during the meal. For example, if Ed ordered shrimp salad, then he could not order shrimp for the second course. You may assume that the items containing vegetables contain carrots and that the fruit salad contains apples. How many such meals are possible?

Ice climbers use various tools together, such as crampons and ice axes, to scale the sides of mountains. Using the tools together rather than separately makes a difficult climb much easier.

13

Algebra

S o far, you haven't needed much algebra to solve the problems in this book. This chapter will focus on algebra as a tool for problem solving. We saved this chapter for the last part of the book for the following reasons:

- If you have taken any typical high school mathematics class, algebra is already a very familiar problem-solving strategy. We postponed having you solve problems algebraically because we wanted you to strengthen your confidence in your problem-solving abilities by using several strategies that didn't require algebra.

- Algebra is emphasized as a problem-solving strategy in many texts. In fact, most texts feature a five-step problem-solving process: read the problem, choose a variable, write an equation, solve the equation, check the solution. This process can give the impression that all problems you'll ever encounter can be solved with an equation. If you can't come up with the equation, you might say, "I can solve the equation once I have it, but I can never set it up." The skills you developed in the earlier chapters of this book—such as drawing a diagram, solving subproblems, and using guess-and-check—will help you build algebraic equations.

- As you advance in the study of mathematics, finding physical representations of problems becomes increasingly difficult. Even problems that are direct adaptations of real-world problems, such as the rate of flow of water through a pipe, require such complex models that reasonable representations are impractical. Therefore, as you progress in your mathematics studies, you need to become increasingly capable of converting problems into mathematical equations—this is a necessary skill.

  But many people won't study or use math at a level where models are difficult. This is why the many problem-solving strategies in this book are so important—they are greatly needed. A person solving a real-world problem is more likely to have to draw a picture than to write an equation.

- Algebra alone is not *the* problem-solving strategy. Of course algebra is a tremendously effective tool, but some problems cannot be solved algebraically. In fact, many problems can be solved much more effectively when some other problem-solving strategy is used in conjunction with algebra.

Algebra is a powerful tool that falls under the major problem-solving theme of Organizing Information. Like many other tools, it reaches its peak power when it's used in conjunction with complementary tools. This chapter will focus on using algebra in conjunction with the problem-solving strategies you've learned about in this book. We assume that you already have a working knowledge of algebra, so this book doesn't include algebra instruction. Instead, it offers instruction on combining algebra with other problem-solving strategies.

We will revisit many problems from previous chapters, especially Chapter 6: Guess-and-Check. In that chapter we mentioned that guess-and-check really helps to set up the algebra in a problem that requires an equation. The problems in Chapter 6 were solvable by using only guess-and-check, but in this chapter you'll use guess-and-check as a means to get to an equation. (Some of the equations will involve one variable and some will involve two.)

SATURDAY AT THE FIVE-AND-DIME GARAGE SALE

 Sandy held a garage sale, during which she charged a dime for everything but accepted a nickel if the buyer bargained well. At the end of the day she realized she had sold all 12 items and raked in a grand total of 95 cents. She had only dimes and nickels. How many of each coin did she have?

See if you can re-create the guess-and-check chart for this problem without looking back at Chapter 6.

Here is the chart:

Dimes	Nickels	Value of Dimes	Value of Nickels	Total Value	Rating
5	7	$0.50	$0.35	$0.85	low
8	4	$0.80	$0.20	$1.00	high

The chart ends before the right answer is reached. Now the objective is to set up an equation. Mike and Pat each solved this problem algebraically after they set up a guess-and-check chart.

Here's Mike's reasoning for using algebra instead of guess-and-check to solve the problem: "Sometimes guess-and-check takes too long. I'm usually pretty good at it, but I tend to get bored. So I made a couple of guesses, and then I tried to set up the equation. Since I was guessing the number of dimes, I decided to call the number of dimes d. So I wrote down d in the dimes column under the 8."

Dimes	Nickels	Value of Dimes	Value of Nickels	Total Value	Rating
5	7	$0.50	$0.35	$0.85	low
8	4	$0.80	$0.20	$1.00	high
d					

"Then I tried to figure out what to put in the nickels column. I noticed that in my guesses so far, the dimes column and the nickels column added up to 12. So the difference between 12 and d should be the number of nickels. So I wrote down $d - 12$ in the nickels column. I was working with my friend Amy, and she pointed out that $d - 12$ was wrong. For instance, if $d = 8$, then $d - 12$ would be -4 and that wouldn't make sense. She said it should be $12 - d$. I checked that with the two guesses I had already made, and it made sense because $12 - 8 = 4$ and $12 - 5 = 7$. So I put $12 - d$ in the nickels column."

Dimes	Nickels	Value of Dimes	Value of Nickels	Total Value	Rating
5	7	$0.50	$0.35	$0.85	low
8	4	$0.80	$0.20	$1.00	high
d	12 − d				

"Again I looked back at my guesses. Where did I get the amount of money in the Value of Dimes and Value of Nickels columns? I realized right away that they came from the number of dimes times 10 cents and the number of nickels times 5 cents. So all I had to do was multiply d times 10 cents and $12 - d$ times 5 cents. So I did that."

Dimes	Nickels	Value of Dimes	Value of Nickels	Total Value	Rating
5	7	$0.50	$0.35	$0.85	low
8	4	$0.80	$0.20	$1.00	high
d	$12 - d$	$(0.10)d$	$(0.05)(12-d)$		

"It seemed like things were working really well so far. Finally, I figured out that my Total Value column came from adding up the Value of Dimes and Value of Nickels columns. So I wrote that down. Then I realized that this total value was supposed to be 95 cents. So I set the Total Value column equal to 95 cents, and I had my equation. While I was writing this, I decided that it would be easier to use cents instead of dollars, so I changed all the dollar values to cents by multiplying them by 100."

Dimes	Nickels	Value of Dimes	Value of Nickels	Total Value
5	7	50	35	85
8	4	80	20	100
d	$12 - d$	$10d$	$5(12-d)$	$10d + 5(12 - d) = 95$

"Of course, solving this equation was really easy."

$$10d + 5(12 - d) = 95$$
$$10d + 60 - 5d = 95$$
$$5d + 60 = 95$$
$$5d = 35$$
$$d = 7$$

"It's funny, but when I used to solve problems in algebra class, I would always write down the value of the variable as the answer to the problem. So I would write down $d = 7$ as the answer. But guess-and-check really helps me to answer the question asked in this problem. 'How many of each did she have?' I'd only figured out dimes so far, so I went back to my chart and figured out that the number of nickels she had was five because $12 - 7 = 5$. So the answer is she has seven dimes and five nickels."

Pat solved this problem in a similar way, but she decided to use two variables instead of one. So where Mike used $12 - d$ to represent nickels, Pat used n to represent nickels. Her chart looks like this:

# of Dimes	# of Nickels	Total Coins	Value of Dimes	Value of Nickels	Total Value	Rating
5	5	10	$0.50	$0.25	$0.75	low-low
2	14	16	$0.20	$0.70	$0.95	high-right
8	4	12	$0.80	$0.20	$1.00	right-high
d	n	$d + n$	$(0.10)d$	$(0.5)n$	$(0.10)d + (0.5)n = 0.95$	

Pat came up with a system of two equations and two variables. One equation is $(0.10)d + (0.5)n = 0.95$, or $10d + 5n = 95$ if you change dollars to cents. But what is her other equation? It comes from the third column in the chart. The total number of coins is $d + n$ and is supposed to equal 12, so the other equation is $d + n = 12$. Solving:

$$d + n = 12$$
$$10d + 5n = 95$$

$$-5d + -5n = -60$$
$$\underline{10d + 5n = 95}$$
$$5d = 35$$
$$d = 7$$

$$d + n = 12$$
$$7 + n = 12$$
$$n = 5$$

So again, the answer to the problem is seven dimes and five nickels.

FARMER JONES

Farmer Jones raises ducks and cows. She tries not to clutter her mind with too many details, but she does think it's important to remember how many animals she has and how many feet those animals have. She thinks she remembers having 54 animals with 122 feet. How many of each type of animal does Farmer Jones have? Again, re-create the guess-and-check chart for this problem. Then set up the equation, or equations, to solve the problem algebraically.

Imogen used the guess-and-check chart shown below. She guessed the number of ducks. To find the number of cows, she simply subtracted the number of ducks from 54 because there were 54 animals altogether. She easily figured out the number of feet for each kind of animal and checked to see if there were 122 feet.

Ducks	Duck Feet	Cows	Cow Feet	Total Feet	Check
20	40	34	136	176	high
40	80	15	56	136	high
50	100	4	16	116	low
d	$2d$	$54 - d$	$4(54 - d)$	$2d + 4(54 - d)$	

Imogen was checking the Total Feet column, and she knew the total feet had to be 122 feet, so the equation was right there for the taking: $2d + 4(54 - d) = 122$. (**Remember** that when you set up an equation, you need to find two things that are supposed to equal each other.)

$$2d + 4(54 - d) = 122$$
$$2d + 216 - 4d = 122$$
$$-2d + 216 = 122$$
$$-2d = -94$$
$$d = 47$$

Therefore, there are 47 ducks and 7 cows. (She found the number of cows by subtracting the 47 ducks from 54 animals.)

When you move from guess-and-check to algebra to solve a problem, you must do exactly what you did in the guess-and-check version but you must use a different "language." In the Farmer Jones problem, you got from ducks to duck feet simply by multiplying by 2. The first guess was 20 ducks, so the number of duck feet was $2 \times 20 = 40$. This is a very simple procedure, but some students have a difficult time translating the guess-and-check language into the algebra language because they're unsure of how to proceed. To move from one language to the other, ask the question "What did I do to get this number?" Whatever the answer is, the procedure for the arithmetic guess and the algebraic guess is the same. Because the arithmetic procedure was to multiply by 2, the algebraic procedure is also to multiply by 2. So, to move from ducks, d, to ducks feet, you'd simply multiply d by 2.

Once you have the algebraic language you want, the next thing to do is to write the equation. An **equation** is simply two **expressions** connected with an equals sign. If the two expressions are supposed to be equal, then you have a valid equation. In most problems, the equation jumps out of the last or next-to-last column. In the Farmer Jones problem, the equation came from the last numeric column (Total Feet) and a known amount (122) was supposed to equal the total feet.

ALL AROUND THE PLAYING FIELD

The perimeter of a rectangular playing field measures 504 yards. Its length is 6 yards shorter than twice its width. What is its area? Set up the guess-and-check chart for this problem and then write the equation.

Sheri's chart is shown below.

Width	Length	Perimeter	
100	194	588	High
60	114	348	Low
80	154	468	Low

Sheri was guessing the width, so she decided to let that be her variable and she called it w. Now, where did she get the length? "The problem says that the length was 6 yards shorter than twice the width. For instance, $100 \times 2 = 200$ would be twice the width. The length is 6 yards shorter than that, so $200 - 6 = 194$. So if I'm letting w stand for width, then length must be $2w - 6$. The perimeter is twice the sum of the length and width. So it's 2 times the quantity $w + 2w - 6$, and it's supposed to be 504 yards."

Width	Length	Perimeter	
100	194	588	High
60	114	348	Low
80	154	468	Low
w	2w − 6	2(w + 2w − 6) = 504	

When using algebra to solve problems, be careful to set up the equation correctly. Sheri had little difficulty changing her guesses into an algebraic representation, using only three columns to solve this problem. But **be careful:** Using too few columns for guess-and-check charts is asking for trouble. If it works, fine, but if you find yourself getting stuck on these types of problems, make a habit of setting up more columns. Here's another way Sheri could have set up her guess-and-check chart:

Width	2 × Width	Length	Perimeter	
100	200	194	588	High
60	120	114	348	Low
80	160	154	468	Low
w	2w	2w − 6	2(w + 2w − 6) = 504	

The second column isn't completely necessary, but it helps by showing all the information pertinent to the problem. Again, if you find that you're a little confused by a problem, try using more columns. Those who have trouble understanding their own charts tend to be those who try to do a problem with too few columns.

Solving the equation is straightforward.

$$2(w + 2w − 6) = 504$$
$$2(3w − 6) = 504$$
$$6w − 12 = 504$$
$$6w = 516$$
$$w = 86$$

So, the length is 2(86) − 6 = 166. Check the perimeter:
86 + 166 = 252, and 252 × 2 = 504. The length is 166 yards, and the
width is 86 yards. But the question asked for the area. The area of the
field is 166 yards × 86 yards = 14,276 square yards.

ORIGAMI

A group of exchange students from Japan went to a convalescent home to
sing songs for the seniors and to demonstrate origami, the art of Japanese
paper folding. Groups of students and seniors sat together at tables so the
students could teach the seniors to fold origami models. As it turned out, at
each table there was either 1 student at a table with 3 seniors, or 2 students
at a table with 4 seniors. There were 23 students and 61 seniors in all. How
many tables were being used? Work this problem before continuing.

Manmeet solved this problem. "I started out using guess-and-check
because the problem really confused me. I guessed the number of each
kind of table and then figured out how many students (ST) and how
many seniors (SN) were at each one. I checked by figuring out the total
number (T) of students and seniors and then comparing the totals to
23 and 61. I used 1|3 to stand for tables with 1 student and 3 seniors,
and 2|4 for the other kind."

1|3 tables			2|4 tables			Total ST 23	SN 61	Rating
T	ST	SN	T	ST	SN			
10	10	30	10	20	40	30	70	high-high
5	5	15	5	10	20	15	35	low-low
8	8	24	8	16	32	24	56	high-low
5	5	15	9	18	36	23	51	right-low
5	5	15	10	20	40	25	55	high-low

"At this point, I was really frustrated. I was guessing two things, but
I wasn't sure how to get closer to the right answer. I also thought that
my first two guesses meant that the right answer was somewhere
between 10 and 5 for each kind of table. But that didn't seem to work

either. So I stopped using guess-and-check and switched to algebra. I called the number of 1|3 tables x and the number of 2|4 tables y. Then I just did the same thing to x and y that I'd done to the number guesses."

	1|3 tables			2|4 tables		Total ST 23	SN 61	
T	ST	SN	T	ST	SN	ST	SN	Rating
10	10	30	10	20	40	30	70	high-high
5	5	15	5	10	20	15	35	low-low
8	8	24	8	16	32	24	56	high-low
5	5	15	9	18	36	23	51	right-low
5	5	15	10	20	40	25	55	high-low
x	x	$3x$	y	$2y$	$4y$	$x+2y$	$3x+4y$	

"Then I knew that the total number of students had to be 23 and the total number of seniors had to be 61, so I just wrote two equations and solved them."

$$x + 2y = 23$$
$$3x + 4y = 61$$

$\rightarrow$
$\rightarrow$

$$-2x - 4y = -46$$
$$\underline{3x + 4y = 61}$$
$$x = 15$$

$$x + 2y = 23$$
$$15 + 2y = 23$$
$$2y = 8$$
$$y = 4$$

"There were 15 tables that held 1 student and 3 seniors, and 4 tables that held 2 students and 4 seniors. I checked this too. There are $15 \times 1 + 4 \times 2 = 23$ students and $15 \times 3 + 4 \times 4 = 61$ seniors, which works out."

Cloe is two years less than four times as old as Zeke. Cloe is also one year more than three times as old as Zeke. How old is each? Solve this problem by using guess-and-check to set up the algebra before continuing.

The guess-and-check chart from Chapter 6 is shown below.

ZEKE'S AGE	4x ZEKE	CLOE'S AGE 4x ZEKE −2	3x ZEKE	CLOE'S AGE 3x ZEKE +1	RATING
1	4	2	3	4	WRONG
2	8	6	6	7	CLOSER
4	16	14	12	13	HIGH (3RD COL. HIGHER THAN 5TH)
b	$4b$	$4b - 2$	$3b$	$3b + 1$	

In the Zeke's Age column, Zeke's age is represented by b. Cloe's age is represented by two expressions, $4b - 2$ and $3b + 1$. In the guess-and-check version of this problem, the problem was finished when the numbers in the third and fifth columns were the same. We'll use this concept of two equal expressions in the algebra version also: To set up our equation, we need to connect the expressions $4b - 2$ and $3b + 1$.

$$4b - 2 = 3b + 1$$
$$b - 2 = 1$$
$$b = 3$$

So Zeke is 3. This means that Cloe is 10, because $4(3) - 2 = 10$ and $3(3) + 1 = 10$.

As you use guess-and-check to work a problem, you begin to understand it better. Then you can convert it to algebra more easily.

Augustus is trying to make chocolate milk. So far he has made a 10% chocolate milk solution (this means that the solution is 10% chocolate and 90% milk). He has also made a 25% chocolate milk solution. Unfortunately, the 10% solution is too weak and the 25% solution is way too chocolaty. He has a whole lot of the 10% solution, but he has only 30 gallons of the 25% solution. How many gallons of 10% solution should he add to the 25% solution to make a mixture that is 15% chocolate? (Augustus is sure the 15% solution will be absolutely perfect.) Work this problem before continuing.

The guess-and-check and subproblems solution from Chapter 7 is shown below.

Gallons of 10% Solution	Gallons of Choc in 10% Soln	Gallons of 25% Solution	Gallons of Choc in 25% Soln	Total Gallons of Choc	Total Gallons of Mix	% of Choc in Tot Mix	Rate
5	0.5	30	7.5	8	35	22.9%	high
30	3	30	7.5	10.5	60	17.5%	high
50	5	30	7.5	12.5	80	15.6%	high
g	$0.1g$	30	7.5	$0.1g + 7.5$	$g + 30$	$\dfrac{(0.1g + 7.5)}{(g + 30)}$	

The expression for the second-to-last column looks complicated, but it's easy to see where it comes from when we break it down into parts: It is simply a ratio of the numbers in the two preceding columns. That is, the numerator is from the Total Gallons of Chocolate column and the denominator is from the Total Gallons of Mixture column.

We arrive at the following algebraic expressions in the same way that we arrived at the guess-and-check numbers. That is, we do the same thing to g that we did to all of the guesses. The final equation comes from the chart and from knowing that our guesses are supposed to result in a 15% mixture.

$$\frac{(0.1g + 7.5)}{(g + 30)} = 0.15$$
$$0.1g + 7.5 = 0.15(g + 30)$$
$$0.1g + 7.5 = 0.15g + 4.5$$
$$-0.05g = -3$$
$$g = \frac{-3}{-0.05}$$
$$g = 60 \text{ gallons}$$

So 60 gallons of the 10% mixture are required.

Note that if Augustus had wanted his mixture to be 14.65% chocolate, using guess-and-check would have taken a long time. Using algebra would have been as quick as it was when he was looking for a mixture of 15% chocolate. Guess-and-check is very useful for setting up an algebraic equation. You don't *have* to use guess-and-check to set up the algebra, but it isn't a bad idea and could save you a lot of grief. If you are at all unsure of the equation you need, then set up a guess-and-check chart first.

Here is another mixture problem with which to exercise your newfound skill.

SALT SOLUTION

A pet store sells salt water for fish tanks. Unfortunately, recently hired Flounder has mixed a salt solution that is too weak. He's made 150 pounds of 4% salt solution. The boss wants a 7% salt solution. Help Flounder out by giving him two options for reaching the 7% solution:

a. Add some salt. How much?

b. Evaporate some water. How much?

Work this problem before continuing.

Steve, Brenda, and Gil worked on this problem.

STEVE: Poor Flounder, this one sounds tough.

BRENDA: Come on, guys, we can do this. Let's set up a guess-and-check chart. What do we know, and what do we need?

GIL: We have 150 pounds of solution, and it is 4% salt. How many pounds of it is salt, then?

STEVE: Sounds like a subproblem. Four percent of 150 is 6. So there are 6 pounds of salt and, therefore, 144 pounds of water in the original solution.

BRENDA: Which part should we do first?

GIL: It probably doesn't matter. Let's do part a. Here's my guess-and-check chart. I guessed the salt added. The first three columns never change.

Lbs Soln	Lbs Salt	Lbs Water	Salt Added	Total Salt	Total Soln	% Salt
150	6	144	1	7	151	$\frac{7}{151} = 4.6\%$
150	6	144	10	16	160	$\frac{16}{160} = 10\%$

BRENDA: I think I follow this. You guessed the salt added. Then you added that to the 6 pounds of salt you already had in the solution to get the Total Salt column. How did you get the Total Solution column?

STEVE: Oh, I get that. You're just pouring more into the solution, so you need to add how much you put in to how much was already there. He added the salt-added value to the 150 pounds of solution that was already there. That gave him how much total solution there was.

BRENDA: Okay, I get it. Then he divided the amount of salt by the total solution amount to get the percent salt. Of course, it comes out as a decimal, so he changed it to a percentage.

GIL: Right. And the correct answer has to be in between 1 and 10 gallons added.

BRENDA: I think we ought to use algebra. Guessing could take forever. It's probably a decimal answer anyway.

GIL: Okay, let's use algebra. How do we do that?

STEVE: Easy, just use a variable as a guess. Put x in the Salt Added column and do the same thing to x that you did to the numbers.

BRENDA: So the Total Salt column would be $x + 6$. The Total Solution column is $x + 150$. And the Percent Salt column is their ratio, just like with the numbers.

Lbs Soln	Lbs Salt	Lbs Water	Salt Added	Total Salt	Total Soln	% Salt
150	6	144	1	7	151	$\frac{7}{151} = 4.6\%$
150	6	144	10	16	160	$\frac{16}{160} = 10\%$
150	6	144	X	$x + 6$	$x + 150$	$(x + 6)/(x + 150)$

GIL: But where do we get the equation?

BRENDA: Easy. The Percent Salt column is supposed to be 7%, right? So set $\dfrac{(x + 6)}{(x + 150)}$ equal to 0.07. Then solve it.

GIL: Are you sure? This seems too easy for this kind of problem.

BRENDA: Try it. It works.

$$\frac{x + 6}{x + 150} = 0.07$$
$$x + 6 = 0.07(x + 150)$$
$$x + 6 = 0.07x + 10.5$$
$$0.93x = 4.5$$
$$x = \frac{4.5}{0.93}$$
$$x = 4.84 \text{ pounds (rounded)}$$

GIL: So he needs to add 4.84 pounds of salt. That's a lot of salt. Maybe he would be better off evaporating some water.

BRENDA: Well, let's try that one. Set it up by guess-and-check again. I'm not going to bother writing down the first three columns like last time. I'll guess water evaporated.

Water Subtract'd	Water Total	Solution Total	% Salt
4	140	146	$6/146 = 4.1\%$
20	124	130	$6/130 = 4.6\%$

STEVE: Wow, this is taking forever. Let's try algebra. Put y in the Water Subtracted column.

Water Subtract'd	Water Total	Solution Total	% Salt
4	140	146	$6/146 = 4.1\%$
20	124	130	$6/130 = 4.6\%$
y	$144 - y$	$150 - y$	$6/(150 - y)$

BRENDA: So we want $\dfrac{6}{(150 - y)}$ to be 7%, or 0.07.

$$\frac{6}{150 - y} = 0.07$$
$$6 = 0.07(150 - y)$$
$$6 = 10.5 - 0.07y$$
$$-0.07y = -4.5$$
$$0.07y = 4.5$$
$$y = \frac{4.5}{0.07}$$
$$y = 64.29 \text{ pounds}$$

BRENDA: Wow, that's a lot of water to evaporate. Poor Flounder. It's going to be tough, whatever he does.

If the answer to the problem is not an integer, guess-and-check could literally take all day. Abandoning guess-and-check for algebra in situations like these is the best way to solve the problem.

The next problem is different. It is not a typical Algebra 1 problem.

SEASON'S STATS

Franny, Carl, and Amichung compared their season statistics during the post-season banquet for their high school baseball team. Franny had three times as many singles as Carl. Carl had four times as many doubles as Amichung. Each of them had exactly the same number of hits. None of the three had any hits besides singles and doubles (they were slap hitters). The three of them as a group had exactly as many singles as doubles. Added together, the three of them had fewer than 200 hits in all. How many singles and how many doubles did each of them have? Work this problem before continuing.

Rick approached the problem this way: "I was really confused by this problem, so I decided to use guess-and-check. I started by guessing the number of singles that Carl had. First I guessed Carl had 2 singles. It says that Franny had three times as many singles as Carl, so Franny had 6 singles. Then I was stuck. I looked at the problem again and saw that Carl had four times as many doubles as Amichung. So I guessed Amichung had 5 doubles, and this meant that Carl had 20 doubles. My chart looked like this so far. Columns with asterisks were the ones I guessed."

Carl		Franny		Amichung	
sing*	doub	sing	doub	sing	doub*
2	20	6			5

"Then I was stuck again. I didn't know how to check the guess. I reread the problem and found that they had fewer than 200 hits altogether. That didn't seem to help much. Then I read that each player had the same number of hits. That helped a lot. Since I already had both types of Carl's hits filled in, I saw that Carl had 22 hits (for this guess). So Franny and Amichung must also have had 22 hits apiece. Since Franny had 6 singles, she must have had 16 doubles. Since Amichung had 5 doubles, he must have had 17 singles. I filled this in on the chart."

| Carl | | Franny | | Amichung | |
sing*	doub	sing	doub	sing	doub*
2	20	6	16	17	5

"Now, what? I still didn't know if this was right. It was definitely less than 200 hits altogether (66 to be exact in this case), but so what? There were lots of possibilities that would give less than 200 hits. Then I read that the three of them as a group had exactly the same number of singles as doubles. So I needed another column on my chart. I added it up and got 25 singles and 41 doubles."

| Carl | | Franny | | Amichung | | Total | |
sing*	doub	sing	doub	sing	doub*	sing	doub
2	20	6	16	17	5	25	41

"Now I could see that this was incorrect, but it gave me something to check. I knew this might take forever, but I went on anyway. I decided that it would be easier if I left one of the guesses the same and changed the other one. I left Carl with 2 singles and changed Amichung to 6 doubles. So Franny had 6 singles (three times as many as Carl), and Carl had 24 doubles (four times as many as Amichung). So there were 26 hits in all, which gave Franny 20 doubles (she already had 6 singles) and Amichung 20 singles (he already had 6 doubles). The total number of singles was 28, and the total number of doubles was 50. This seemed to be getting worse, so in my next guess I gave Carl more singles."

| Carl | | Franny | | Amichung | | Total | |
sing*	doub	sing	doub	sing	doub*	sing	doub
2	20	6	16	17	5	25	41
2	24	6	20	20	6	28	50
3	24	9	18	21	6	33	48

"At this point, I decided to use algebra. I was guessing Carl's singles, so I made that x, and I made Amichung's doubles y. With the numbers, I had tripled Carl's singles to get Franny's singles. So Franny's singles must be $3x$. I had quadrupled Amichung's doubles to get Carl's doubles, so Carl's doubles must be $4y$."

| Carl | | Franny | | Amichung | | Total | |
sing*	doub	sing	doub	sing	doub*	sing	doub
2	20	6	16	17	5	25	41
2	24	6	20	20	6	28	50
3	24	9	18	21	6	33	48
x	$4y$	$3x$			y		

"The thing I did next with the numbers was to add up the total number of hits for each player and then make the other players have that many hits. So Carl had $x + 4y$ hits. So far, Franny had $3x$ hits. If her doubles were d, then $3x + d$ = total hits = $x + 4y$. Solving for d, I got $d = 4y - 2x$. So Franny must have $4y - 2x$ doubles. **Notice** that her total hits are right because they're what Carl had.

"I did the same thing for Amichung. So far he had y doubles. If I let him have n singles, then $n + y = x + 4y$ total hits. So $n = x + 3y$ singles."

| Carl | | Franny | | Amichung | | Total | |
sing*	doub	sing	doub	sing	doub*	sing	doub
2	20	6	16	17	5	25	41
2	24	6	20	20	6	28	50
3	24	9	18	21	6	33	48
x	$4y$	$3x$	$4y - 2x$	$x + 3y$	y		

"Then I looked back at what I did with the numbers. For each guess, I figured out the total number of singles and the total number of doubles, then looked to see if they were the same:

Singles: $x + 3x + (x + 3y) = 5x + 3y$

Doubles: $4y + (4y - 2x) + y = 9y - 2x$."

| Carl | | Franny | | Amichung | | Total | |
sing*	doub	sing	doub	sing	doub*	sing	doub
2	20	6	16	17	5	25	41
2	24	6	20	20	6	28	50
3	24	9	18	21	6	33	48
x	$4y$	$3x$	$4y - 2x$	$x + 3y$	y	$5x + 3y$	$9y - 2x$

"Since I wanted total singles to equal total doubles, I set the number of singles equal to the number of doubles. I had two variables, so I wasn't sure what would happen. I decided to get the x's on one side and the y's on the other side."

$$5x + 3y = 9y - 2x$$
$$7x = 6y$$

"I realized this would be true if x were 6 and y were 7. I also realized it would be true if x were 12 and y were 14. Anytime the ratio of $x{:}y = 6{:}7$, there would be a solution. So I decided to guess $x = 6$ and $y = 7$, meaning Carl had 6 singles and Amichung had 7 doubles. Then I tried giving Carl 12 singles and Amichung 14 doubles."

| Carl | | Franny | | Amichung | | Total | |
sing*	doub	sing	doub	sing	doub*	sing	doub
2	20	6	16	17	5	25	41
2	24	6	20	20	6	28	50
3	24	9	18	21	6	33	48
x	$4y$	$3x$	$4y - 2x$	$x + 3y$	y	$5x + 3y$	$9y - 2x$
6	28	18	16	27	7	51	51
12	56	36	32	54	14	102	102

"It worked for $x = 6$ and $y = 7$, giving a total of 102 hits. When I guessed $x = 12$ and $y = 14$, it gave 204 total hits. But the problem said the number of hits was less than 200. So the first solution must be the only solution. So the answers are Carl had 6 singles and 28 doubles, Franny had 18 singles and 16 doubles, and Amichung had 27 singles and 7 doubles. Whew!"

The next two problems use diagrams in conjunction with algebra.

THE SHADOW

A man 6 feet tall is walking away from a streetlight that is 15 feet tall. How long is the man's shadow when he is 10 feet away from the light?

Work this problem before continuing. **Note** that guess-and-check doesn't really help here, but a diagram helps a lot.

Suzanne drew the diagram shown below. "I drew the picture and saw where the shadow would be. I labeled the length of the shadow x."

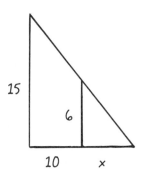

"It looked to me like the triangles were similar. The ratio of the height of the pole to the height of the man should be in the same proportion as what to what? Comparing the big triangle to the small triangle, the vertical side of the big triangle compared to the vertical side of the small triangle should have the same ratio as the bottom side of the big triangle to the bottom side of the small triangle. So I set up an equation. Solving it, I got the following for x."

$$\frac{15}{6} = \frac{10 + x}{x}$$
$$15x = 6(10 + x)$$
$$15x = 60 + 6x$$
$$9x = 60$$
$$x = \frac{60}{9} = \frac{20}{3}$$

"So the man's shadow is $^{20}/_3$ or $6^2/_3$ feet long."

Brian is supposed to run around the basketball court inside the gym at the beginning of each day's volleyball practice. The court measures 70 feet by 120 feet. But Brian is lazy and cuts off each corner as he runs around. When he is 6 feet from the end of the court, he runs diagonally to a point 6 feet from the side of the court. He does this on each of the four corners. How many feet does Brian cut from one lap? Work this problem before continuing.

This problem needs a diagram of the court. The diagram below shows the court and the four corners that are cut off.

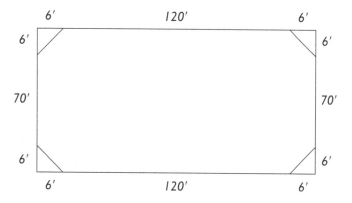

The problem breaks down into subproblems. First, find the length of the diagonal of one of the triangles. Find the difference between the diagonal length and the distance around the corner. Then multiply the answer by 4 to find the total number of feet Brian is eliminating.

We can use algebra to find the length of the diagonal.

To solve this subproblem, you need to know the Pythagorean theorem: The sum of the squares of the legs of a right triangle is equal to the square of the hypotenuse.

$$6^2 + 6^2 = x^2$$
$$36 + 36 = x^2$$
$$72 = x^2$$
$$8.48 = x \qquad \text{(Take the square root of 72.)}$$

So Brian runs about 8.5 feet instead of running around the corner, which measures 12 feet. This results in his cutting off 3.5 feet from each corner. Multiplying by the four corners gives a total number of 14 feet cut from each lap. So Brian is cheating himself out of 14 feet of running. Instead of running the 380 feet around the court, he is running only 366 feet.

Algebra is a very effective problem-solving strategy for many types of problems, but it is not the *only* strategy available to you. When algebra is used in conjunction with other problem-solving strategies, it is especially effective.

Problem Set A

1. ALGEBRA THIS TIME

Go back to the problems from Problem Set A in Chapter 6 or to any Problem Set B problems that you used guess-and-check to solve. Choose three of those problems, and write and solve equations for them.

2. MORE COINS

Bill has $3.25 in nickels and dimes. He has eight more nickels than dimes. How many of each does he have?

3. SUPPLEMENTS

The larger of two supplementary angles is six degrees more than twice the smaller of the two angles. What is the measure of each angle?

4. BIKE RIDE

Blaise rode his bike to his friend Elroy's house, which was 15 miles away. After he had been riding for half an hour, he got a flat tire. He walked his bike the rest of the way. The total trip took him 3 hours. If his walking rate was one-fourth as fast as his riding rate, how fast did he ride?

5. CHAMPIONSHIP GAME

A group of students were transported to the championship basketball game on buses and vans. When one bus and two vans unloaded, there were 55 students. A few minutes later, two more buses and one van unloaded 89 students. In all, three buses and eight vans drove students to the game. How many students went to the game?

6. FISHING POLES

Daniel and Gary are fishing. They each have several fishing poles, and each pole has several worms on its line. Daniel's poles each have 6 worms on their lines. Gary's poles each have 11 worms on their lines. Between the two of them, Daniel and Gary have 13 poles and 103 worms. How many poles does each boy have?

7. CAR WASH

Alyse and Jeremy are washing their father's car. Alyse can wash it by herself in 20 minutes. Jeremy can wash it by himself in 30 minutes. How long does it take them to wash the car if they work together?

8. INTEREST

Lakeitha earned $12,000 more in her accounting job this year because she received her CPA certification. She decided to invest the money, which was split between two different savings accounts. One account was a certificate of deposit that paid 7.25% annual interest. The other was a money market account that paid 5.4% annual interest. At the end of one year, she had made $730. How much did she invest in the money market account?

9. CHEMISTRY

A chemist mixes two solutions. One is 24% acid (the rest is water), and the other is 41% acid. About how much of each solution does she need to produce 50 gallons of a solution that is 31% acid? Answer to the nearest hundredth of a gallon.

10. **LADDER**

A woman wants to put a ladder against the wall of her house and climb up to fix the gutter. The gutter is 14 feet above the ground. Unfortunately, there is an 8-foot-high retaining wall standing 3 feet away from her house. The ladder can't be placed between the retaining wall and the house, so it must be placed on the outside of the retaining wall. The ladder will go over the retaining wall (it can touch it) and then up to the roof. How long a ladder does she need?

11. **WRITE YOUR OWN**

Write your own algebra problem. Start in the same way that you created your guess-and-check problem in Chapter 6, by first creating the situation and then the answer. Then write the rest of the problem. Consider creating a problem that has a decimal answer, like a mixture problem.

Problem Set B

1. **HOW MANY ZEROS?**

The expression $n!$ is read "n factorial" and means $n(n-1)(n-2)(n-3)$ $(n-4)(n-5)\ldots(3)(2)(1)$. Thus, 6! means $6 \times 5 \times 4 \times 3 \times 2 \times 1 = 720$ and 10! means $10 \times 9 \times 8 \times 7 \times 6 \times 5 \times 4 \times 3 \times 2 \times 1 = 3{,}628{,}800$. **Notice** that 6! ends with one digit of zero and that 10! ends with two digits of zero. How many digits of zero does 5000! end with?

2. **FORMING PENTOMINOES**

Pentominoes are figures formed by connecting five squares so that they share a common side (see the illustrations of the valid and invalid pentominoes below). How many different pentominoes are there? **Note** that reflections and rotations are not considered to be different.

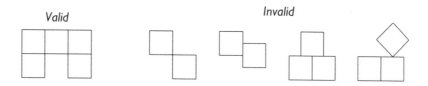

Valid   Invalid

3. VALLEY SPRINGS

Valley Springs Juicers bought two different kinds of grapes to make juice. The green grapes cost $500 per ton. The red grapes cost $200 per ton. The buyer ended up paying an average of $280 per ton for the grapes. What is the ratio of tons of green grapes to tons of red grapes?

4. ALL IN THE FAMILY

People of Latino heritage traditionally have two last names. The first one is from their father, and the second one is from their mother. For example, a woman named María Sánchez Jones would have had a father with the last name Sánchez and a mother with the last name Jones (the other last names are irrelevant to this discussion).

Suppose a man named José García López marries a woman named María Sánchez Jones. She would then drop Jones and become María Sánchez de García, adding on her husband's name after the word *de*. So she is now María Sánchez, "wife of García."

If that couple then has a child, the child will use the last names García Sánchez. Regardless of whether that child is a boy or a girl, the name that is passed on to his or her offspring is García. The sample family tree below illustrates that.

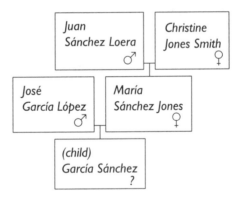

Write the names of the following people in the correct places on a family tree diagram. **Notice** that some people have been listed twice, once with their maiden names and once with their married names. (The *F* indicates a female, and *M* indicates male.

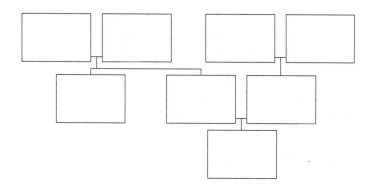

1. Dolores Lara Baez (F)

2. Alberto Rodijo Saenz (M)

3. Marisela Saenz de Rodijo (F)

4. Consuelo Baez García (F)

5. Rafael Lara Echeve (M)

6. Dolores Lara de Rodijo (F)

7. Ana Luísa Rodijo Saenz (F)

8. Marisela Saenz Vaquero (F)

9. Concepción Rodijo Lara (F)

10. Juan Carlos Rodijo Gómez (M)

11. Consuelo Baez de Lara (F)

5. WHEN I'M 64

This is a game for two people: Taking alternate turns, choose a whole number from 1 to 8. Keep a running total. (For example, if you pick 2 and your opponent picks 6, the total is now 8. Then maybe you pick 5, so now the total is 13, and so on.) The object of the game is to make the score exactly 64 on your turn. (If it were your turn and the running total at that point was 62, you would say 2, making the score 64, and you would be the winner.) You are going to choose the first number. What number should you pick to guarantee a win for yourself, and what strategy should you follow?

Meteorologists analyze small differences in quantifiable weather data at various places and times to establish a weather pattern that can aid in their predictions.

14

Finite Differences

The major problem-solving theme of Organizing Information is very evident in the strategy of finite differences, which ties together many of the strategies you've already learned: systematic lists, looking for patterns, subproblems, easier related problems, and algebra. The strategy of finite differences provides you with a very powerful way to organize information and often leads to equations that you can use to solve problems. Several of the problems you looked at in earlier chapters can be solved with this new strategy, which you'll come to understand through an example. Recall the following version of the How Many Squares? problem from Chapter 9.

HOW MANY SQUARES? REVISITED

Find a formula for the number of squares on a checkerboard that has n squares along each side. (This is an n-by-n checkerboard.) Set up a pattern for this problem before going on.

In Chapter 9: Solve an Easier Related Problem, you set up a chart to determine the number of squares in a one-by-one square, a two-by-two square, and so on, up to an eight-by-eight square. This version of the problem asks you to find a formula for an *n*-by-*n* square. The chart from Chapter 9 is shown below.

Size of checkerboard	Number of squares
1-by-1	1
2-by-2	$4 + 1 = 5$
3-by-3	$9 + 4 + 1 = 14$
4-by-4	$16 + 9 + 4 + 1 = 30$

Angie and Isaac created this chart, and in discussing this problem they conjectured that there might be a formula for problems like this. This chapter is about finding such formulas.

We can express Angie and Isaac's chart in a slightly different way, and we can also expand it:

Side of checkerboard	Number of squares
1	$1 = 1$
2	$5 = 1 + 4$
3	$14 = 1 + 4 + 9$
4	$30 = 1 + 4 + 9 + 16$
5	$55 = 1 + 4 + 9 + 16 + 25$
6	$91 = 1 + 4 + 9 + 16 + 25 + 36$
7	$140 = 1 + 4 + 9 + 16 + 25 + 36 + 49$
8	$204 = 1 + 4 + 9 + 16 + 25 + 36 + 49 + 64$
9	$285 = 1 + 4 + 9 + 16 + 25 + 36 + 49 + 64 + 81$
10	$385 = 1 + 4 + 9 + 16 + 25 + 36 + 49 + 64 + 81 + 100$

The pattern Angie and Isaac came up with to solve this problem in Chapter 9, adding the next square number to each previous answer, shows up in our expanded chart. So,

$$1 + 2^2 = 5$$

$$5 + 3^2 = 14$$

$$14 + 4^2 = 30 \text{ and so on.}$$

This chapter will explore this particular pattern in great detail, and you will learn how you can use what you notice about this pattern to figure out a formula or an equation for many different functions.

To begin, consider the following functions, or input-output charts. Find a pattern in each problem and predict the output for the inputs 5 and 137. **Note** that the input value is called x and the output value is called y.

FUNCTIONS

Find the pattern in each function, then fill in the y-values for the x-values 5 and 137.

1.

x	y
0	3
1	7
2	11
3	15
4	19
5	−?−
137	−?−

2.

x	y
0	−2
1	5
2	12
3	19
4	26
5	−?−
137	−?−

3.

x	y
0	−4
1	1
2	12
3	29
4	52
5	−?−
137	−?−

Fazal worked on this problem. "The first function wasn't that hard to figure out. I quickly saw the pattern that each y-value increased by 4. So I decided to write this into the chart, putting +4 between each set of numbers. Doing that made it quite obvious that the output for $x = 5$ was $y = 23$."

x	y	
0	3	
		+4
1	7	
		+4
2	11	
		+4
3	15	
		+4
4	19	
		+4
5	23	

"But I got really stuck trying to figure out the output for $x = 137$. I decided to go on to the next problem. On this problem I could see that the y-values increased by 7 each time. So it was no problem figuring out that the y-value for $x = 5$ was $y = 33$. But again, I had no clue on $x = 137$.

x	y	
0	-2	
		+7
1	5	
		+7
2	12	
		+7
3	19	
		+7
4	26	
		+7
5	33	

"The third problem was harder. I looked at the differences between successive y-values again, but this time it wasn't quite so obvious what was going on.

x	y	
0	-4	
		+5
1	1	
		+11
2	12	
		+17
3	29	
		+23
4	52	
5	?	

"After staring at it for a while, I noticed that the *differences* were going up by 6. So I made another column of the differences of the differences. I wasn't sure this would help me, but I did it anyway.

x	y		
0	-4		
		+5	
1	1		+6
		+11	
2	12		+6
		+17	
3	29		+6
		+23	
4	52		+6
5	?		

"I decided that if that worked, then the difference between the y-value of 52 and the next y-value would have to be 29. This was because the difference of 23 had to go up by 6, which would make it 29. Using this, I calculated the next y-value to be 81. But I still didn't know how to get the y-value for $x = 137$."

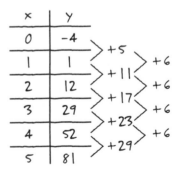

x	y		
0	-4		
		+5	
1	1		+6
		+11	
2	12		+6
		+17	
3	29		+6
		+23	
4	52		+6
		+29	
5	81		

Finite differences can help Fazal with the problem of determining the y-value for a particular x-value. When you use the strategy of finite differences, you assign a sequence of whole-number values to x, then analyze the differences between the y-values to generate the *original equation* used to compute the y-values of that function. This strategy is the strategy of working backwards applied to the output of a function. Fazal already found the key patterns between successive y-values in each of the problems. The strategy of finite differences will allow him (and you) to use those difference patterns to find an equation for each function, an equation that relates the input to the output. (The strategy of finite differences will work only for polynomial functions. It will not work for exponential functions, trigonometric functions, or other functions that are not polynomial.)

Now consider the two functions below. The function below on the left is the first problem Fazal worked on. The function below on the right is an easier problem that is related to the one on the left. What is the equation for the function on the right? In other words, what equation relates the value of x to the value of y? Write your equation as $y = -?-$.

x	y			x	y	
0	3	+4		0	0	+4
1	7	+4		1	4	+4
2	11	+4		2	8	+4
3	15	+4		3	12	+4
4	19	+4		4	16	+4
5	23	+4		5	20	+4

You should see that the y-value is always 4 times the x-value. This relationship can be expressed with the equation $y = 4x$. What does that have to do with the function on the left? **Note** that if you compare the y-values term by term, the y-values for the function on the left are always 3 greater than the corresponding y-values for the function on the right. This means that the equation for the function on the left is $y = 4x + 3$. Now Fazal can figure out the y-value when $x = 137$. Substituting 137 for x, $y = 4(137) + 3 = 551$.

But suppose you don't figure out the helpful easier related problem when you are working on finding the equation. For example, what is a useful easier related problem for the third function Fazal worked on? Is there another way to get the equation, without finding an easier related problem? The answer, of course, is yes, or there wouldn't be much purpose to this chapter. The way to find equations for functions of this type is to use the strategy of finite differences.

The equation for our first function, $y = 4x + 3$, can be expressed in general form as $y = mx + b$. In algebra this equation is called the slope-intercept form of an equation of a line, and it defines a linear function. (**Note** that most algebra classes use m and b for linear equations in slope-intercept form a, b, and c for the quadratic formula. However, the meaning of the letter b is inconsistent between these two equations, even though they are taught in the same class. To avoid whatever you think b is or b should be, we've chosen not to use it and we use e and f in this book instead of m and b.) We'll use f and e for reasons that will become clear later in the chapter. You can actually use whatever letters you want, and it won't make any difference at all.

Look closely at the equation $y = fx + e$. Assigning different values to f and e, make up three different equations and enter the values into function charts, letting x be all integers between 0 and 5. For example, when $f = 4$ and $e = 3$, the equation is $y = 4x + 3$, and this equation generates the function chart we've been working with. Create the charts for three different functions before reading on.

Earvin made up these functions:

$f = 3$ $e = 1$			$f = -2$ $e = 9$			$f = 1$ $e = -4$	
$y = 3x + 1$			$y = -2x + 9$			$y = 1x - 4$	
x	y		x	y		x	y
0	1		0	9		0	-4
1	4		1	7		1	-3
2	7		2	5		2	-2
3	10		3	3		3	-1
4	13		4	1		4	0
5	16		5	-1		5	1

Now examine each of these functions, indicating the differences as Fazal did with his functions. Also do this for the functions you made up yourself.

$f = 3 \quad e = 1$
$y = 3x + 1$

x	y	
0	1	
1	4	$+3$
2	7	$+3$
3	10	$+3$
4	13	$+3$
5	16	$+3$

$f = -2 \quad e = 9$
$y = -2x + 9$

x	y	
0	9	
1	7	-2
2	5	-2
3	3	-2
4	1	-2
5	-1	-2

$f = 1 \quad e = -4$
$y = 1x - 4$

x	y	
0	-4	
1	-3	$+1$
2	-2	$+1$
3	-1	$+1$
4	0	$+1$
5	1	$+1$

Notice that the second function features y-values that decrease and that the differences are -2. What do the differences have to do with the original equations? You should see right off that the values of f, the **coefficient** of the x-term in the general equation, are the same as the differences. So for the second function with the differences of -2, $f = -2$. **Note,** also, that the values of e in the original equations are the same as the y-values when x equals zero.

What is the equation for the chart shown below? (This was the second problem Fazal worked on.)

x	y	
0	-2	
1	5	$+7$
2	12	$+7$
3	19	$+7$
4	26	$+7$
5	33	$+7$

Note that the common difference is 7, so the value of f must equal 7. The y-value for $x = 0$ is $y = -2$, so e equals -2. Therefore, the equation is $y = 7x - 2$. This can easily be checked with the x- and

y-values. For example, when $x = 5$, $y = 7(5) - 2 = 33$, which is correct. Fazal tried to figure out the y-value when x was 137. Now that he knows the equation for the function, he can easily do it: $y = 7(137) - 2 = 957$.

LINEAR FUNCTION GENERAL CHART

Does using this process work to find equations for functions every time? Why? Consider the general equation for a linear function, $y = fx + e$. Make a function chart for this equation, using the values 0 through 5 for x. Do this before reading on.

First, plug in the x-values of 0 through 5 into the equation $y = fx + e$ to get the chart shown at right.

Next, figure out the differences between successive terms, as we did earlier. For this chart, you have to algebraically subtract each term from the term that follows it. For example, the first two y-values in the chart are e and $(f + e)$. Subtracting the first from the second gives $(f + e) - e = f$. The next difference is $(2f + e) - (f + e) = f$. The difference turns out to be f every time.

This general (or master) chart shows that the common difference will always be the value of f, and that the value of e will always be given by the value of y when x equals 0.

$y = fx + e$

x	y
0	e
1	$f + e$
2	$2f + e$
3	$3f + e$
4	$4f + e$
5	$5f + e$

$y = fx + e$

x	y	
0	e	
		$+f$
1	$f + e$	
		$+f$
2	$2f + e$	
		$+f$
3	$3f + e$	
		$+f$
4	$4f + e$	
		$+f$
5	$5f + e$	

Now look back at the third problem Fazal worked on earlier shown at the top of the next page,

x	y
0	-4
1	1
2	12
3	29
4	52
5	?

First differences: +5, +11, +17, +23, +29
Second differences: +6, +6, +6, +6, +6

This problem had a common difference, but Fazal didn't see it until it showed up in the second set of differences. This situation didn't happen for equations of the form $y = fx + e$. So the general form for this equation must be different. Do you recall ever seeing a function that behaved this way, showing a common difference in the second set of differences? A well-known function is shown below. What is the equation for it?

x	y
0	0
1	1
2	4
3	9
4	16
5	25
6	36

First differences: +1, +3, +5, +7, +9, +11
Second differences: +2, +2, +2, +2, +2

You probably recognize this function as $y = x^2$. If so, you might suspect that a function for which the second difference is a constant comes from some sort of quadratic equation.

The general form for a quadratic function is $y = gx^2 + fx + e$. As you did for the earlier Linear Function General Chart problem, make the general function chart for this equation by substituting x-values from 0 through 5. (**Note** that when $g = 0$, this chart is the same as one for $y = fx + e$.) Do this problem before reading on.

The quadratic function general chart is shown below on the left. Computing the first set of differences involves a little bit more algebra than you used in the chart for $y = fx + e$. For example, consider the values of y for $x = 2$ and $x = 3$. You must subtract the first of these function values from the second, so $(9g + 3f + e) - (4g + 2f + e) = 5g + f$. Be careful to compute the values consistently and in order, subtracting the first from the second, the second from the third, and so on. **Note** that with each difference, the e term drops out. The chart with the first set of differences filled in is shown below on the right.

$$y = gx^2 + fx + e$$

x	y
0	e
1	$g + f + e$
2	$4g + 2f + e$
3	$9g + 3f + e$
4	$16g + 4f + e$
5	$25g + 5f + e$

$$y = gx^2 + fx + e$$

x	y	
0	e	
		$g + f$
1	$g + f + e$	
		$3g + f$
2	$4g + 2f + e$	
		$5g + f$
3	$9g + 3f + e$	
		$7g + f$
4	$16g + 4f + e$	
		$9g + f$
5	$25g + 5f + e$	

These differences are not constant, so you must subtract again. This time take the difference of the differences, as shown at the top of the next page.

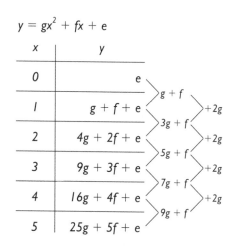

$$y = gx^2 + fx + e$$

x	y
0	e
1	g + f + e
2	4g + 2f + e
3	9g + 3f + e
4	16g + 4f + e
5	25g + 5f + e

This time the second difference turns out to be 2g every time. This is the constant we were seeking. In the third function Fazal worked on, the second difference was constant. The second difference was also constant in the chart for $y = x^2$.

We can use our chart for the equation $y = gx^2 + fx + e$ as a general chart to figure out the equation for any function for which the second difference is constant. Let's compare our general chart with the chart for the function $y = x^2$ to see how we would find an unknown equation.

$$y = -?-$$

x	y
0	0
1	1
2	4
3	9
4	16
5	25

+1, +2
+3, +2
+5, +2
+7, +2
+9

$$y = gx^2 + fx + e$$

x ,	y
0	e
1	g + f + e
2	4g + 2f + e
3	9g + 3f + e
4	16g + 4f + e
5	25g + 5f + e

g + f, +2g
3g + f, +2g
5g + f, +2g
7g + f, +2g
9g + f

The key to the strategy of finite differences is comparing a general chart with the problem you're working on and matching up places in the charts that are the same. **Note** that in this problem's chart, the $y = -?-$ chart shown above, the second difference is always 2. In the general chart, the second difference is always $2g$. Equating these two differences—because they are in exactly the same place in both charts, indicated in dark red—gives $2g = 2$, which means $g = 1$. So, up to this point the equation for this problem's function is $y = 1x^2 + fx + e$. We now need to determine the values for f and e.

Again compare two sections of the charts that correspond. For example, the difference between the x-values 0 and 1 is 1 on the problem chart and $g + f$ on the general chart. (These sections are indicated in light blue on both charts.) This gives $g + f = 1$. To solve this equation, **remember** that we already know $g = 1$. So $1 + f = 1$, which gives $f = 0$.

Instead we could have matched up the differences between $x = 4$ and $x = 5$. In our problem chart, that difference is 9. In the general chart, that difference is $9g + f$. Equating these gives $9g + f = 9$. Again, remembering that $g = 1$ gives us $9(1) + f = 9$, so $f = 0$. This is the same value we got by matching up the differences between the x-values 0 and 1. A word of caution, though. Be sure to compare the parts of the charts that are *exactly the same.* For example, you wouldn't want to compare the differences between $x = 2$ and $x = 3$ on one chart with the differences between $x = 3$ and $x = 4$ on the other chart. That would lead to an incorrect value of f.

Finally, let's determine the value of e. In the problem chart, when $x = 0$, y also equals 0. In the general chart, when $x = 0$, $y = e$. (These sections are indicated in light red on both charts.) Therefore, e must equal zero.

Respectively, the values of g, f, and e are 1, 0, and 0. Therefore, the equation for our problem function is $y + 1x^2 + 0x + 0$, or just $y = x^2$. We already knew that this was the equation for this function. However, illustrating this process shows us that it will work for generating quadratic equations that we *don't* already know.

Now consider the third problem Fazal worked on earlier. Compare it with the general chart and figure out the equation for the function. Do this problem before reading on.

$y = -?-$

x	y		
0	-4		
		+5	
1	1		+6
		+11	
2	12		+6
		+17	
3	29		+6
		+23	
4	52		+6
		+29	
5	81		

$y = gx^2 + fx + e$

x	y		
0	e		
		$g + f$	
1	$g + f + e$		$+2g$
		$3g + f$	
2	$4g + 2f + e$		$+2g$
		$5g + f$	
3	$9g + 3f + e$		$+2g$
		$7g + f$	
4	$16g + 4f + e$		$+2g$
		$9g + f$	
5	$25g + 5f + e$		

Compare the parts of the charts that are the same. It's a good idea to find the value of g first, then f, and then e. The last column of the table (that is, the second difference) is 6. This corresponds to $2g$ on the general chart. So $2g = 6$, which means $g = 3$.

In the problem chart, the difference between the x-values 0 and 1 is 5, which matches up with $g + f$ in the general chart.

$g + f = 5$
$3 + f = 5$ Recall, $g = 3$.
$f = 2$

Finally, when $x = 0$, y is -4, which corresponds to e on the general chart. So $e = -4$.

Thus, the equation is $y = 3x^2 + 2x - 4$. Check it by substituting in $x = 4$. When $x = 4$, then $y = 3(4^2) + 2(4) - 4 = 52$, which is correct. You can use this equation to find the value of y for any x in this function. In Fazal's problem, he needed to find y when $x = 137$. So $y = 3(137^2) + 2(137) - 4 = 56,577$.

Find the equation for each function below. Then use your equations to find the missing y-values, indicated by −?−. Work these before going on.

x	y
0	−5
1	−2
2	5
3	16
4	31
5	50
48	−?−

x	y
2	14
3	11
4	8
5	5
6	2
7	−1
82	−?−

Sarah, Michele, and Iram worked on this problem.

SARAH: This problem looks like a tough nut to crack. What should we do? And we've got a pair of them.

MICHELE: Let's figure out what the differences are.

x	y	
0	−5	
1	−2	−3
2	5	+3
3	16	+11
4	31	+15
5	50	+19

IRAM: Wait a second. You have the first two differences wrong.

MICHELE: I do? What is wrong with them?

SARAH: I see what Iram means. From -5 to -2 it goes up 3, not down 3. So it should be $+3$. That would have been a real lemon if we had blown that one.

IRAM: Right. And from -2 to 5, that goes up 7. Think of owing someone two dollars and then earning seven dollars. You would pay off the person you owed and still have five dollars. So $-2 + 7 = 5$.

MICHELE: Okay, I see. (She changed her chart to the new one shown at right.) Now let's find the second differences.

x	y	
0	-5	
		+3
1	-2	
		+7
2	5	
		+11
3	16	
		+15
4	31	
		+19
5	50	

MICHELE: So it comes out constant on the second difference. That means it's a quadratic equation. So the general equation is $y = gx^2 + fx + e$.

x	y		
0	-5		
		+3	
1	-2		+4
		+7	
2	5		+4
		+11	
3	16		+4
		+15	
4	31		+4
		+19	
5	50		

SARAH: So we need the master chart for a quadratic. Who wants that plum job?

IRAM: Wait, I think I have it in my notebook someplace.

MICHELE: Don't bother looking, Iram. We can just create it from scratch. I'm not into memorizing stuff. I just know how to create it.

SARAH: I agree. I'll do it. This is pretty peachy. (Here's the chart Sarah created.)

$$y = gx^2 + fx + e$$

x	y			
0	e			
		g + f		
1	g + f + e		2g	
		3g + f		
2	4g + 2f + e		2g	
		5g + f		
3	9g + 3f + e		2g	
		7g + f		
4	16g + 4f + e		2g	
		9g + f		
5	25g + 5f + e			

MICHELE: Now, what do we do again?

IRAM: Compare the master chart with the chart for the problem we are doing.

MICHELE: Oh yeah. (She put the problem chart next to the master chart.) Okay, 2g matches up with 4 in our problem.

x	y		
0	-5		
		+3	
1	-2		+4
		+7	
2	5		+4
		+11	
3	16		+4
		+15	
4	31		+4
		+19	
5	50		

$$y = gx^2 + fx + e$$

x	y			
0	e			
		g + f		
1	g + f + e		2g	
		3g + f		
2	4g + 2f + e		2g	
		5g + f		
3	9g + 3f + e		2g	
		7g + f		
4	16g + 4f + e		2g	
		9g + f		
5	25g + 5f + e			

IRAM: Right. So 2g must equal 4 and therefore, g = 2.

SARAH: No problem. The next one is a little trickier. You have to make sure you are comparing apples to apples.

MICHELE: What? Come on, Sarah, forget the food and be serious.

IRAM: I know what she means. The difference between 0 and 1 is g + f on the master chart. On our problem it is 3. So g + f = 3.

$$y = gx^2 + fx + e$$

x	y	first diff	second diff
0	−5		
1	−2	+3	
2	5	+7	+4
3	16	+11	+4
4	31	+15	+4
5	50	+19	+4

x	y	first diff	second diff
0	e		
1	$g + f + e$	$g + f$	
2	$4g + 2f + e$	$3g + f$	$2g$
3	$9g + 3f + e$	$5g + f$	$2g$
4	$16g + 4f + e$	$7g + f$	$2g$
5	$25g + 5f + e$	$9g + f$	$2g$

MICHELE: Cool. I get it. We wouldn't want to match up $g + f$ with 7, because 7 is the difference between $x = 1$ and $x = 2$.

SARAH: Right. That would be comparing apples and oranges.

MICHELE: Got it. Anyway, $g + f = 3$ and we already know that g is 2, so f has to be 1.

IRAM: Right. And e is obviously −5 because that is the y number when the x number is 0.

MICHELE: So the equation is $y = 2x^2 + x − 5$. We'd better check it.

SARAH: That's a good idea. Let's use $x = 4$. There is less risk of making a mistake there. We shouldn't check things with $x = 0$, 1, or 2 because it might turn out right and really be wrong. Using $x = 4$ is safe because 4 is a square, and I could sure use a square meal right now. Okay, so $y = 2(4^2) + 4 − 5$, which is 31. And 31 is what it is supposed to be.

MICHELE: Okay, now we need to know what y is when x is 48. So $y = 2(48^2) + 48 − 5 = 4651$.

SARAH: You know, these problems are fun. I know people who don't carrot all about problems like this.

IRAM: Very funny, Sarah. Now look at the next one. It's different.

MICHELE: It doesn't start at $x = 0$.

IRAM: Right. But I guess we can find the differences anyway. (The differences Iram calculated are shown at the top of the next page.)

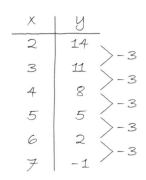

x	y	
2	14	
		−3
3	11	
		−3
4	8	
		−3
5	5	
		−3
6	2	
		−3
7	−1	

MICHELE: How come those are −3 and not +3?

IRAM: It's just like in the last problem. The numbers are going down, so it's −3.

MICHELE: Okay, got it. It came out constant the first time, so it must be an easy one. Aren't these called linear equations?

SARAH: Yeah, they are. I don't know why, though. What I know about vocabulary doesn't amount to a hill of beans.

IRAM: So let's compare this with the master chart for $y = fx + e$. I think I can generate it, even though I'm sure I have it in my notebook somewhere. (Here is what Iram wrote down next to the problem chart.)

$$y = fx + e$$

x	y		x	y	
			0	e	
					+f
			1	$f + e$	
					+f
2	14		2	$2f + e$	
		−3			+f
3	11		3	$3f + e$	
		−3			+f
4	8		4	$4f + e$	
		−3			+f
5	5		5	$5f + e$	
		−3			+f
6	2		6	$6f + e$	
		−3			+f
7	−1		7	$7f + e$	

SARAH: I may be a couch potato, but I don't see why you wrote down the master chart like that.

IRAM: I was trying to follow your advice about apples and oranges, Ms. Pineapple. I am trying to show the comparison between two things that are the same.

MICHELE: Good idea. But how should we handle the holes in the problem chart?

SARAH: I worked with Mel on a problem like this. We were really confused about those missing *y*-values too.

IRAM: Well, either we don't worry about them and just compare the similar parts of both charts, or we could work backwards and figure out the values for $x = 0$ and $x = 1$.

SARAH: Or we could meet halfway and do both. Let's do it both ways and see if we get the same answers.

IRAM: Compare similar parts of the two charts first. That gives us $f = -3$. And opposite $x = 2$ we have $14 = 2f + e$.

$$14 = 2(-3) + e$$
$$14 = -6 + e$$
$$e = 20$$

So the equation is $y = -3x + 20$. This checks when $x = 6$ because $-3(6) + 20 = 2$.

MICHELE: If we work backwards on our chart, we have to *add* 3 to go *up* the chart, since we subtract 3 going down the chart. We get $e = 20$ anyway since that is the number opposite 0. And f would still be -3 since that is the common difference. So it must be right.

x	y	
0	20	
		−3
1	17	
		−3
2	14	
		−3
3	11	
		−3
4	8	
		−3
5	5	
		−3
6	2	
		−3
7	−1	

SARAH: Now we need *y* when $x = 82$. So $y = -3(82) + 20$, which is -226. That seems right since it really starts going down. Grape job, girls!

IRAM: That was a berry good job, wasn't it?

MICHELE: You're starting to sound like Sarah. See ya later. I think I'm going to go have lunch. As they say in England, "Cherry-o!"

The trio did a good job on this problem. **Notice** that they were careful to compare parts of their master charts with like parts of the problem charts, even when some of the intermediary values for x and y were missing. Also, they checked their equations after they'd found them.

HANDSHAKES

Suppose that at the first meeting of the House of Representatives, all 435 members shook hands with each of the other members. How many handshakes took place? Work this problem before continuing.

Kowasky worked on this problem. "This problem seemed pretty hard. When I get a hard problem, I always want to make it easier. So I figured, suppose only one representative showed up. Then there wouldn't be too many handshakes. If two showed up, there would be one handshake. Let's say three showed up— call them U, S and A. U shakes hands with S, and then with A, and S shakes hands with A. That's three handshakes. When I got to four people, I drew a diagram. I counted lines in the diagram, which represented six handshakes."

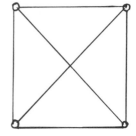

"Then I started making a chart and looked for a pattern."

People	Handshakes
0	0
1	0
2	1
3	3
4	6

"I figured I had better do five people. It was getting harder to make a diagram, but then I thought if there were four people there, they made 6 handshakes. If a fifth person came into the room, he would shake hands with the four people that were there already. So that would make 10 handshakes. Then a sixth person would shake five hands, so that would be 15 handshakes for six people.

"I added this to my chart and looked to use finite differences, since it would take forever to extend this pattern all the way to 435."

People	Handshakes		
0	0		
		+0	+1
1	0		
		+1	+1
2	1		
		+2	+1
3	3		
		+3	+1
4	6		
		+4	+1
5	10		
		+5	+1
6	15		

"I saw that the constant difference happened the second time. That meant that the equation was quadratic, of the form $y = gx^2 + fx + e$."

"I generated the master chart for that equation. I could have looked it up, but it's kind of fun to generate. I compared it with my chart for this problem."

$y = ?$

x	y
0	0
1	0
2	1
3	3
4	6
5	10
6	15

First differences: $+0$, $+1$, $+2$, $+3$, $+4$, $+5$
Second differences: $+1$, $+1$, $+1$, $+1$, $+1$

$y = gx^2 + fx + e$

x	y
0	e
1	$g + f + e$
2	$4g + 2f + e$
3	$9g + 3f + e$
4	$16g + 4f + e$
5	$25g + 5f + e$
6	$36g + 6f + e$

First differences: $g + f$, $3g + f$, $5g + f$, $7g + f$, $9g + f$, $11g + f$
Second differences: $2g$, $2g$, $2g$, $2g$, $2g$

"Then I just had to compare similar parts of the two charts. The second constant difference is 1, which is equal to 2g. So if 2g = 1, then g = 1/2."

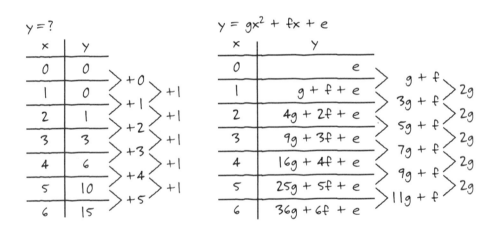

"Then I wanted to figure out what f was. The difference between x = 2 and x = 3 was 2, and that equals 5g + f. I used these values because I wasn't sure this problem made sense for fewer than two people."

$$y = ?$$

x	y
0	0
1	0
2	1
3	3
4	6

+0, +1, +2, +3, +4 → +1, +1, +1, +1

$$y = gx^2 + fx + e$$

x	y
0	e
1	g + f + e
2	4g + 2f + e
3	9g + 3f + e
4	16g + 4f + e

g + f, 3g + f, 5g + f, 7g + f, 9g + f → 2g, 2g, 2g, 2g

$$5g + f = 2$$
$$5(\tfrac{1}{2}) + f = 2 \qquad \text{remember } g = \tfrac{1}{2}$$
$$2.5 + f = 2$$
$$f = -\tfrac{1}{2}$$

"Finally I wanted e. The y-value for $x = 3$ was 3. In the master chart the value was $9g + 3f + e$."

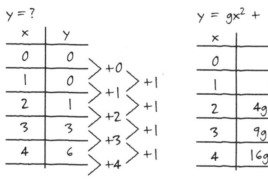

$$y = ?$$

x	y
0	0
1	0
2	1
3	3
4	6

+0, +1, +2, +3, +4 → +1, +1, +1, +1

$$y = gx^2 + fx + e$$

x	y
0	e
1	g + f + e
2	4g + 2f + e
3	9g + 3f + e
4	16g + 4f + e

g + f, 3g + f, 5g + f, 7g + f, 9g + f → 2g, 2g, 2g, 2g

$$9g + 3f + e = 3$$
$$9(\tfrac{1}{2}) + 3(-\tfrac{1}{2}) + e = 3 \qquad \text{recall } g = \tfrac{1}{2} \text{ and } f = -\tfrac{1}{2}$$
$$4.5 - 1.5 + e = 3$$
$$3 + e = 3$$
$$e = 0$$

"I noticed that I would have gotten the same value of *e* if I had just used the value next to *x* = 0 in the chart. So my equation was $y = (1/2)x^2 - (1/2)x$, where *x* represents the number of representatives and *y* represents the number of handshakes. I checked this with six people."

$$y = (\tfrac{1}{2})x^2 - (\tfrac{1}{2})x$$
$$y = (\tfrac{1}{2})6^2 - (\tfrac{1}{2})6$$
$$y = (\tfrac{1}{2})36 - 3$$
$$y = 18 - 3$$
$$y = 15, \quad \text{and that's what I got before.}$$

"Finally, I needed to find the number of handshakes for all 435 representatives."

$$y = (\tfrac{1}{2})x^2 - (\tfrac{1}{2})x$$
$$y = (\tfrac{1}{2})(435^2) - (\tfrac{1}{2})(435)$$
$$y = (\tfrac{1}{2})(189225) - 217.5$$
$$y = 94612.5 - 217.5$$
$$y = 94395$$

"There had to be 94,935 handshakes. That's a lot of handshakes. I think there must have been a lot of tired hands. And if the senators were there too, wow!

"This problem used a lot of strategies. I started with an easier related problem, then a diagram, then a pattern, and finally, finite differences. A lot of these strategies seem to work in concert really well."

Now look again at the How Many Squares? Revisited problem from the beginning of this chapter. To solve this problem, you will also have to create the cubic general chart.

HOW MANY SQUARES? REVISITED

Find a formula for the number of squares on any size *n*-by-*n* checkerboard. Set up a pattern for this problem before continuing.

When we last left this problem, the chart shown below had been developed. Angie and Isaac are back to discuss this problem.

SIDE SQRS	# OF SQRS
1	1
2	5
3	14
4	30
5	55
6	91
7	140
8	204
9	285
10	385

ANGIE: I think we can use finite differences to figure out the formula for this problem.

ISAAC: I agree. Let's go for it. First find all the differences.

SIDE SQRS	# OF SQRS			
1	1			
		+ 4		
2	5		+ 5	
		+ 9		+ 2
3	14		+ 7	
		+ 16		+ 2
4	30		+ 9	
		+ 25		+ 2
5	55		+ 11	
		+ 36		+ 2
6	91		+ 13	
		+ 49		+ 2
7	140		+ 15	
		+ 64		+ 2
8	204		+ 17	
		+ 81		+ 2
9	285		+ 19	
		+ 100		
10	385			

ANGIE: Wow, I've never seen one that took three differences to come out a constant.

ISAAC: Yeah. I wonder what we should do. It can't be linear or quadratic.

ANGIE: Huh?

ISAAC: You know linear is $y = fx + e$ and quadratic is $y = gx^2 + fx + e$.

ANGIE: Oh yeah. Because those take one difference and two differences. So what does that mean? Does it have to be a cubic equation?

ISAAC: I guess so. It's got to have an x^3 in it. I wonder what that looks like?

ANGIE: Probably $y = x^3 + x^2 + x + e$.

ISAAC: Don't we need some coefficients in there?

ANGIE: Yeah, okay. How about $y = hx^3 + gx^2 + fx + e$?

ISAAC: Sounds good. Let's try and generate the master chart for it.

CUBIC GENERAL CHART

Generate the general chart for the general form of a cubic function, $y = hx^3 + gx^2 + fx + e$. Do this before continuing.

The general chart is at the top of the next page.

ANGIE: Okay, I think I've got it.

ISAAC: Me too. Let's compare.

ANGIE: Wow, we got the same thing. I think we really understand this stuff.

ISAAC: We do. Now let's compare this master chart with our chart.

ANGIE: Okay, let's start with the last column. In the master chart, the last column is $6h$. In our chart, the last column is 2.

$$y = hx^3 + gx^2 + fx + e$$

x	y
0	e
1	h + g + f + e
2	8h + 4g + 2f + e
3	27h + 9g + 3f + e
4	64h + 16g + 4f + e
5	125h + 25g + 5f + e
6	216h + 36g + 6f + e

First differences:
- h + g + f
- 7h + 3g + f
- 19h + 5g + f
- 37h + 7g + f
- 61h + 9g + f
- 91h + 11g + f

Second differences:
- 6h + 2g
- 12h + 2g
- 18h + 2g
- 24h + 2g
- 30h + 2g

Third differences:
- 6h
- 6h
- 6h
- 6h

SIDE SQRS	# OF SQRS
1	1
2	5
3	14
4	30
5	55
6	91
7	140
8	204
9	285
10	385

First differences:
- + 4
- + 9
- + 16
- + 25
- + 36
- + 49
- + 64
- + 81
- + 100

Second differences:
- + 5
- + 7
- + 9
- + 11
- + 13
- + 15
- + 17
- + 19

Third differences:
- + 2
- + 2
- + 2
- + 2
- + 2
- + 2
- + 2

ANGIE: So if $6h = 2$, then h is 3.

ISAAC: No it's not. It's one-third: $h = 1/3$.

ANGIE: Oh right, sorry, I divided the wrong way.

ISAAC: Now let's compare the third columns. The top number in the third column of our chart is 5. The top number in the third column of the master chart is $6h + 2g$. So $6h + 2g = 5$.

ANGIE: No, $6h + 2g$ is the second difference related to the $x = 0$ and $x = 1$ values. But we never had $x = 0$ in our chart, so we need to compare 5 to $12h + 2g$.

$y = hx^3 + gx^2 + fx + e$

x	y
0	e
1	$h + g + f + e$
2	$8h + 4g + 2f + e$

$\Rightarrow\ h + g + f\ \Rightarrow\ 6h + 2g\ \Rightarrow\ 6h$

$\Rightarrow\ 7h + 3g + f\ \Rightarrow\ 12h + 2g\ \Rightarrow\ 6h$

$\Rightarrow\ 19h + 5g + f\ \Rightarrow\ 18h + 2g\ \Rightarrow\ 6h$

SIDE SQRS	# OF SQRS
1	1
2	5
3	14
4	30
5	55
6	91

$\Rightarrow + 4\ \Rightarrow + 5\ \Rightarrow + 2$

$\Rightarrow + 9\ \Rightarrow + 7\ \Rightarrow + 2$

$\Rightarrow + 16\ \Rightarrow + 9\ \Rightarrow + 2$

$\Rightarrow + 25\ \Rightarrow + 11\ \Rightarrow + 2$

$\Rightarrow + 36\ \Rightarrow + 13\ \Rightarrow + 2$

$\Rightarrow + 49\ \Rightarrow + 15\ \Rightarrow + 2$

ISAAC: Oh, I see what you mean. We need to make sure the positions in the two charts correspond exactly. Okay, so $12h + 2g = 5$.

$$12h + 2g = 5$$
$$12\left(\tfrac{1}{3}\right) + 2g = 5 \qquad h = \tfrac{1}{3}$$
$$4 + 2g = 5$$
$$2g = 1$$
$$g = \tfrac{1}{2}$$

ANGIE: Great. Now let's go to the second column and make sure we are comparing the same things.

$$y = hx^3 + gx^2 + fx + e$$

x	y
0	e
1	h + g + f + e
2	8h + 4g + 2f + e

$$h + g + f \ > \ 6h + 2g \ > \ 6h$$
$$7h + 3g + f \ > \ 12h + 2g \ > \ 6h$$
$$19h + 5g + f \ > \ 18h + 2g \ > \ 6h$$

SIDE SQRS	# OF SQRS
1	1
2	5
3	14
4	30
5	55
6	91

$$+ 4 \ > \ + 5 \ > \ + 2$$
$$+ 9 \ > \ + 7 \ > \ + 2$$
$$+ 16 \ > \ + 9 \ > \ + 2$$
$$+ 25 \ > \ + 11 \ > \ + 2$$
$$+ 36 \ > \ + 13 \ > \ + 2$$
$$+ 49 \ > \ + 15 \ > \ + 2$$

ISAAC: Okay, $7h + 3g + f = 4$. Those are the differences between $x = 1$ and $x = 2$.

ANGIE: Right. I can solve that for f.

$$7h + 3g + f = 4$$
$$7\left(\tfrac{1}{3}\right) + 3\left(\tfrac{1}{2}\right) + f = 4 \qquad h = \tfrac{1}{3}, \ g = \tfrac{1}{2}$$
$$\tfrac{7}{3} + \tfrac{3}{2} + f = 4$$
$$\tfrac{23}{6} + f = 4$$
$$f = \tfrac{1}{6}$$

ANGIE: Okay, now what is e? Isn't it just the top number in the y column?

ISAAC: It would be if we had a value for $x = 0$. It should be zero since with no squares you wouldn't have any squares. But let's compare:

$$y = hx^3 + gx^2 + fx + e$$

x	y
0	e
1	$h + g + f + e$
2	$8h + 4g + 2f + e$

$\Rightarrow h + g + f \Rightarrow 6h + 2g \Rightarrow 6h$

$\Rightarrow 7h + 3g + f \Rightarrow 12h + 2g \Rightarrow 6h$

$\Rightarrow 19h + 5g + f \Rightarrow 18h + 2g \Rightarrow 6h$

SIDE SQRS	# OF SQRS
1	1
2	5
3	14
4	30
5	55
6	91

$\Rightarrow + 4 \Rightarrow + 5 \Rightarrow + 2$

$\Rightarrow + 9 \Rightarrow + 7 \Rightarrow + 2$

$\Rightarrow + 16 \Rightarrow + 9 \Rightarrow + 2$

$\Rightarrow + 25 \Rightarrow + 11 \Rightarrow + 2$

$\Rightarrow + 36 \Rightarrow + 13 \Rightarrow + 2$

$\Rightarrow + 49 \Rightarrow + 15 \Rightarrow + 2$

$$h + g + f + e = 1$$
$$\tfrac{1}{3} + \tfrac{1}{2} + \tfrac{1}{6} + e = 1$$
$$1 + e = 1$$
$$e = 0$$

ANGIE: You were right, e is 0. Okay, so what's our equation?

ISAAC: It's $y = (1/3)x^3 + (1/2)x^2 + (1/6)x$, where x is the number of squares on a side and y is the total number of squares in the figure.

ANGIE: Great! Let's test it. Suppose $x = 8$. We know that answer is supposed to be 204.

$$y = (\tfrac{1}{3})x^3 + (\tfrac{1}{2})x^2 + (\tfrac{1}{6})x$$
$$y = (\tfrac{1}{3})8^3 + (\tfrac{1}{2})8^2 + (\tfrac{1}{6})8$$
$$y = (\tfrac{1}{3})(512) + (\tfrac{1}{2})(64) + (\tfrac{1}{6})8$$
$$y = {}^{512}\!/_3 + 32 + {}^4\!/_3 = 204$$

ANGIE: It checks.

ISAAC: All right. So for a checkerboard that is n-by-n, there will be $(1/3)n^3 + (1/2)n^2 + (1/6)n$ total squares on it.

ANGIE: These finite differences are pretty cool. I think I could even figure out an equation that started with x^4 if I had to.

The strategy of finite differences provides a very powerful way to find equations that are polynomial in nature. It is really useful when used in conjunction with easier related problems, patterns, and sometimes, diagrams. This strategy organizes the information in a problem in a new way and quickly leads to equations. But be careful: It doesn't work on all equations. Consider the chart at right. It was created by the function $y = 2^x$. The chart at the top of the next page shows what happens when it is evaluated with finite differences.

x	y
0	1
1	2
2	4
3	8
4	16
5	32
6	64
7	128
8	256
9	512

Notice that the differences keep repeating themselves. This type of a pattern is very typical of exponential functions. For fun, you might want to investigate the pattern that arises from attacking the function $y = 3^x$ with finite differences. Be sure you consider x-values up to at least 9. The repeating pattern that shows up here with the function $y = 2^x$ doesn't occur, but something else interesting does happen.

x	y				
0	1				
		+1			
1	2		+1		
		+2		+1	
2	4		+2		+1
		+4		+2	
3	8		+4		+2
		+8		+4	
4	16		+8		+4
		+16		+8	
5	32		+16		+8
		+32		+16	
6	64		+32		+16
		+64		+32	
7	128		+64		+32
		+128		+64	
8	256		+128		
		+256			
9	512				

There are other booby traps in finite differences. Consider the chart shown below.

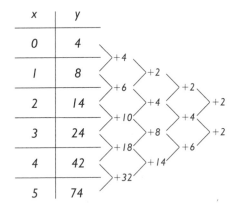

x	y				
0	4				
		+4			
1	8		+2		
		+6		+2	
2	14		+4		+2
		+10		+4	
3	24		+8		+2
		+18		+6	
4	42		+14		
		+32			
5	74				

It appears that there is a constant difference of 2 in the fourth column, which indicates that the equation is fourth degree, but you can see only two values. You should have more information to convince you of the validity of the pattern. If you're working on a problem for which you generated the data—as you did for the Handshakes or How Many Squares? Revisited problems—generate a few more pieces of data. Then you'll have a better idea of whether or not your pattern is correct. No pattern is guaranteed to go on forever, so be careful.

Another potential difficulty with the strategy of finite differences is making a mistake in a chart. Mistakes completely mask any patterns that are present, and the mistakes compound themselves as you move on to more columns. Any common difference that is supposed to be present will disappear because of one mistake. Check out the chart shown below.

A simple subtraction mistake leads to all kinds of chaos. Be careful, especially when dealing with negative and positive numbers. (By the way, did you find the subtraction mistake?)

Used accurately, finite differences is a great strategy that ties together the strategies of systematic lists, looking for patterns, subproblems, easier related problems, and algebra. You can use finite differences to find the equation for any polynomial function. Enjoy the strategy; it can be a lot of fun.

Problem Set A

EIGHT FUNCTIONS
Find the equation for each function.

a.

x	y
0	6
1	13
2	20
3	27
4	34
5	41

b.

x	y
0	6
1	12
2	20
3	30
4	42
5	56

c.

x	y
0	4
1	3
2	6
3	13
4	24
5	39

d.

x	y
0	5
1	1
2	−3
3	−7
4	−11
5	−15

e.

x	y
0	−2
1	3
2	20
3	55
4	114
5	203

f.

x	y
4	10
5	16
6	22
7	28
8	34
9	40

g.

x	y
2	3
3	10
4	19
5	30
6	43
7	58

h.

x	y
0	1
1	−1
2	9
3	43
4	113
5	231

2. TRIANGULAR NUMBERS

Find a formula for the triangular numbers.

3. PENTAGONAL NUMBERS

Find a formula for the pentagonal numbers.

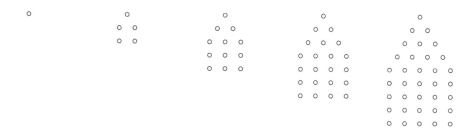

4. DIAGONALS

How many diagonals are there in a polygon with n sides?

5. GREAT PYRAMID OF ORANGES

A very bored grocer was stacking oranges one day. She decided to stack them in a triangular pyramid. There was one orange in the top layer, three oranges in the second layer, six oranges in the third layer, and so on. Each layer except the top formed an equilateral triangle. How many oranges would it take her to build a pyramid 50 layers high?

6. WRITE YOUR OWN

Create your own pattern that can be solved with finite differences. Start with the equation that you are going to use, then create the chart. If you get ambitious, try creating a situation that will give you the numbers in your chart, as in the Great Pyramid of Oranges problem in this problem set.

Problem Set B

1. **CELEBRATION TIME**

Luke and Dicey decided to celebrate. They didn't know what they were celebrating, but it sounded like fun. They started with dinner. It cost them one-third of their money, plus $4.50 more for a tip. Then they spent $3.75 each on admission to the county fair, and they immediately purchased tickets for an open-air concert for half their money plus one more dollar. They bought a bottle of antacid with $2.50 of their remaining money, and then spent one-third of what they had left on the trip home. At this point, feeling sick and exhausted, they had only $5.00 left. How much money did they spend on their celebration?

2. **WILSHIRE BOULEVARD**

Ardith, Burris, Chris, Dawn, and Eartha all live on Wilshire Boulevard, which is a very long street. Ardith lives at one end of the street. Driving down the street from Ardith's house, you would first get to Burris's house, then Chris's, Dawn's, and finally Eartha's. The five of them had lunch one day and discussed the distances between their houses. The number of blocks between each pair of houses is different. These ten numbers, arranged in numerical order, are 15, 21, 27, 36, 42, 48, 63, 69, 84, and 111. If Ardith lives closer to Burris than Dawn lives to Eartha, determine the distances between each pair of adjacent houses.

3. **FIVES AND ONES**

Monica, Jurmaii, Carol, Andy, and Tomás each have some $1 bills. Monica has one of them, Jurmaii has two, Carol has three, Andy has four, and Tomás has five. Each person may also have a $5 bill. None of them has any other kind of money.

At least one person has more money than Jurmaii and less money than Tomás. Monica does not have less money than both Carol and Andy. Tomás does not have more money than both Monica and Jurmaii. The person with the most money has six dollars more than the person with the least amount of money. How much does each person have?

4. REGIONS IN A CIRCLE

A circle can be separated into seven different regions by three straight lines across the circle. The regions will not be the same size. Before you go on, be sure you can draw a circle and separate it into seven regions by drawing three straight lines.

What is the maximum number of regions that will be formed by drawing 100 straight lines across the circle? (Some of these regions will be very small!)

5. PRICEY PETS

The members of a boys' club went to a very large pet store. The club's advisor wanted to find out how much the pets cost, because some of the boys said they wanted one. He noticed some signs at various places in the store. The sign above the fish tank said "Buy 16 fish and 8 cats for the price of 7 dogs." The sign above the cat cage said "Buy 11 cats and 7 dogs for the price of 9 fish." The sign above the dog cage said "Buy 3 dogs and 9 fish for the price of 8 cats." The advisor ended up helping one of the boys buy a fish and a dog. The fish cost $42 less than the dog. At this time, the advisor discovered that exactly one of the three signs was incorrect. Which sign was wrong, and how much did a cat cost?

Baseball statistics are organized in many ways so that fans, players, and coaches can evaluate different aspects of a player's performance.

15

Other Ways to Organize Information

At the California State Fair in Sacramento, there are two types of tickets. Adults' tickets cost $6, and children's tickets cost $4. Before the fair opened, the assistant manager realized that with the large number of people who would crowd into the gates when they opened at 10 a.m., the time it would take the cashiers to add up the ticket price for each group would slow down the line. So she devised the matrix shown on the next page to speed things up. All a cashier had to do was ask each customer, "How many adults, and how many children?" Then, by finding the number of adults on the top of the matrix and the number of children down the side, the cashier could find the appropriate dollar amount to collect. Look in the matrix below to determine the cost for five adults and seven children.

ADULTS

	0	1	2	3	4	5	6	7	8	9	10
0	0	6	12	18	24	30	36	42	48	54	60
1	4	10	16	22	28	34	40	46	52	58	64
2	8	14	20	26	32	38	44	50	56	62	68
3	12	18	24	30	36	42	48	54	60	66	72
4	16	22	28	34	40	46	52	58	64	70	76
5	20	26	32	38	44	50	56	62	68	74	80
6	24	30	36	42	48	54	60	66	72	78	84
7	28	34	40	46	52	58	64	70	76	82	88
8	32	38	44	50	56	62	68	74	80	86	92
9	36	42	48	54	60	66	72	78	84	90	96
10	40	46	52	58	64	70	76	82	88	94	100

CHILDREN (rows, 0–10)

With the ticket information organized in this way, the cashiers can save a lot of time when they figure out what each family owes for its tickets. Did you get $58 for the family described above? How much would admission for your family cost?

You have explored many problem-solving strategies in this book. The strategies have been separated to fall under three major problem-solving themes: Organizing Information, Changing Focus, and Spatial Organization. The last three chapters of the book feature various other strategies that fall under these three themes.

Throughout this book you've learned techniques for organizing information. The strategies of systematic lists, eliminating possibilities, matrix logic, looking for patterns, guess-and-check, unit analysis, algebra, and finite differences all require that you organize information in some way. (There are elements of the Organizing Information theme in the strategy of working backwards, although working backwards fits primarily into the Changing Focus theme.) When you organize a problem's information in a meaningful way, the problem is usually much easier to solve. This chapter will explore more ways of organizing information.

The next problem first appeared in Chapter 13: Algebra.

The next problem first appeared in Chapter 13: Algebra.

SEASON'S STATS

Franny, Carl, and Amichung compared their season's statistics during the post-season banquet for their high school baseball team. Franny had three times as many singles as Carl. Carl had four times as many doubles as Amichung. Each of them had exactly the same number of hits. None of the three had any hits besides singles and doubles (they were slap hitters). The three of them as a group had exactly as many singles as doubles. Added together, the three of them had fewer than 200 hits in all. How many singles and how many doubles did each of them have? Do this problem before continuing on.

In Chapter 13, Rick started his solution with a systematic list and guess-and-check. To make things easy on himself, he'd kept his guesses of the number of singles the same and had changed his guesses of the number of doubles. Ryan continued Rick's line of reasoning a little further, as shown in the chart below. (The * columns are the numbers they guessed.)

| Carl | | Franny | | Amichung | | Total | |
sing*	doub	sing	doub	sing	doub*	sing	doub
2	20	6	16	17	5	25	41
2	24	6	20	20	6	28	50
2	28	6	24	23	7	31	59
2	32	6	28	26	8	34	68

Ryan noticed many patterns. "If you read down each column, some patterns showed up. In Carl's Doubles column the numbers increased by 4 each time. The same thing happened in Franny's Doubles column.

In Amichung's Singles column the numbers increased by 3. In the Total Singles column the numbers increased by 3, and in the Total Doubles column the numbers increased by 9. Wanting to see if this would keep happening, I started over with three singles for Carl and returned Amichung to five doubles."

Carl		Franny		Amichung		Total	
sing*	doub	sing	doub	sing	doub*	sing	doub
3	20	9	14	18	5	30	39
3	24	9	18	21	6	33	48
3	28	9	22	24	7	36	57
3	32	9	26	27	8	39	66

"The same thing happened. I also noticed that in my new chart the difference between the total singles and doubles started at 9 (found by subtracting: 39 − 30) and went up to 15 (48 − 33), then 21 (57 − 36), and so on—a difference of 6. In the previous chart, the difference started at 16 (found by subtracting: 41 − 25) and went up to 22 (50 − 28), 28 (59 − 31), and so on—also a difference of 6. I realized that if I could make this difference zero, I would solve the problem. I looked for a better way of organizing the information.

"Since I had two variables to work with, I decided that a two-dimensional array might be useful. I set one up, with the numbers running down the outside left-hand column being the guesses for Carl's singles, and the numbers running across the top row being the

AMICHUNG'S DOUBLES

CARL'S SINGLES		5	6	7	8	9	10	11	12	13
	2	16	22	28	34	40				
	3	9	15	21	27	33				
	4	2	8	14	20	26				
	5	−5	1							
	6									
	7									
	8									

guesses for Amichung's doubles. The numbers in the array are the differences between the total number of singles and the total number of doubles. The first four numbers in the first two rows are from my two earlier charts. The rest of the numbers in the chart [the red numbers] are from the observed patterns."

"I noticed that there were some neat patterns here too. Going across each row, the numbers increase by 6. Going down each column, the numbers decrease by 7. If you go diagonally down to the right, the numbers decrease by 1. So I knew that I would reach zero very soon. I didn't bother finishing the whole chart; I just continued until I reached a zero."

AMICHUNG'S DOUBLES

		5	6	7	8	9	10	11	12	13
	2	16	22	28	34	40				
	3	9	15	21	27	33				
CARL'S SINGLES	4	2	8	14	20	26				
	5	−5	1	7	13	19				
	6	−12	−6	0 bingo						
	7	−19								
	8	−26								

"So Carl must have had six singles, and Amichung must have had seven doubles. These are the same answers that Rick got."

~~~~~~

You first encountered the next problem in Problem Set A of Chapter 3: Eliminate Possibilities. You probably solved it with a combination of strategies—making a systematic list and eliminating possibilities. In this chapter, we will look at a different way to organize the information in this problem.

THE THREE SQUARES

Three cousins, Bob, Chris, and Phyllis, were sitting around watching football on TV. The game was really boring, so they started talking about how old each of them were. Bob (the oldest) noticed that they were all between the ages of 11 and 30. Phyllis noticed that the sum of their ages was 70. Chris (the youngest) burst out, "Gee, if you write the square of each of our ages, all the digits from 1 to 9 will appear exactly once in the digits of the three squares." How old was each person? Do this problem before continuing on. See if you can organize the information in the problem in a new way.

The solution for this problem was contributed by Ed Migliore, a mathematics teacher at Monterey Peninsula College in Monterey, California. It uses the strategy of eliminating possibilities as well as organizing information in a new way.

"First I made a list of numbers from 11 to 30 and their squares. I didn't bother to include numbers like $11^2 = 121$ since there are repeated digits, which obviously was not allowed."

AGE	SQUARE	AGE	SQUARE
13	169	23	529
14	196	24	576
16	256	25	625
17	289	27	729
18	324	28	784
19	361	29	841

"I set up a chart on graph paper. The numbers on the top row are the digits 1 through 9. The numbers down the side are the numbers between 11 and 30 that I squared. I just checked off the digits that appeared in each square. For example, $25^2 = 625$, so I put an X in each of the 2, 5, and 6 columns."

NUMBER	1	2	3	4	5	6	7	8	9
13	X					X			X
14	X					X			X
16		X			X	X			
17		X						X	X
18		X	X	X					
19	X		X			X			
23		X			X				X
24					X	X	X		
25		X			X	X			
27		X					X		X
28				X			X	X	
29	X			X				X	

Ed went on. "The only 3's appear in the squares for 18 and 19. So either 18 or 19 must be in the list. Assume it is 18 [an example of seeking contradictions]. This means that 3, 2, and 4 all appear in 18^2 and therefore can't appear in any other number. So eliminate all of the numbers that have 3's, 2's, or 4's in them. This eliminates 16, 17, 19, 23, 25, 27, 28, and 29 [as shown on the next page]."

NUMBER	1	2	3	4	5	6	7	8	9
13	X					X			X
14	X					X			X
~~16~~		*			*	*			
~~17~~		*						*	*
18		X	X	X					
~~19~~	*		*			*			
~~23~~		*		*					*
24					X	X	X		
~~25~~		*			*	*			
~~27~~		*					*		*
~~28~~				*			*	*	
~~29~~	*			*				*	

"The only number left with a 7 is $24^2 = 576$, so 24 must be one of the ages. But 576 also contributes a 5 and a 6, and the only remaining ages of 13 and 14 have squares that both contain 6's. So the assumption that 18 is one of the ages proves false, so 18 may be crossed off.

NUMBER	1	2	3	4	5	6	7	8	9
13	X					X			X
14	X					X			X
16		X			X	X			
17		X						X	X
~~18~~		*	*	*					
19	X		X			X			
23		X			X				X
24					X	X	X		
25		X			X	X			
27		X					X		X
28				X			X	X	
29	X			X				X	

This also means that 19 is one of the ages for sure, since it is the only other number whose square can contribute the 3. Now I had a bunch of crossed out values from my false assumption. I had to clean up my chart before I could proceed [as shown on the previous page].

"Knowing that 19 is one of the ages means that the digits 1, 3, and 6 are contributed by 19^2 and I can cross off all of the other numbers whose squares contain 1, 3, or 6. This eliminates 13, 14, 16, 24, 25, and 29."

NUMBER	1	2	3	4	5	6	7	8	9
~~13~~	*					*			*
~~14~~	*					*			*
~~16~~		*			*	*			
17		X						X	X
~~18~~		*	*	*					
19	X		X			X			
23		X			X				X
~~24~~				*		*	*		
~~25~~		*			*	*			
27		X					X		X
28				X			X	X	
~~29~~	*			*				*	

"The only number left that contains a 5 is 23^2. So 23 must be one of the ages. I circled it and eliminated the other numbers that contained 2's, 5's, and 9's. This eliminated 17 and 27. The only number left in the list was 28, so it had to be in the final list also. So the ages are 19, 23, and 28."

NUMBER	1	2	3	4	5	6	7	8	9
~~13~~	*					*			*
~~14~~	*					*			*
~~16~~		*			*	*			
~~17~~		*						*	*
~~18~~		*	*	*					
19	X		X			X			
23		X			X				X
~~24~~					*	*	*		
~~25~~		*			*	*			
~~27~~		*					X		X
28				X			X	X	
~~29~~	*			*				*	

"So Chris (the youngest) is 19, Phyllis is 23, and Bob (the oldest) is 28."

Notice that in Ed's final chart, each of the digits 1 through 9 that appeared in the squares appears in only one column. It is also interesting that Ed never used the clue that the ages had to add up to 70—this clue is superfluous to solving the problem. The way that Ed organized the problem's information made the solution very easy to reach. His approach is somewhat similar to the matrix logic approach from Chapter 4.

The high schools in and around Sacramento, California, participate in a series of monthly mathematics competitions called Mathletes. Each Mathlete team consists of five members, each member must take three of the five tests given in the competition, and each test is taken by three team members. For many years the tests were given in arithmetic, Algebra 2, Algebra 1, trigonometry, and geometry (the test categories were recently revised and now include problem solving).

Ken was the coach of the Mathlete team at Luther Burbank High School for many years. When he first started coaching, for each event he made up a schedule like the one at the top of the next page.

Arith	Alg II	Alg I	Trig	Geom
John	Hoa	Khanh	Hoa	Hoa
Julie	Khanh	Julie	Khanh	John
Dahlia	John	Dahlia	Julie	Dahlia

The advantage of this schedule was that each team member could look at the schedule before each particular test started to see whether or not to take that test. But it wasn't immediately apparent on the schedule which three tests each team member would take—they had to search for that information. In addition, Ken had a hard time figuring out whether each person was taking three tests.

Another Mathlete coach showed Ken a matrix that she used.

	Arith	Alg II	Alg I	Trig	Geom
Hoa		X		X	X
Khanh		X	X	X	
John	X	X			X
Julie	X		X	X	
Dahlia	X		X		X

In her matrix it was easy to see which test was being taken by which person. It was also easy to immediately see which three tests each person would take. For the coach, it was evident that each person was taking three tests, and each test was being taken by three people. And it was really easy to change if necessary.

In the Storage Sheds problem in Problem Set A from Chapter 2: Systematic Lists, you were asked to find all possible rectangular sheds that could be made with panels whose lengths measured 8, 10, 12, and 15 feet. Michelle did the problem with the chart shown on the next page. Each X represents a side panel. (**Note** that because opposite sides are the same length, she used only two X's instead of four.)

8	10	12	15	
XX				8×8
X	X			8×10
X		X		8×12
X			X	8×15
	XX			10×10
	X	X		10×12
	X		X	10×12
		XX		12×12
		X	X	12×15
			XX	15×15

There is often more than one way to organize information, as many of the examples in this chapter demonstrate. Experiment with different methods of organization as you do the problems in the problem set. Don't be afraid to throw out what you have and start over.

Problem Set A

1. **COFFEE STAIN**

   At an amusement park, all the cashiers used a matrix that contained the prices for various combinations of children's and adults' tickets, similar to the matrix described at the beginning of this chapter. Toward the end of one day, entries to the park were getting rather slow. The manager, Patty, closed down all the entry gates except one. Unfortunately, the cashier spilled coffee on his matrix. All he could read were the numbers shown on the next page, and he wasn't even sure that they were all right, although he figured most of them were.

Re-create the matrix, changing the fewest numbers possible, and determine what the prices are for adults' and children's tickets. Also determine which numbers in the matrix are incorrect.

ADULTS

CHILDREN	0	1	2	3	4	5	6	7	8
0									
1				59					
2				58					110
3		34					99		
4			57			93			
5				74				126	
6		55							
7						114			
8									

2. THE OTHER THREE SQUARES

Three other cousins of the three cousins we met earlier noticed that their ages were all under 40 and that the squares of each of their ages contained all the digits from 0 to 9 exactly once. What were their ages?

3. TWO BILLS

I once met a father and a son, both named Bill. Bill Senior said, "I moved to Florida in 1965." Bill Junior said, "I was a sophomore in high school when my father moved to Florida." Bill Senior said, "Bill turned 16 in his sophomore year." The conversation took place in 1991. What were the possible ages for Bill Junior?

On a recent airline flight, six people from the same company were seated in rows 1, 2, and 3. Each had booked the flight at different times, so they all may have been charged different amounts. The people in the window seats had fares that were $5 apart (such as $14, $19, and $24). One person in an aisle seat had a fare equal to her seat partner's. Another person in an aisle seat had a fare that was one and a half times her seat partner's. The third person in an aisle seat had a fare that was twice her seat partner's. The total fare for all six was $1,025. All fares were in whole dollar amounts. How much was the second most expensive fare?

5. AHSME

The Mathematical Association of America sponsors a high school mathematics contest every year called the American High School Math Exam. The contest consists of multiple-choice questions that include five possibilities for each question. For many years, the scoring system for the 30-question test was as follows: Each right answer was worth 4 points. Each wrong answer was worth -1 point. Each unanswered question was worth zero points. Each contest participant started with a score of 30 points. Thus, for a person who got 6 right, 3 wrong, and left 21 unanswered, the score would be $30 + (6 \times 4) + (3 \times -1) + (21 \times 0) = 51$ points. To qualify for the second round of competition, a person had to score 95 points.

Around 1988 the scoring system changed. The new scoring system is as follows: 5 points for a right answer, zero points for a wrong answer, 2 points for no answer, and each participant starts with zero points. Thus, the example of 6 right, 3 wrong, and 21 unanswered would result in $(6 \times 5) + (3 \times 0) + (21 \times 2) = 72$ points. To qualify for the second round of competition, a person has to score 100 points.

Analyze these two different scoring systems and discuss which system you think gives a person a better chance of qualifying for the next round. For each system, decide on the best strategy of reaching the second round, given that you are sure of the answers to 10 questions and have narrowed down 10 other questions to two choices.

6. TWO-INPUT FUNCTION

The following is a function with two inputs. The first input is x, and the second input is y. What is the rule for calculating the output?

Input	Output	Input	Output	Input	Output
2, 3	17	1, 5	29	7, 4	44
4, 1	17	9, 2	40	1, 4	20
3, 7	61	0, 5	25	2, 5	33
4, 3	25	5, 2	24	4, 2	20
3, 9	93	2, 4	24	3, 8	76

Problem Set B

1.   ALGEBRA AND FRENCH

There are 53 students in the freshman class.

1. Twenty students are enrolled in both algebra and French.

2. Seven students taking language are not taking math.

3. Two-thirds of all language students are taking French.

4. The number of algebra students not taking language is one-third the number of math students not taking language.

5. Three-fourths of all math students are taking algebra.

6. There are 42 language students and 33 algebra students.

7. Ten algebra students are taking a language other than French.

8. The number of French students not taking math is three less than the number of math students not taking language.

How many students are taking a math class other than algebra and a language class other than French? How many students are not taking a math class?

2.   MOVIE THEATER

Five adults and their five young children went to a movie. The adults all sat together and the children sat together, with one empty seat between the two groups. As the lights dimmed and the movie began, the children realized they had sat behind a group of tall basketball players and they asked the adults to trade places with them. However, to be considerate to the people behind them, they all decided to follow these principles:

1. They could move into the next seat if it were empty.

2. They could leapfrog over only one person into an empty seat.

3. Nobody would backtrack. All moves had to be toward their new seats.

How many moves were necessary for the two groups to switch places?

3. **LOTSA FACTORS**

Including 1 and itself, how many positive-integer factors does 1,746,360,000 have?

4. **DICEY DIFFERENCES**

You are playing a new dice game. You roll two regular dice and then subtract the smaller number from the larger number. (If the dice show the same number, then it doesn't make any difference which way you subtract.) What is the difference most likely to occur?

5. **AREA AND PERIMETER**

Find the dimensions of all rectangles that have area equal to twice the perimeter, where both the length and the width are whole numbers. (Ignore units.)

Like the correct path through a maze, the solution to a problem can be easy to see when you change your point of view.

16

Other Ways to Change Focus

This chapter is about various strategies that fall under the major problem-solving theme of Changing Focus. Some problems are best solved by looking at them in a completely different way. For example, subproblems direct your attention away from the question asked and onto lesser, more manageable subgoals. Easier related problems require that you temporarily suspend your work on the original problem and concentrate on easier versions of the same problem. And when working backwards, you go to the end of a problem to see how everything in the problem leads up to that point. This chapter explores three other ways to change focus. We call these ways *change your point of view, solve the complementary problem,* and *change the representation.*

Movie and television directors have often used a changing-focus strategy when filming a movie or a TV program. The old TV show *Mission: Impossible* used this technique quite often. The camera would focus on a character in the foreground, then gradually move the focus to someone in the background—usually someone the person in the foreground was unaware of! If you've ever looked through a window on a rainy day, you probably experienced a similar sensation. While looking out the window, you didn't see the raindrops *on* the window until you focused your eyes on them.

Section 1: Change Your Point of View

You may have experienced some conflicts in your life that you and your family could not resolve. Possibly you sought the advice of a friend or a family counselor. This person was able to bring a new, fresh, and objective point of view to your situation and perhaps was able to help you resolve your conflicts. Sometimes you can solve your own individual problems by adopting a similar strategy. Looking at your situation the way someone else sees it may help you find a solution.

Similarly, being able to **change your point of view** may help you solve a mathematical problem that you think is impossible. You may have seen the following problem before. The solution to this problem is a good illustration of the strategy of changing your point of view.

NINE DOTS

Without lifting your pencil from start to finish, draw four line segments through all nine dots.

The solution has nothing to do with how wide the dots are or that possibly the lines determined by them are not parallel. The dots are mathematically defined—they have no width, and they determine sets of parallel lines.

Work this problem before continuing.

The solution to this problem is very simple. But finding the solution is not easy. Generally people feel constrained to make the solution fit within the confines of the square determined by the nine dots. The key here is to be flexible enough to allow your thinking to diverge from the zone indicated by the dots. You must change your point of view, moving your focus away from the structure of the square and allowing yourself to draw outside it. This type of thinking is commonly referred to as "thinking outside the box." (You can find the answer to this problem before the real-world problem solving feature at the end of this chapter.)

You could use a computer to solve the next problem, but that would be taking a sledgehammer approach. This chapter is about finding creative ways to look at problems in a different light. Think creatively as you solve this problem.

THE HUMAN FACTOR

Mayra is a human computer. She has appeared on talk shows to show off her amazing ability with numbers. One type of problem Mayra is very adept at is this: A person from the audience will give Mayra a number, and Mayra will immediately be able to tell how many one-digit factors that number has. For example, if you were in the audience and you said 50, Mayra would say 3 because 50 has 3 one-digit factors (namely, 1, 2, and 5).

One day, Mayra was on a well-known talk show, and some wise guy in the audience asked Mayra to tell him how many one-digit factors the numbers from 1 to 100 had. The answer was not 9, because Mayra had to count each factor for a particular number, then add that count to the number of factors for each of the other numbers from 1 to 100. So, for instance, even though the factor 5 appears in the factorization of 50, it also appears in the factorization of 45, so it must be counted once for each of those numbers. Mayra quickly "programmed" her brain to give her the answer, and she had it in a few moments. What was her answer?

Work this problem before continuing.

This problem encompasses many strategies. Arlene took one possible approach to this problem. "I decided to list all of the numbers from 1 to 100 and write down all their factors. Then I counted up the factors that were only one digit."

A portion of Arlene's list appears at right.

At this point, Jessica joined her. As Jessica would say later, "It seemed like this was going to take an awfully long time. So I suggested to Arlene that maybe there was an easier way. We looked at her list together to see if we noticed something."

Number	Factors
1	1
2	1, 2
3	1, 3
4	1, 2, 4
5	1, 5
6	1, 2, 3, 6
7	1, 7
8	1, 2, 4, 8
9	1, 3, 9
10	1, 2, 5, 10
11	1, 11
12	1, 2, 3, 4, 6, 12
13	1, 13
14	1, 2, 7, 14

ARLENE: When Jessica came over, I resented it at first. I mean, I had a perfectly reasonable way to do this problem, and I was doing fine. I knew it was going to take a long time, but I tend to be a very diligent, hardworking student [she was] and I figured I could do it. Sometimes, when I see a way that will work, I just continue with that method, even though it may take a while. It's better than not doing anything.

JESSICA: I tend to be lazy [she was], so I wanted to find an easier way. I had a feeling that Arlene was a little bothered by my presence, and I thought about leaving her alone, but lots of times two heads are better than one. So I asked Arlene if she noticed anything about her list.

ARLENE: After I recovered slightly from my resentment, I did as she asked. And of course, right away I noticed that I had written down 1 every time, 2 every other time, 3 every third time, et cetera.

JESSICA: After Arlene pointed this out, it seemed as though there was a really easy way to solve the problem. All we had to do was count up the number of 1's, 2's, 3's, 4's, 5's, 6's, 7's, 8's, and 9's that appeared in the list. But we didn't have to make the whole list to do that. There were obviously going to be 100 ones and 50 twos.

ARLENE: We had a little trouble with the number of threes. Then I realized that the last three would occur in the number 99, so there would be 33 threes.

JESSICA: All we had to do was divide each number into 100. If it didn't come out evenly, we had to round down. For example, how many 6's are there? Well, $100 \div 6$ is $16\frac{2}{3}$. The last 6 therefore occurs as a factor of 96, and we can ignore the remainder because the next 6 shows up as a factor of 102 and we weren't supposed to go that far.

Factor	Times It Appears
1	100/1 = 100 times
2	100/2 = 50 times
3	100/3 = 33 times
4	100/4 = 25 times
5	100/5 = 20 times
6	100/6 = 16 times
7	100/7 = 14 times
8	100/8 = 12 times
9	100/9 = 11 times
Total	281 times

ARLENE: So there are 281 one-digit factors of the first 100 numbers. Jessica was right, there was an easier way.

JESSICA: And it just goes to show that two heads are better than one.

Jessica and Arlene changed their point of view to solve this problem. They completely changed their approach to the problem when it became apparent that the original approach was going to take a long time. Instead of attacking the problem by checking each number to see how many factors it had, they changed their focus to the number of times a given factor appeared in the list of the first 100 numbers. This method counted exactly the same thing but organized the count in a much more manageable fashion, which made the problem a lot easier.

You must be "a little lazy" to use this strategy effectively. If you are willing to proceed with "the long way," you likely won't even look for an easier way. However, a little laziness is a good motivator in looking for the shorter way.

AVERAGE SPEED

Jacques left his home in Austin and drove to San Antonio. On the way there, he drove 40 miles per hour (there was a lot of traffic). On the way back, he drove 60 miles per hour. What was his average speed? Work this problem before continuing.

Since 50 is the average of 40 and 60, the answer 50 miles per hour appears to be the answer. But this answer is incorrect. Try changing your point of view. Instead of looking at the speed, concentrate on the time and the distance. **Notice** that there is no stated distance in this problem. This causes some difficulty, so use an easier related problem. One way to make this problem easier is to make up a distance. What we learn from the easier problem could help us solve the original problem. Because you might not be sure this approach works, make up at least two distances and figure out the problem for both.

A good distance to use would be 120 miles. One hundred twenty is the least common multiple of both 40 and 60. This should keep some of the other numbers in the problem simple.

Using 120 miles as the distance, Jacques traveled 40 miles per hour on the way from Austin to San Antonio. So this trip took him 3 hours. On the way back, he traveled 120 miles at 60 miles per hour. This trip took 2 hours. The total distance traveled was 240 miles. It took 5 hours to travel that far.

$$\frac{240 \text{ miles}}{5 \text{ hours}} = 48 \text{ miles per hour}$$

Verify this answer by using a distance different from 120 miles. The answer comes out the same. If you move your point of view away from speed and instead focus on time, this problem becomes easy to solve.

In the movie *Patch Adams,* the character of Patch Adams (played by Robin Williams) has a discussion with Mendelson (played by Harold Gould). Mendelson holds up four fingers and asks Patch how many fingers Patch sees. He responds, "Four." But Mendelson claims that the answer is incorrect. "You are looking at the problem," he says. "Look past the problem. See the solution." When Patch looks past the problem (the fingers) he no longer sees four fingers. He sees eight.

Try this great example of changing your point of view. Hold up four fingers at arm's length and look past them to an object across the room. Now how many fingers do you see? By focusing on an object past your fingers, your fingers will blur and you will actually see *eight* fingers. The point here is that when you are confronted with a problem, you sometimes have to change your point of view to be able to solve it. In the movie, Patch realizes that doctors need to make this change in their point of view, and this is a breakthrough in his thinking. He feels that doctors tend to focus on the disease and not on the patient, and he believes that doctors need to cure patients, not diseases. By focusing on the patient instead of the disease, Patch becomes a better doctor.

Section 2: Solve the Complementary Problem

Some problems are more easily approached by a "comin' around the back" approach. That is, instead of solving the problem that is asked, try finding the opposite of what is asked. Consider a problem from probability: How many ways are there to roll two dice and have them sum to a one-digit number? Instead of answering this question, answer the opposite question: How many ways are there to get a sum of 10, 11, or 12? This is much easier to do. A 10 can be rolled as (6, 4), (5, 5), or (4, 6). An 11 can be rolled as (5, 6) or (6, 5). A 12 can be rolled as (6, 6). So there are six ways to roll 10, 11, or 12. Therefore, because there are 36 ways to roll two dice, there must be 30 ways to roll a one-digit number.

This approach, to **solve the complementary problem**, is another way to change focus. You might be familiar with the word *complement*—not *compliment,* like "gee, your hair looks nice today," but *complement,* which refers to two things that are different yet fit together. Here are some of Webster's definitions:

- That which completes or brings to perfection

- Something added to complete a whole; either of two parts that complete each other

- In geometry, two angles that sum to 90 degrees

- In music, the difference between a given interval and the complete octave

The key in all these definitions is the idea of two parts making a whole. In the dice problem, the sums of 2 through 9 complement the sums of 10 through 12, and vice versa, because the complete set of possible sums includes those from 2 through 12.

Keep in mind that this strategy of solving a complementary problem provides another way to change focus. Rather than solving the stated problem, instead solve the complementary problem (if it is easier). Use this strategy to solve the next problem.

BOOK REPORT

Seiko had to do a book report. She was supposed to read five books, in any order, then write an essay comparing and contrasting the books. She could choose from the list below. In how many ways could she choose five books?

Of Mice and Men by John Steinbeck

The Bean Trees by Barbara Kingsolver

The Joy Luck Club by Amy Tan

The Color Purple by Alice Walker

The Call of the Wild by Jack London

Catch-22 by Joseph Heller

Work this problem before continuing.

Seiko was handy with solving the complementary problem. "I thought about making a systematic list of all the ways I could choose five books. But then I realized that each entry in my list would always contain five of the books and leave one out. Figuring out the number of ways to leave a book out is a lot easier to do. There are six books, and each of them would be left out one time, so there are six ways to choose five books. The complementary problem was much easier to solve."

Complementary events come up in many different areas of life. A baseball manager attempting to determine which of his pitchers will be relievers must first determine who will be starting. Mechanics can figure out what is broken by noting what is working. Head counts are taken on field trips because the point of counting heads is to determine if anybody is missing.

Some other strategies and problems in this book incorporated the idea of complementary situations. When you solved a matrix logic problem, you knew that each person either was or wasn't matched up with something else. Your objective was to determine the matchups, and you often did this by eliminating the complementary possibilities. In Chapter 13: Algebra, the pet-store employee in the Salt Solution problem was asked to raise the concentration of salt in a solution. He could have accomplished this task by either of two complementary actions: adding salt or evaporating water.

AREA

Find the area of the shaded region. Work this problem before continuing.

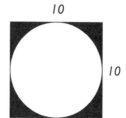

The shaded area is a complement of the circle when both are viewed as parts of the square. This section focuses on complementary problems, and this problem clearly illustrates the concept of two problems that fit together well as complements. Nobody in his or her right mind would try to find the area of the shaded section directly (though it can be done). Instead, it is far easier to take the subproblem-complementary problem approach to it. That is, rather than finding the area of the regions that *are* shaded, it is much easier to find the area of the region that is *not* shaded and subtract it from the square.

In this case, the area of the square is 100 square units. The area of the circle is $\pi(5^2)$, which is approximately 78.54 square units. The complementary problem here is finding the area of the circle. This area complements the area of the shaded regions. By subtracting, we find that the answer is approximately 21.46 square units.

OFFICE NETWORK

I hate our office computer network. It seems to be "down" more than it is "up." Take the last eight days since I came back from vacation, for example. I work an eight-hour shift, but the network works less. The first three days back were fine. It was working the whole time I was. But the fourth day, it was down for the first half hour of my shift and then went down again 15 minutes before I left. The next day I had to wait a half hour longer than I had to wait the previous day for it to come up, and it went down 15 minutes earlier than the day before—the network almost seems to have a brain. The sixth day it did the same thing: It came up half an hour later than on the fifth day, and went down 15 minutes earlier. That same pattern carried on to the seventh day. How many hours total was the network operational during my last seven shifts? Work this problem before continuing.

You could solve this problem by calculating how much the network was operational each day and adding it all up. But there is an easier approach. Say the magic words *solve the complementary problem.* For this problem it is easy to calculate the amount of time the network would have been working if it had been up during the person's entire shift for seven days.

8 hours/day × 7 days = 56 hours

Now figure out how much time the network was down. On the fourth day, it was down for a half hour in the morning and for 15 minutes in the afternoon. So it was down for 45 minutes on the fourth day. The next day, it was down for half an hour more in the morning and 15 minutes more in the afternoon, so it was down 45 + 45 minutes on the fifth day. This pattern continued on the sixth day, 45 + 45 + 45, and again on the seventh day, 45 + 45 + 45 + 45. Therefore, the network was down 10 × 45, or 450 minutes, which is 7 ½ hours. Subtract 7.5 from the 56 we originally calculated, and we're left with 48.5 hours. It was much easier to find how much time the network was down and subtract from the 56 hours than it would have been to calculate how much time it was functional.

THE TENNIS TOURNAMENT

A big regional tennis tournament in New Orleans drew 378 entries. It was a single elimination tournament, in which a player was eliminated from the tournament when she lost a match. How many matches were played to determine the champion? Work this problem before continuing.

Henrick solved this problem with a diagram and easier related problems. "I looked at this problem and wanted to scream. It was way too hard. So I changed it to only two people in the tournament. That was a much easier problem, and it had an easy solution: one match. Then I used three people. This was a little harder. If the players were A, B, and C, I figured A could play B while C had a bye. Then the winner would play C for the championship. That would be two matches. Four players seemed harder. I decided to make one of those elimination charts like they use in tennis tournaments and the NCAA basketball tournaments."

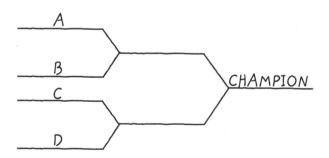

"From this I could see that there would be three matches. I suspected that the number of matches needed was one less than the number of players, but I really wasn't sure. That's when LaVonn came to help me."

LaVonn picked up the solution. "I saw that Henrick had a good pattern going, but it seemed like he would never really be sure if he was right. It suddenly occurred to me that maybe we could look at the complementary problem. Instead of determining the number of matches necessary to determine a winner, I figured out how many matches were necessary to determine all the losers. Since there is only one winner, everyone else must lose. Each match produces a winner and a loser. The winner goes on, but the loser is eliminated. When the tournament is over, all players but one have lost. So there must be exactly that many matches: one less than the number of players in the tournament. So in a tournament that has 378 players, there must be 377 losers and therefore 377 matches to determine a champion."

(For more about tree diagrams and tournament charts, see Chapter 17: Other Forms of Spatial Organization.)

Section 3: Change the Representation

Change the representation is a strategy that combines changing focus with some other strategy. Generally, you use the strategy of drawing a diagram when you change the representation, but there are other ways. For instance, you might use a systematic list to organize your problem information, but you could convert your list to a matrix. In the new representation, all sorts of hidden relationships become clear.

A problem may seem to lend itself to a particular strategy, or it may seem hard to approach with any strategy. Such problems may be good candidates for changing the representation. If you can represent the problem in some other form, you may be able to solve it more easily. Again, a little laziness is helpful.

You may have solved this famous problem about cards in an earlier problem set.

You have ten cards numbered 1, 2, 3, 4, 5, 6, 7, 8, 9, and 10. Your task is to arrange them in a particular order and put them in a stack, hold the stack in your hand, and then do the following: Put the top card on the table face up, put the next card on the bottom of the stack in your hand, put the next card on the table, put the next card on the bottom of the stack, and so on, continuing to alternate cards that go on the table and under the stack, until all ten cards are on the table.

That, of course, is really easy to do. The trick is to lay the cards on the table in numerical order. In other words, the first card you put on the table will be number 1, the next card you put on the table will be number 2, the next card you put on the table will be number 3, and so on, until the last card placed on the table will be number 10.

In what order should the cards be arranged in the original stack so that this will happen? See if you can represent this problem in a completely different way (we used a diagram) and solve it more easily. Work this problem before continuing.

Originally, you probably solved this problem with a physical representation in conjunction with working backwards. This problem can also be easily solved by changing the representation. Draw ten lines in a circle, as shown at right. Label one of them the first (top) card in the stack. Write the number 1 on that line.

Then go to the next line. (This solution will proceed in a clockwise direction, but you could just as easily go counterclockwise.) The next line represents the second card in the stack. This card will be put under the stack, so skip this line. The next line will be the third card in the stack. This will be card number 2. Label this line 2. Skip the next line because that card will go under the stack. Label the next line 3. Skip the next. Then label 4. Skip the next, then label 5. Skip the next.

Top card
_1_

Top card
_1_

5   2

4   3

The next line you come to is line number 1, but this line represents a card that has already been put on the table, so it would no longer be in the stack. The next empty line will be card 6. Skip the next empty line because this card will be put under the stack. Continue in this way until reaching card 10.

Top card

8 1 6

5   2

9   10

4 7 3

The final order proceeds from the top (card 1) clockwise to the last card (card 8). So the order is 1, 6, 2, 10, 3, 7, 4, 9, 5, 8. Try it. **Note** that completely changing the way the problem was represented made the problem much easier to solve.

Ed also used the strategy of changing the representation on this problem, but he used a different representation. "I wrote down ten blanks in a row to represent the ten cards. Then I numbered the first blank 1, the third blank 2, the fifth blank 3, and so on. The second, fourth, sixth, et cetera, blanks I labeled A, B, C, D, E."

1 A 2 B 3 C 4 D 5 E

"The cards numbered 1–5 would be the first five cards laid down on the table. The cards labeled A–E would be the five cards put under the stack. So I drew arrows to show them being put under the stack."

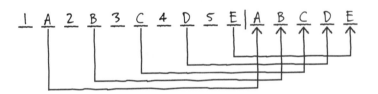

"After card E, the next card should be the 6. That means that card A should be 6. Then card B goes under the stack again, card C becomes 7, card D goes under the stack and card E becomes 8."

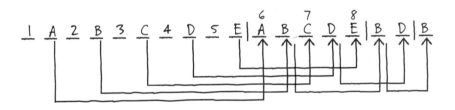

"Then card B goes under the stack again, and card D becomes 9. So card B is 10."

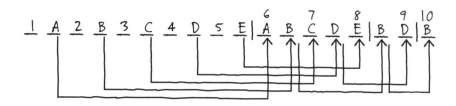

"Finally I went back into the original list and labeled A–E with the numbers they turned out to be. So now I knew the order of the cards."

1 6 2 10 3 7 4 9 5 8

Changing the representation is another way of changing the focus. It can be a very good strategy, though it may be difficult to apply to most problems.

By the way, here's the solution to the problem that opens the chapter.

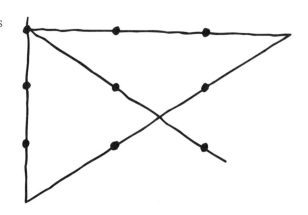

Real-World Problem Solving

At the Annual Meeting of the National Council of Teachers of Mathematics in San Diego, California, in April 1996, mathematics teacher Alan Barson from Beaver College in Glenside, Pennsylvania, told the story of a man in New York City's Central Park who played the following card game: The game was played with nine cards, each showing one of the digits 1 through 9. Two players took turns choosing one of the cards. The object of the game was to be the first player who had three cards that added up to 15. Consider the sample game below.

PLAYER 1 TAKES	PLAYER 2 TAKES
4	6
2	9
8	5
3	

At this point the game is over and player 1 wins the game because he has 3, 4, and 8, and those add up to 15. **Note** that player 2 did not win when he had 6 and 9, because you need *three* cards that add up to 15. Try playing this game with someone.

The man playing the game—let's call him Hugo—never lost this game. Either he would always tie the game or he would win. (As you'll see as you read on, Hugo had an unseen edge. The unsuspecting person who plays the game thinks the game is fair, but the person running the game employs a very clever strategy so that he will not lose.) Alan wondered why Hugo never lost, but he didn't figure it out until much later in his life. Hugo was not really playing a card game; he was playing the game of tic-tac-toe. In the game of tic-tac-toe, you need three X's or three O's in a row of a three-by-three grid to win. Hugo had created a three-by-three magic square that contained the digits 1 through 9. Each row, column, and diagonal of his magic square contained three numbers that added up to 15. He'd memorized this magic square, and when his opponent took a number, he made a mental X on his magic square. Then he would use a mental O to indicate his own move. In this way, he could always force either a tie (cat's game) or a win.

If you've played a lot of tic-tac-toe in your life, you probably have strategies you use that prevent you from losing. But usually when you play tic-tac-toe, your opponent knows that *she* is playing tic-tac-toe too. Imagine playing tic-tac-toe against someone who doesn't even know she's playing tic-tac-toe! She'd make some very strange moves. But you could always force a tie or a win.

If you wonder how this works, make the three-by-three magic square for this game, using the digits 1 through 9. Each row, column, and diagonal of your square must add to 15.

Now try playing this game with someone. Create the nine cards that contain the digits 1 through 9. Then sit at a table, opposite your opponent. Alternate taking cards. Hold your magic square in your lap and use it to play tic-tac-toe while you're also playing the card game. It will take some practice, but you can do it.

This game is a perfect example of changing the representation. Hugo had changed a relatively difficult game into a game of tic-tac-toe, which is much easier to play. In mathematics, this type of situation is called an **isomorphism** (a one-to-one correspondence of mathematical sets). The tic-tac-toe game is said to be isomorphic to the game in the park.

~~~

The three strategies in this chapter all require insight, imagination, and creativity. You must be able to see a problem in a different perspective. The result of changing the focus is that the problem becomes easier to solve in its new form than it was in its old form. If a problem seems too difficult and an easier related problem doesn't seem to help too much, then try changing your focus to a different approach to solve it.

Problem Set A

1. MORE DOTS

Without lifting your pencil from start to finish, draw six line segments through all 16 dots. The solution has nothing to do with how wide the dots are or that possibly the lines determined by them are not parallel. The dots are mathematically defined as points—they have no width, and they determine sets of parallel lines.

2. FEARLESS FLY

This is a famous problem. Two bicyclists, Frances and Fred, rode toward each other. Each traveled 20 miles per hour, and they started off 10 miles apart. A frivolous fly flew furiously fast at 50 miles per hour from Frances to Fred. The fly started on Frances's handlebars as Frances and Fred started riding. It flew to Fred's handlebars and then back to Frances's and back to Fred's, always following the bike path. (No self-respecting fly flies a beeline.) It continued in this way until Frances and Fred reached each other. How far did the fly travel?

3. TOOTHPICKS

Using six toothpicks, make four triangles of the same size.

4. PERFECT SQUARES

How many perfect squares are there between 2,000 and 20,000?

5. COMPLEMENTARY EVENTS

What is the complementary event for each given situation?

    a. You roll a die one time and get a six.

    b. You roll a die one time and get an odd number.

    c. You roll a die two times and don't get any sixes.

    d. You roll a die five times and get six every time.

    e. There are 40 people in the same room, and they all have different birthdates.

6. PAYDAY

Marissa recently got a smaller-than-usual weekly paycheck. She normally works from 8:00 a.m. to 5:00 p.m., with an hour for lunch, five days a week. Her pay is $7.50 per hour, but she gets paid only for the hours she works. On Monday she left at 3:30 to go see her son play softball. On Tuesday she was 45 minutes late getting back from lunch because she got a flat tire. On Wednesday she left at 2:15 to go to her night class. On Thursday she had a doctor's appointment in the morning and didn't get to work until 10:30. On Friday, she took a three-hour lunch break to pick her brother up at the airport. Then at 4:10, she left early to beat weekend traffic. How much did she get paid for the week?

7. THE LIKELIHOOD OF BEING LATE

The airline you're flying on has an on-time rate of 98% for the route you are taking. The bus from the airport to the convention center has an on-time rate of 95%, but if you are late, of course, you will miss the bus and be late arriving at the convention. What are your chances of being late?

8. ANOTHER CARD ARRANGEMENT

This problem is similar to the Card Arrangement problem in this chapter. Start with all the cards in one suit in the deck: ace, 2, 3, 4, 5, 6, 7, 8, 9, 10, jack, queen, and king. Arrange the cards in a particular order in your hand. Then spell the name of each card, putting one card on the bottom of the stack for each letter in the name of the card. So for an ace, you would say "A-C-E ace," putting three cards on the bottom of the stack and laying the fourth one face up on the table (which will be the ace). Then continue by saying, "T-W-O two," putting three cards on the bottom of the stack and laying the fourth one (a two) on the table just as you say "two." Continue in this way all the way through jack, queen, and king, each time ending the spelling by saying the card you just spelled as you lay it face up on the table. What order do the cards have to be in originally for this to all work out?

9. **KNIGHT MOVES**

This problem comes from our friend and mentor Tom Sallee. Suppose you arranged chess knights on a three-by-three chess board as shown below.

White Knight 1		White Knight 2
Black Knight 1		Black Knight 2

A knight's move is one space in any direction (horizontally or vertically), then two spaces in either perpendicular direction. (That's equivalent to two spaces and then one space in the perpendicular direction—knights can jump over pieces in their path.) Two knights may not occupy the same space at the same time. Only one knight may move at a time.

a. How many moves does it take for the white knights to change places with the black knights?

b. How many moves does it take for White Knight 1 to change places with Black Knight 1?

10. NEW GAME IN CENTRAL PARK

When Alan Barson figured out what Hugo was doing (see the real-world problem solving feature in this chapter), he went back to Central Park to see if Hugo was still there. Hugo wasn't, but his son was and he was playing a related game. This time, each of the nine cards contained a word. The words were

BRIM   FORM   HEAR   HOT   SHIP   TANK   TIED   WASP   WOES

Players alternated choosing words. The object of the game was to be the first person to possess three words that contained the same letter. For example, if you chose *form, hot,* and *woes,* you would have three words that contained the letter *o.* Hugo's son was also using the strategy of change the representation and was actually playing tic-tac-toe. He'd made a three-by-three magic square, but had put a word into each square instead of a number. Each row, column, and diagonal of the magic square contained three words that shared a common letter. Make the magic square.

Problem Set B

1. COMPUTER ERROR

A computer was printing a sequential list of positive integers, but because of a glitch in the software, it neglected to print any numbers that were integral powers of integers (the powers were larger than 1). Thus, the list began 2, 3, 5, 6, 7, 10, 11, 12, 13, 14, 15, 17, ... How many numbers in this list had fewer than four digits?

2. PALINDROME CREATOR

How many three-digit numbers have the following special property? Take a three-digit number. Reverse the digits to create a new three-digit number (this number may be the same as the original number). Add the two numbers together. The result is a *palindrome,* a number that reads the same backwards and forwards. Neither the original number nor the new number can start with 0.

3. THE AMAZING RESTIN

The Amazing Restin is a psychic. She can figure out anything anybody is thinking, as long as she is lying down. She gives performances all over the country. One of her favorite gimmicks features words: Her assistant thinks of a five-letter word. Then the Amazing Restin proceeds to guess five-letter words, and her assistant tells her how many letters the word he thought of shares with the word she guessed. One day, she guessed five words and he told her that each of her words shared exactly two letters with the word he had in mind. Here are the five words she guessed.

BLUNT   VOTER   SPICE   BUOYS   MADLY

What word did the assistant have in mind?

4. MULTIPLES

Place the digits 0 through 9 into the circles below, subject to the following rule: Each pair of digits that are joined by a line must form a two-digit number (in either order) that is divisible by either 8 or 13. So, for example, the digits 4 and 8 could be connected with a line because 48 is divisible by 8. (**Note** that 84 is not divisible by either 8 or 13, but that doesn't matter. As long as it works in one of the orders it's okay.) There are two solutions, but they are basically the same—just two digits are switched.

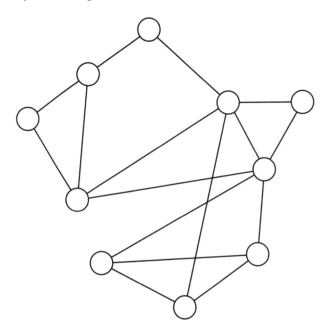

A man who lives in the South Pacific is planning a rowboat trip. His rowboat will hold him plus enough food to last three weeks. By a strange coincidence, several small islands about one week's rowing apart are near the island he lives on. He plans on rowing to the fifth island, which is a large island with grocery stores similar to those on the main island he lives on now. But the four small islands between his island and the other big island have no stores, and he will not be able to buy any food on those islands. So he realizes that he will have to row out to an island, store some food, and return to the main island for more supplies. Show how he should organize his food supplies so he can get to the fifth island. How many weeks will his trip take altogether?

A graph can be a dramatic and persuasive way to show that a product is earning a profit or losing money for its manufacturer.

17

Other Forms of Spatial Organization

W e have already discussed strategies that fall under the major problem-solving theme of Spatial Organization: diagrams, physical representations, and Venn diagrams. This chapter will explore three more strategies that fall under this theme: graphs, scale drawings, and tree diagrams.

Section 1: Use a Graph

Some problems are best represented with a **graph**. Graphs are used in many places to represent real-world situations. For example, newspapers are full of various types of graphs. Graphs can clearly show the relationship between **variables** in a way that is difficult to see otherwise.

CHICKEN NUGGETS

A local fast-food vendor sells chicken nuggets for the following prices:

SERVING SIZE	PRICE
6 nuggets	$2.40
10 nuggets	$3.60
15 nuggets	$5.10
24 nuggets	$7.80

Draw a graph of this information. Then answer the following questions:

a. What is the equation for this graph?

b. What is the slope for the graph? What is the real-world significance of the slope?

c. What is the *y*-intercept for this graph? What is the real-world significance of the *y*-intercept?

d. How much would it cost to buy a serving size of 50 chicken nuggets?

e. Another restaurant sells 13 nuggets for $4.25 and 20 nuggets for $6.75. Use the graph to find out whether these are good deals compared to those of the restaurant above. Then use the equation for the graph to check your answer.

A group of students worked on this problem.

BETTY: This seems impossible. How are we supposed to answer all these questions?

NANCY: Oh, come on, Betty. That's what you always say, but then you're the first one done. We can do this.

BETTY: Okay, where do we start? I guess we should draw the graph. But what should we put on the *x*-axis?

SHAUNA: I think we should put the price on the *x*-axis.

SHELLY: No. The price depends on the number of nuggets purchased. You're always supposed to put the **dependent variable** on the *y*-axis and the **independent variable** on the *x*-axis.

BETTY: Okay. So *x* is the number of nuggets, and *y* is the total price. (Here's the graph she drew.)

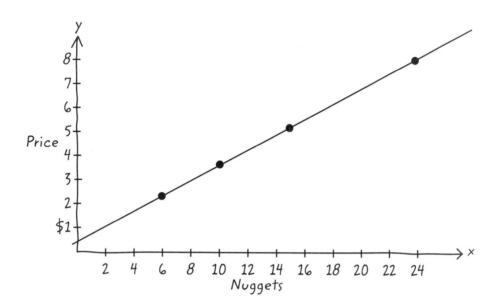

BARBARA: What does the line mean?

BETTY: The points on the line give all possible combinations of the number of nuggets and the corresponding price. So, for instance, 8 nuggets would cost $3.00.

BARBARA: I see. Let's try to figure out the equation for this thing. What do we need to do?

SHELLY: We need the **slope**, and we need the **y-intercept**. Then we can write the equation, using $y = mx + b$.

NANCY: I can figure out the slope. It's just rise over run. So if we choose the run from 6 nuggets to 10 nuggets, the price goes up, or rises, $1.20. A price change of $1.20 for 4 nuggets is $0.30 per nugget. That's the ratio of rise over run.

SHAUNA: That must be what the question means about the real-world significance of the slope. It's just price per nugget. That's interesting. I never thought of that before.

SHELLY: Since m stands for the slope, the equation must be $y = 0.30x + b$. But how do we get b?

BARBARA: Well, b is just the y-intercept. Let's look at the graph. It looks like the line goes through the y-axis somewhere around $0.50.

NANCY: Let's work backwards. If it costs $0.30 per nugget, then 6 nuggets should cost $1.80. But 6 nuggets really cost $2.40. That's an extra $0.60, which is where the graph crosses the y-axis.

BETTY: Or we could have plugged 6 nuggets and $2.40 into the equation that Shelly suggested and solved for b.

$$y = \left(\frac{\$0.30}{\text{nugget}}\right)\left(x \text{ nuggets}\right) + b$$

$$\$2.40 = \left(\frac{\$0.30}{\text{nugget}}\right)\left(6 \text{ nuggets}\right) + b$$

$$\$2.40 = \$1.80 + b$$

$$b = \$0.60$$

BETTY: Wow, even the units work out.

SHELLY: So our equation is $y = 0.30x + 0.60$. The slope is the price per nugget, but what is the significance of the y-intercept?

NANCY: Well, if you bought zero nuggets, it would cost $0.60. That's what I was trying to say before. That's weird. How come it costs so much to buy nothing? You must be paying for something.

SHAUNA: Maybe you're paying for the privilege of buying your chicken nuggets there.

BETTY: Or maybe for the forks and spoons and napkins. Or maybe it's just profit. Or the packaging.

NANCY: Okay, I get the message. There could be a lot of things you're paying for. I wonder if all restaurant food is priced like that.

SHELLY: Probably. Question d asks for the price of 50 nuggets. We can figure that out with our equation or our graph.

BETTY: I didn't use paper big enough for the graph. But I think 50 nuggets would cost between $15 and $16.

NANCY: According to the equation, the price is $y = 0.3(50) + 0.60$, which is 15.60. That matches your estimate, Betty.

BARBARA: How are we going to answer the last question?

BETTY: Let's plot those points on the graph. The point (13, 4.25) is below the line, and (20, 6.75) is above the line.

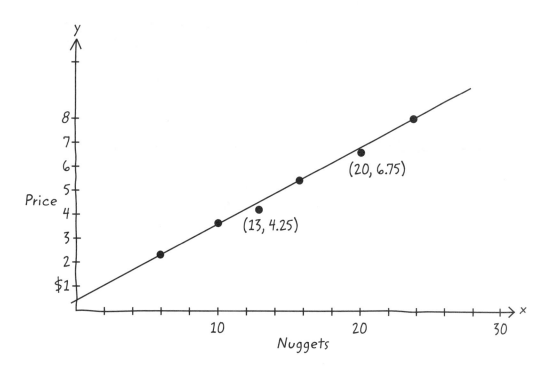

BARBARA: What does that mean?

SHELLY: Well, if the point is under the line, the cost is less than it should be, so it's a good deal. And if the point is above the line, the cost is more than it should be, so it's a bad deal.

BARBARA: That makes sense. Can we also use the equation to figure that out?

NANCY: Sure, I think so.

SHAUNA: Yes, we can. Use the equation to figure out how much 13 nuggets would cost at the first restaurant: $y = 0.3(13) + 0.60 = 4.50$. That means $4.25 is a good deal, better than $4.50.

BETTY: And 20 would cost $0.3(20) + 0.60 = 6.60$, and $6.60 is cheaper than the other restaurant's price of $6.75, a bad deal.

SHELLY: Wow, this was a really neat problem. The graph and the algebra together are pretty convincing.

As this discussion illustrates, you can use either graphing or algebra to solve the Chicken Nuggets problem, but combining the two strategies will provide a more sound and convincing solution. An advantage of graphing is that you can represent information visually. Work the following problem with similar methods.

PHONE CALLS

Lisa Family just got a new phone installed in her room so that she can chat with her friend Ernie without monopolizing the Family family phone. During spring break, Ernie went on vacation for five days. Lisa called him once a day each of the five days he was gone, even though it was a long-distance call. The shortest of these calls was 6 minutes and cost $1.26. A 7-minute call cost Lisa $2.07. Here's a chart of the other three calls she made to Ernie.

TIME (IN MINUTES)	COST
11	$2.26
17	$4.57
22	$4.46

Determine the connect fee and the cost per minute for the two rate schedules Lisa called under: day rate and evening rate. (A connect fee is the charge levied the instant a phone conversation begins.) **Note** that both the day rate and the evening rate are linear relationships. Work this problem before continuing.

The following graph is going to play a crucial, though not complete, role in solving this problem. Here are the graph points plotted with time in minutes (t) on the horizontal axis and cost (c) on the vertical axis.

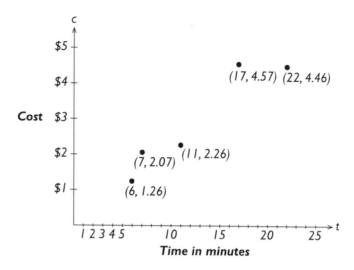

Because we know that Lisa called under two different rate schedules, we can reasonably assume that we need to determine the graphs of two linear functions. Three points in particular (the 6-, 11-, and 22-minute calls) line up easily. The remaining two points also form a line, slightly steeper and slightly higher than the first. The slope of each line represents the cost per minute. The c-intercept of the higher line reflects the higher connect fee. Because day calls cost more than evening calls, we can assume that the higher and steeper line represents the day calls.

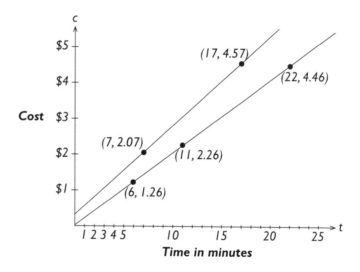

Now that we've identified the calls associated with the day rates and the evening rates, we can determine the slope and the c-intercept for each line. First consider the evening calls, using the two points (6, 1.26) and (11, 2.26). You can find the slope by calculating the rise over the run.

$$\frac{\text{rise}}{\text{run}} = \frac{\$2.26 - \$1.26}{11 \text{ minutes} - 6 \text{ minutes}} = \frac{\$1.00}{5 \text{ minutes}} = \frac{\$0.20}{\text{minute}}$$

The slope, m, must be 0.20, which is the evening per-minute rate. The equation form $y = mx + b$ translates to $c = mt + b$ in this problem. Solve for b, the c-intercept, to find the connection charge.

$$c = mt + b$$
$$2.26 = 0.20(11) + b$$
$$2.26 = 2.20 + b$$
$$0.06 = b$$

The connection charge is $0.06, so the first-minute rate for an evening call is $0.26 and each additional minute costs $0.20. The equation you can use to find the cost for any evening call at this rate is $c = 0.20t + 0.06$, where c is the cost of the call and t is the number of minutes talked.

To find the day rate, we again find the slope and the c-intercept.

$$\frac{\text{rise}}{\text{run}} = \frac{\$4.57 - \$2.07}{17 \text{ minutes} - 7 \text{ minutes}} = \frac{\$2.50}{10 \text{ minutes}} = \frac{\$0.25}{\text{minute}}$$

We solve for b to find the c-intercept, the connection charge.

$$c = mt + b$$
$$2.07 = 0.25(7) + b$$
$$2.07 = 1.75 + b$$
$$0.32 = b$$

Therefore, the cost of the day phone calls is $0.25 for each minute, with a $0.32 connection charge. The first minute costs $0.57, and each additional minute costs $0.25. The equation you can use to find the cost for any day call at this rate is $c = 0.25t + 0.32$.

The graph in this solution showed us two rates that applied to Lisa's phone calls: two calls were plotted on one linear graph that represented the day rate, and the other three calls were plotted on the other linear graph that represented the evening rate. In addition to grouping items in a problem into one category or another, you can use a graph to extend the results to data not specified in the problem.

Note that the linear model for this particular function is not entirely accurate. Phone costs do not rise at a constant per-minute rate, so they do not actually correspond to linear graphs. Rather, they are examples of what are called **step functions**. In the problem, the charge for Lisa's 11-minute call is given as $2.26. This would also be the charge for a 10-minute-and-1-second call, a 10-minute-and-2-second call, and so on, all the way up to an 11-minute call. But as soon as the twelfth minute begins, the charge goes up to $2.46. The graph that follows shows this step function for only the evening calls. On the graph, note that an open circle means that the left-hand endpoint does not belong to the line segment. A closed circle means that the right-hand endpoint does belong to the line segment. The endpoints indicate rate changes, so if a call is exactly 3 minutes, it will be charged at the lower rate. The line drawn as the original graph connects the right-hand endpoints of the steps.

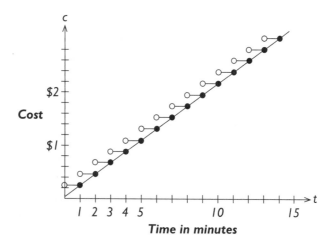

Time in minutes

The Family family wants to take another vacation. They have decided to drive their van to a destination 600 miles away. If they drive at a reasonable speed, how much time should they set aside for the trip? Plot a graph that shows various driving speeds (in miles per hour) on the *x*-axis and driving time (in hours) on the *y*-axis. Work this problem before continuing.

Doug solved this problem with a systematic list and a graph. "I didn't really understand this problem at first. So I started making a list of possible speeds and times. I realized right away that if they traveled 60 miles per hour, it would take 10 hours of driving. And if they traveled 30 miles per hour, it would take 20 hours of driving. I decided to make a systematic list showing a lot of the possibilities—but not all of them because the list would be endless."

SPEED	TIME
1 mph	600 hrs
2	300
3	200
4	150
5	120
6	100

"At this point, I realized that I should try to put this information in a graph. But I knew I needed some more varied data or my graph was going to be pretty dull. So I decided to skip some possible speeds.

SPEED	TIME		SPEED	TIME
1 mph	600 hrs		50 mph	12 hrs
2	300		60	10
3	200		70	8.57
4	150		75	8
5	120		80	7.5
6	100		100	6
10	60		120	5
20	30		300	2
30	20		600	1
40	15			

"Although some of these pairs of numbers were a little unrealistic, like driving 600 miles per hour (although that could be reasonable for an airplane), I didn't think my graph would be complete without them. As the problem directed, I put speed on the *x*-axis and time on the *y*-axis, because the time it takes the Familys to reach their destination depends on how fast they drive."

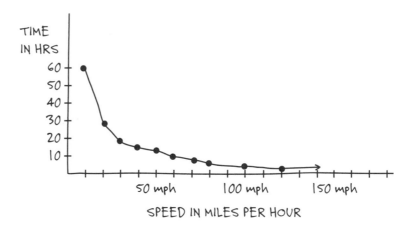

SPEED IN MILES PER HOUR

"The graph looks pretty neat, but I guess the results are obvious because anybody knows that the faster you drive, the sooner you'll get there. A more interesting graph would show the time you'd spend waiting for the highway patrol to write out your tickets if you'd been driving 90 miles per hour, or the time you'd spend in the hospital if you'd been driving 250 miles per hour."

FAT CONTENT

Many ads for food indicate either the percentage of fat the food contains or to what percentage the food is fat-free. For example, an ad might say "Our burgers are 90% fat-free," or perhaps "Our lean hamburger is only 15% fat." A person reading these ads might assume that the percentage of Calories from fat is also only 10% in the first case and 15% in the second case. But this assumption wouldn't be accurate, because the ads indicate the percentage of fat by *weight,* not in *Calories.*

Fat has 9 Calories per gram. Comparatively, carbohydrates and protein each have only 4 Calories per gram. In addition, virtually all foods have moisture content (as well as minerals, etc.), which contains 0 Calories per gram. For example, 2% milk (2% of the weight of the milk comes from fat) is about 89% water. Once this water weight is taken into account, about 34% of the Calories come from fat.

Draw a graph that shows a food's percentage of fat by weight on the x-axis and its percentage of fat in Calories on the y-axis. Assume that this food is 50% water. Then assume the remaining percentage of the food represents carbohydrates and protein. Then use your graph to find what percentage of fat by weight gives 50% of the Calories from fat. Work this problem before continuing.

To draw the graph, you'll need points to plot. Start by inventing weights of fat and of carbohydrates and protein for 100 grams of imaginary food. (This is a good example of creating an easier related problem—using the number 100 often makes working with percentages easier.) Because of our assumption that 50% of the food is water, that means that 50 grams of the food is water. List the number of grams of fat the food contains so you can figure out the number of grams of carbohydrates and protein it contains. For example, if the food contains 5 grams of fat, then it contains 45 grams of carbohydrates and protein (and the remaining 50 grams are water, as we assumed). Because our food weighs 100 grams total, the number of grams of fat will always also be the percentage of fat by weight.

Now calculate the number of fat Calories. Look again at 5 grams of fat and calculate how many Calories of our food that represents.

$$5 \text{ grams} \times \frac{9 \text{ Calories}}{\text{gram}} = 45 \text{ Calories}$$

Because our food is made up of fat *and* of carbohydrates and protein (and water), we also need to calculate the number of Calories of carbohydrates and protein.

$$45 \text{ grams} \times \frac{4 \text{ Calories}}{\text{gram}} = 180 \text{ Calories}$$

So, our food contains a total of 225 Calories: $45 + 180 = 225$. Now we can figure the percentage of Calories from fat compared to the total Calories.

$$\frac{45 \text{ Calories from fat}}{225 \text{ Calories total}} = 20\% \text{ fat}$$

To generate a sufficient list of points to plot, continue in this way, choosing numbers for grams of fat—which are also the percentages of fat by weight—and figuring out the appropriate percentages for Calories. Then draw a graph such as that shown on the next page.

% fat by weight	% fat in Calories
0	0.0
5	20.0
10	36.0
15	49.1
20	60.0
25	69.2
30	77.1
35	84.0
40	90.0
45	95.3
50	100.0

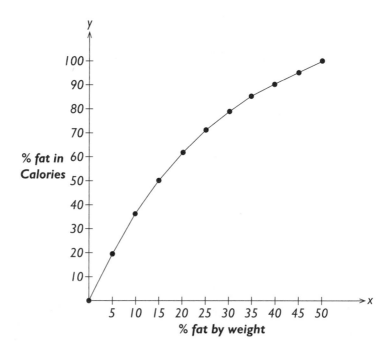

The graph shows that with about 15% fat by weight, the food contains 50% fat in Calories. And remember, we assumed that our sample food had 50% moisture weight. Many foods are more than 50% moisture. The moral of the story is, be a little cautious when you hear that a food is 90% or 85% fat-free, because a lot more of the Calories come from fat than you might expect.

The population served by the Martin Gardner High School District grew drastically starting in the mid-1990s. The enrollments of Gardner High School itself and the neighboring Raymond Smullyan High School also grew. The enrollment capacity of each school is 2200 students. If growth exceeds this figure at either school, the district will need to build a new school. Here are the enrollment data for the two schools.

	ENROLLMENT	
YEAR	MARTIN GARDNER	RAYMOND SMULLYAN
1994	1402	1718
1995	1462	1741
1996	1467	1745
1997	1548	1782
1998	1661	1765
1999	1801	1778

Your task is to make a report to the school district on enrollment growth patterns that will help them decide whether a new school is needed. Do this problem before continuing.

Shannon provided this graph and report.

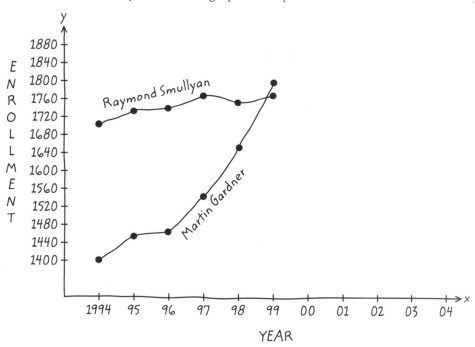

"The Raymond Smullyan High School graph shows an increase of approximately 12 students per year on average, although only one of the one-year changes (1998–1999) was close to this average. For an accurate forecast, it would also be necessary to check other factors reflecting the population, such as housing and employment changes. However, the general trend of the points plotted clearly indicates a gradual, steady growth that will not reach the 2200-student maximum in the next five years.

"On the other hand, the graph for Martin Gardner High School is alarming. Growth there appears to be exponential, and an enrollment forecast based on the graph would give us around 2025 students in 2000 and somewhere around 2400 students in 2001. A new school is needed to serve students in this community within two years, unless the other factors mentioned above will completely stop population growth in the district in the next year. That seems unlikely, so I recommend immediate action to build a new school in the Martin Gardner High School area."

Shannon's analysis for Martin Gardner High School is correct. Because of the 2200-student capacity of the school, enrollment growth could not be permitted to continue the way the graph indicates. The graph allows us to project the rate of growth shown by the plotted data into subsequent years. It also provides a visual picture that supports Shannon's recommendation to the school district, convincing them of the need for immediate action.

DUCKS AND COWS

Farmer Brown has ducks and cows. The animals have a total of 12 heads and 32 feet. How many ducks and how many cows does Farmer Brown have? Solve this problem with a graph before continuing.

Eric solved this problem with a graph. "I set up two equations, one representing heads and the other representing feet. I let x represent ducks and y represent cows. My equations were

$x + y = 12$ (the total number of heads is 12)

$2x + 4y = 32$ (2x is the number of duck feet and 4y the number of cow feet, and the total number of feet is 32)

"Then I graphed each equation, which gave me two straight lines. They intersected at (8, 4), which is 8 ducks and 4 cows."

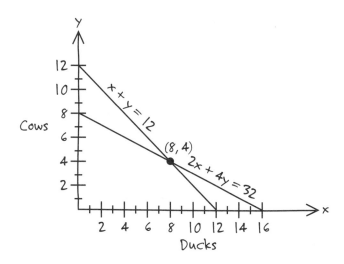

MAXIMUM AREA

A farmer with 100 feet of fencing wants to build a rectangular garden. What should the dimensions of the garden be in order to enclose the maximum area? Work this problem before continuing.

This problem could be solved in any number of ways. You could use guess-and-check or you could generate a systematic list, but you might not be sure you had the best answer. You could also use calculus, a very good technique for solving problems such as this. But this problem can also be solved by graphing, which is how we'll solve it.

First set up the equation to be graphed. Start by drawing a picture of the rectangular garden. The total fencing available measures 100 feet. So, if the top and bottom sides of the garden each measure x feet, then the left- and right-hand sides each measure $(100 - 2x)/2$ feet, which can also be written as $50 - x$ feet.

Thus, the area of the garden is $x(50 - x)$ square feet. By hand, or with a graphing calculator or a computer, graph $y = x(50 - x)$, or simply $y = 50x - x^2$.

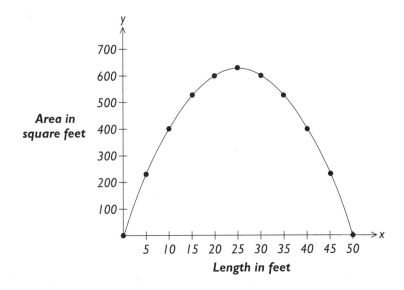

The y-value represents the area of the garden. The x-value represents the length of the top side of the garden. Look for where the y-value is at its highest point (called a **maximum value**). It appears that when x measures 25 feet, the area is at a maximum at 625 square feet.

You don't really need an equation to create the graph. You could also do it by choosing values for the length, calculating the areas, and using the coordinates (length, area) as the points to plot. The graphing process is then essentially the same: The y-value represents the area of the garden, and the x-value represents the length of the top side of the garden.

Graphs are very powerful visual tools for solving problems. A graph can provide a visual image of the situation given in a problem, making the problem and the solution easier to understand.

Section 2: Make a Scale Drawing

Consider the Ducks and Cows problem again.

DUCKS AND COWS

Farmer Brown has ducks and cows. The animals have a total of 12 heads and 32 feet. How many ducks and how many cows does Farmer Brown have? Read the following explanation of how to solve this problem with a special type of scale drawing.

Melissa and Kevin each solved this problem with a **nomograph**. A nomograph is a graph whose axes are parallel to one another instead of at right angles. Just as in a coordinate graph, you can place corresponding values alongside each other to illustrate proportions and relations. Melissa's nomograph is shown below.

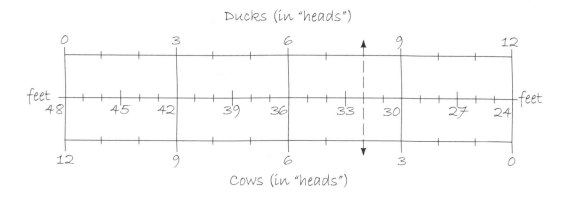

Melissa explained her diagram. "Because the total number of heads is 12, the nomograph is set up so that a vertical line drawn anywhere in the graph will yield a solution of x ducks + y cows = 12 heads. The maximum number of feet possible for 12 heads is 48, and the minimum is 24. Therefore, the range of the number of feet is between 24 and 48.

"To find a solution, move along the feet-axis until the desired number is reached—in this case, 32. Draw a vertical line through that point, and the corresponding numbers on the ducks-axis and on the cows-axis are the solution.

"The answer to '32 feet' is 4 cows and 8 ducks, as shown above. Got it?"

Kevin took a similar approach to this problem. He used a constant of 32 feet, and he looked for the number of heads to add up to 12.

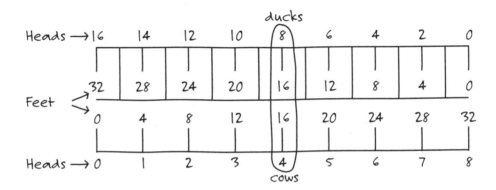

Kevin explained: "With this nomograph, I can locate the correct number of ducks and cows by finding which vertical line intersects numbers that add up to 12 heads, because the feet for each line equals 32. Therefore, the answer is 8 ducks and 4 cows."

The two solutions to the Ducks and Cows problem combined the strategies of using a graph and making a **scale drawing**. In Section 1 of this chapter you learned about drawing graphs to solve problems. In this section you'll learn about making scale drawings to solve problems.

Who uses scale drawings? Matt Tsugawa is a landscape architect. He frequently uses scale drawings to plan landscapes for his clients. He makes a scale drawing of the basic area he'll be working with, such as a backyard or a park. Then, to check the plans for aesthetics, that walkways are the appropriate width, for foliage density, and so on, he draws various plants and trees to scale on transparent overlays and places them over the main drawing. If he doesn't like the results, he creates a new transparency and so doesn't have to eliminate the main drawing.

Police investigators also make scale drawings of traffic-accident scenes. They use their scale drawings—along with some algebra, geometry, trigonometry, unit analysis, and subproblems—to determine the original speeds of the vehicles involved. This process helps determine whether either driver was speeding, which in turn may indicate who was at fault.

Scale drawings depend on unit analysis, as you'll see in the next problem.

MY PATIO

A rectangular patio measures 18 feet by 12 feet. On the patio is a rectangular lounge chair that measures 2 feet by 4 feet 3 inches and a circular picnic table that measures 5 feet 8 inches in diameter. Make a scale drawing of my patio before continuing.

The first step in creating a scale drawing is to choose a scale. It is often easier to use centimeters rather than inches to represent feet so let's pick the scale 1 cm = 2 ft. You must then do some unit analysis to convert real-world measurements to scale measurements. For example, to find the scale measurement of the picnic table's diameter, you must convert 5 ft 8 in. into feet, then scale to centimeters.

$$8 \text{ in.} \times \frac{1 \text{ ft}}{12 \text{ in.}} \approx 0.67 \text{ ft}$$

$$5.67 \text{ ft} \times \frac{1 \text{ cm}}{2 \text{ ft}} = 2.83 \text{ cm}$$

So the table with a diameter of 5.67 ft has a diameter of 2.83 cm in the scale drawing. Using an approximation of 2.8 cm will work well for this problem. The drawing of the patio is shown on the next page.

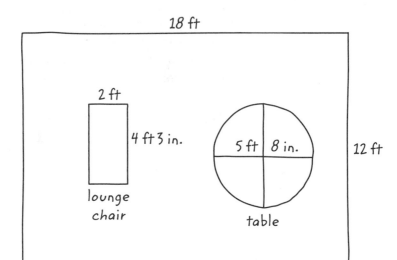

18 ft

2 ft

4 ft 3 in.

lounge
chair

5 ft | 8 in.

table

12 ft

1 cm = 2 ft

Note the difference between unit analysis and scaling. In unit analysis, the fraction you multiply by has the value of 1 (for example, $^{1\,\text{ft}}/_{12\,\text{in.}}$). In scaling, the fraction does not have the value of 1 (such as $^{1\,\text{cm}}/_{2\,\text{ft}}$), but you choose to make 1 cm and 2 ft correspond for the purposes of scaling.

MAYDAY

"Mayday, Mayday!" The call startled Ned, who was stationed in the Coast Guard office. He immediately radioed. "Coast Guard here. What is your position? Over."

"I'm not sure. We left the port at Miami at 7:30. We sailed due southeast for 2 hours at 35 knots. Then we turned about 30° to starboard [right] and sailed for 4 hours at 25 knots. Then we lost our engines and we have been adrift for about an hour and a half. We would have called earlier, but our radio was out. Can you send us some help?"

Ned replied, "I'll work out your position and send out a chopper right away. Over." Ned knew that the ocean current at that time of day was approximately 5 knots due south. A knot (kn) is 1 nautical mile per hour. One **nautical mile** (NM) is about 1.15 land miles. The helicopter speedometer measures land miles per hour. The likely speed of the helicopter was 80 miles per hour (that is, land miles). In what direction should Ned send the helicopter, and how many minutes will it take it to get to the stranded boat?

Make a scale drawing and solve this problem before continuing.

Ned solved this problem as follows: "I knew I could probably use trig for this, but instead I made a scale drawing. I let 1 millimeter equal 1 nautical mile. From a dot representing Miami, I measured a 45° angle in the southeast direction. The 2 hours at 35 knots is 70 nautical miles, so I marked off 70 millimeters with a big dot. From there I measured a 30° angle representing the right turn and marked off 100 millimeters because the 4 hours at 25 knots is 100 nautical miles. From there I drew a line due south and marked off 7.5 millimeters to represent 7.5 nautical miles, the distance the boat would have drifted in an hour and a half with a current of 5 knots.

"Finally, I drew a line from Miami to the boat's last position, and found it to be 171 millimeters, representing 171 nautical miles. The line formed an angle about 64° south of east."

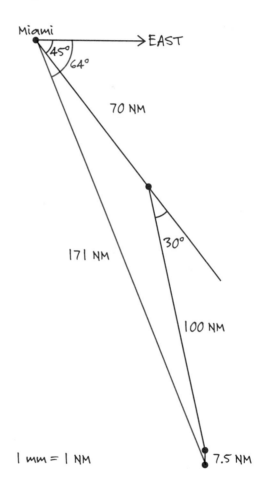

$$171 \text{ NM} \times \frac{1.15 \text{ mi}}{1 \text{ NM}} = 196.65 \text{ mi}$$

"Then I figured out the time, given that the helicopter travels 80 miles per hour."

$$196.65 \text{ mi} \times \frac{1 \text{ hr}}{80 \text{ mi}} \approx 2.46 \text{ hr}$$

$$0.46 \text{ hr} \times \frac{60 \text{ min}}{1 \text{ hr}} = 27.6 \text{ min}$$

"So it would take the helicopter about 2 hours 28 minutes to reach the boat. Of course, in that time the boat would have drifted a little farther south, which means the helicopter wouldn't find the boat at that spot. It would have to turn due south at that point and look for the boat."

Many people use scale drawings to solve real-world problems that deal with space or to visualize problems that involve trigonometry. You can get a much clearer overview of a situation when you make a scale drawing of it.

Section 3: Draw a Tree Diagram

Another common way to organize information is by using a tree diagram. An example of a tree diagram is illustrated in Chapter 2: Systematic Lists. You may have also used tree diagrams to solve some of the other problems in this book. In the real world, tree diagrams show up in tournament scheduling. NCAA basketball tournaments and all tennis tournaments organize their schedules with tree diagrams.

These types of tournaments often feature seedings, or rankings. The best player in the tournament is seeded number 1, the next best player is seeded number 2, and so on. The tournament schedule is organized so that the best player plays the worst player in the first round, the second-best player plays the second-worst player, and so on. Additionally, the schedule is set up so that the number-1 and number-2 seeds cannot meet until the final round. A typical tennis tournament diagram for eight players is shown below.

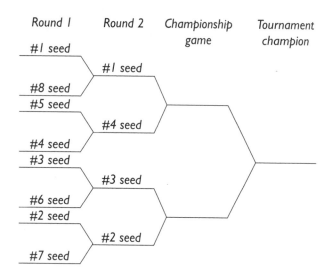

Notice that the sum of the seed numbers for each first-round game is 9. And assuming that the higher seed wins each first-round game, the sum of the seeds for each second-round game is 5. Now assume that the higher-seeded player wins each second-round game, leaving the number-1 and number-2 seeds in the championship game. A similar pattern exists for a tournament of 16 players, 32 players, and so on.

The difference between tournament diagrams like these and typical tree diagrams is that in most tree diagrams the branches grow out to the right.

Steve Weatherly, who taught mathematics at Nevada Union High School in Grass Valley, California, for many years, wrote many of the tree-diagram problems in this chapter. The next problem illustrates how to use a tree diagram to solve problems that involve counting.

Liberty is going to flip four coins at once: a penny, a nickel, a dime, and a quarter. How many ways are there for the four coins to come up? Make a tree diagram of all possible results before continuing.

Liberty made the tree diagram shown below. The coin flips are indicated in order: penny, nickel, dime, quarter.

Penny	Nickel	Dime	Quarter	Possible results P N D Q
			H	HHHH
		H	T	HHHT
	H		H	HHTH
		T	T	HHTT
			H	HTHH
		H	T	HTHT
H	T		H	HTTH
		T	T	HTTT
			H	THHH
		H	T	THHT
	H		H	THTH
		T	T	THTT
			H	TTHH
T		H	T	TTHT
	T		H	TTTH
		T	T	TTTT

Liberty then counted up the ways, shown by the diagram, and found there are 16 results you can get when you flip four coins.

Tree diagrams are very useful for solving problems about probability. The next couple of problems involve probability.

After Liberty counted all the ways she could flip four coins, she wanted to know the probability of getting two heads and two tails when flipping four coins. What is that probability? Solve this problem before continuing.

Liberty looked back at the tree diagram she'd made to solve the Four Coins problem and counted all the places in the diagram where two heads and two tails came up. The diagram shows that two heads and two tails occurred 6 times out of the 16 total times. So the probability of two heads and two tails is $^6/_{16}$, which written as a decimal is .375 or 37.5%.

A bag contains one white ball and two red balls. A ball is drawn at random. If the ball is white, then it is put back into the bag along with an extra white ball. If the ball is red, then it is put back into the bag with two extra red balls. Then another ball is drawn. What is the probability that the second ball drawn is red? Solve this problem before continuing.

Len drew the tree diagram shown at right.

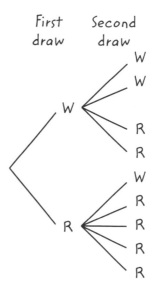

First draw   Second draw

W
W
W
R
R
W
R
R
R
R

Len said, "First I thought the probability was $6/9$. But then I realized that there were two red balls to start with. I figured this diagram was getting way too confusing, so I tried just writing R and W once on each branch, and writing the probability of that branch along the line." He drew the new diagram shown below.

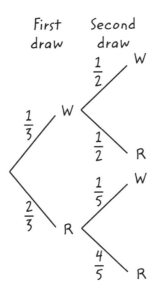

Len went on. "The probability of choosing a white ball on the first draw is 1 out of 3, since there were originally one white ball and two red balls in the bag. If a white ball is chosen the first time, it is put back into the bag along with an extra white ball. So now there are two white balls and two red balls in the bag. So the probability of drawing a white ball on the second draw is $2/4 = 1/2$. The probability of drawing a red ball on the second draw is also $2/4 = 1/2$.

"Then I looked at what happens if a red ball is chosen first. The probability of that happening is $2/3$ because originally there were two red balls and one white ball in the bag. If a red ball is chosen first, then it is put back into the bag along with two extra red balls. So now there are four red balls and one white ball in the bag. The probability of drawing a white ball on the second draw is $1/5$, and the probability of drawing a red ball on the second draw is $4/5$.

"Now I wanted to find the total probabilities for each line. The probability that a white ball is drawn both times is $^{1}/_{6}$. I found this by multiplying $^{1}/_{3} \times ^{1}/_{2}$. So I computed all the probabilities. The notation P(W,W) stands for the probability of getting a white ball on the first draw and a white ball on the second draw.

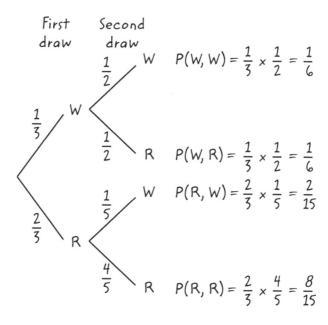

"To check to see if I was doing it right, I added up the total probability.

$$\frac{1}{6} + \frac{1}{6} + \frac{2}{15} + \frac{8}{15} = \frac{5}{30} + \frac{5}{30} + \frac{4}{30} + \frac{16}{30} = \frac{30}{30} = 1$$

"I knew I was calculating correctly, because the total probability was 1. I also noticed that the sum of the top two branches was $^{1}/_{3}$, which was the probability of getting a white ball the first time. Also, the sum of the bottom two branches was $^{2}/_{3}$, and that was the probability of getting a red ball the first time.

"Finally, I calculated the probability of getting a red ball on the second draw. This could happen white, red (W,R) or red, red (R,R). The probabilities were $^1/_6$ and $^8/_{15}$, so I added $^1/_6 + {}^8/_{15}$ and got $^{21}/_{30}$, which reduces to $^7/_{10}$. So there is a 7 in 10 chance, or a 70% chance, of getting a red ball on the second draw."

Another excellent use of tree diagrams is in problems about conditional probability. Problems like the next two are common in statistics classes. This next problem may surprise you. It is an example of the mathematics of drug testing, greatly simplified for the purposes of this book.

DRUG TESTING

A company that conducts individual drug tests to identify the existence of certain substances in a person's system claims that its drug test is 90% accurate. That is to say, given a group of people who use drugs, the test will correctly identify 90% of the group as drug users. And given a group of people who don't use drugs, the test will correctly identify 90% of the group as non-users. Those numbers sound pretty good on the surface, but suppose someone has just taken this drug test and the results are positive. What is the probability that he actually uses drugs?

To solve this problem, we need to know what percentage of the general population uses drugs. Let's use the company's numbers: To test the validity of its drug test, the company tested a sample group of people, knowing that 5% of this group did in fact use drugs. Solve this problem with a tree diagram before continuing.

Take a hypothetical group of 10,000 people. If 5% of these people use drugs, then there are 500 drug users in the group (5% of 10,000 = 0.05 × 10,000 = 500). Let's say that all 10,000 people have taken this drug test. The test will correctly identify a drug user 90% of the time. So, presumably, of the 500 drug users, 450 of them will be identified by the drug test. But because the test is only 90% accurate, 50 of them will *not* be identified by the drug test—these test results are called false negatives. The tree diagram on the next page shows this information.

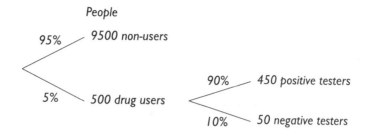

People

95% — 9500 non-users

5% — 500 drug users — 90% — 450 positive testers

10% — 50 negative testers

Now let's look at the 9500 people in our group who do not use drugs. The test is 90% accurate, so it will correctly identify 8550 people as non-users. However, 10% of the people will register as false positive, a test result indicating that they are drug users when they are not. Ten percent of 9500 is 950 people. So 950 people will register as false positives. This information has been added to the tree diagram.

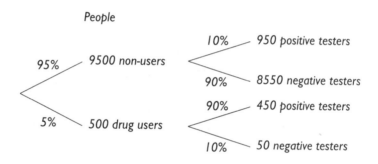

People

95% — 9500 non-users — 10% — 950 positive testers

90% — 8550 negative testers

5% — 500 drug users — 90% — 450 positive testers

10% — 50 negative testers

Now look at all the people who tested positive. There is a total of 450 + 950 = 1400 positive tests. But only 450 of those positive testers are actually drug users. The other 950 positive test results are false positives. So what percentage of the positive testers are actually drug users? If we divide 450 by 1400, we get approximately 32%. So roughly only one in three people who tested positive for drugs with this test are actually drug users. What are the implications of this information for the people who use such drug tests to make decisions and for the people who are affected by those decisions? (**Note** that many drug tests now take into account these issues regarding false positives.)

Using tree diagrams to analyze a situation involving probability is as applicable to an entertainment, such as games of chance, as it is to the important situation presented in the Drug Testing problem. Consider the following.

CARNIVAL GAME

You are at a carnival. A man is offering a game of chance. He will charge you $3 to play the game. The rules are as follows: You are to reach into a bag that contains three orange marbles and seven green marbles, and draw out two marbles. If you draw two green marbles, the man will pay you $2. If you draw one of each color, the man will pay you $3. If you draw two orange marbles, the man will pay you $12. Should you play this game? Remember, it costs $3 to play. Draw a tree diagram for this problem to analyze this situation before continuing.

Nichole solved this problem. "I drew a tree diagram of the situation. The probability of drawing orange the first time is $3/10$ and of drawing green is $7/10$. Then if an orange is drawn first, there are nine marbles left in the bag: two orange and seven green, so for the second draw the probability of drawing orange is $2/9$ and green is $7/9$. If a green ball is drawn first, there are nine marbles left in the bag—three orange and six green—so for the second draw, the probability of drawing orange is $3/9$ and green is $6/9$. I put all of this into my diagram."

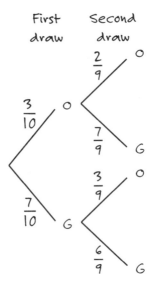

"Then I multiplied to find the probability of each combination of oranges and greens."

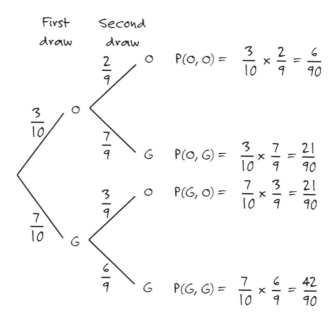

$$P(O, O) = \frac{3}{10} \times \frac{2}{9} = \frac{6}{90}$$

$$P(O, G) = \frac{3}{10} \times \frac{7}{9} = \frac{21}{90}$$

$$P(G, O) = \frac{7}{10} \times \frac{3}{9} = \frac{21}{90}$$

$$P(G, G) = \frac{7}{10} \times \frac{6}{9} = \frac{42}{90}$$

"I then figured out the results of playing the game 90 times. In those 90 times, the following things would happen:

- Draw orange, orange (O, O) and win $12. This would happen 6 out of 90 times. So in those 6 times I would win $72 (6 × 12).

- Draw orange, green (O, G) or green, orange (G, O) and win $3. This would happen 42 out of 90 times ($^{21}/_{90} + {}^{21}/_{90} = {}^{42}/_{90}$). In those 42 times I would win $126 (42 × 3).

- Draw green, green (G, G) and win $2. This would also happen 42 out of 90 times. In those 42 times I would win $84 (42 × 2).

"I made a chart to summarize the winnings."

OUTCOME	AMOUNT WON	TIMES OCCURRED	TOTAL WINNINGS
O, O	$12	6	$72
O, G or G, O	$3	42	$126
G, G	$2	42	$84

"So in the 90 games, I would win $72 + $126 + $84 = $282. The 90 games would cost me $3 each, which would be $270 total. In those 90 games I would come out $12 ahead. So it is to my advantage to play. I could also look at dividing $^{282}/_{90}$ = 3.13. So my **expected value** for each game would be $3.13. Since it only costs $3 to play, this is a good deal."

Of course, commercial games of chance are, more often than not, bad deals. For example, the expected value for a state lottery ticket is usually about $0.50. Considering lottery tickets cost $1 to play, you can expect to win only $0.50 for every dollar you pay, getting back only half of your money. That's a terrible investment. The contests that magazine publishers offer also give you a terrible expected value. For some contests, the expected value of an entry is only $0.15, which isn't even worth the price of the stamp you'd need to send it in. In general, if your expected value for winning is less than you have to pay, you shouldn't waste your money. A question to consider: Why do people play the lottery?

By examining all branches of a tree diagram, you get a very clear vision of the problem and the various possible outcomes. For these reasons, tree diagrams are very effective in statistical analysis.

You could have solved all the problems in this chapter with methods other than graphs, scale drawings, or tree diagrams. However, the purpose of this chapter was to show you that visual representation sometimes has advantages over symbolic manipulation. Drawings bring your visual experience to problems, and vision is the most highly developed sense in many people. Graphs, scale drawings, and tree diagrams enable you to meld the mathematical with the visual, making for an effective, accurate problem-solving medium.

Problem Set A-1

Draw a graph for each problem.

1. REFRIGERATOR

Cher visits a store to buy a new refrigerator and finds two recommended models. The Major brand is $600 and is expected to cost $30 per month for energy use. The Minor brand is $400 and is expected to cost $40 per month for energy use. Which refrigerator would you advise Cher to buy?

2. SODA

Two vendors next door to each other sell soda. One is a hamburger restaurant, the other is a gasoline station and mini-mart. The prices each charges for take-out sodas are shown in the chart below.

Size (ounces)	8	12	16	20	32
Restaurant	$0.59	$0.69		$0.84	
Mini-mart			$0.57	$0.72	$0.99

Each vendor is considering offering a 24-ounce soda. What would be the probable price at each establishment?

3. LETTUCE

Fatima is the produce manager for a local grocery store. Information provided by the grower and shipper states that iceberg lettuce will stay fresh for 21 days at 35°, for 15 days at 40°, for 10 days at 45°, and for 1 day at 70°. During a heat wave Fatima knows that the store will not be able to keep the produce as cool as she would like. How long can she expect the lettuce to last if the store keeps it at about 60°?

4. APPLE ORCHARD

Ms. Pomme has an apple orchard. If she hires 20 workers to pick the apples, it will take them 6 hours. If she hires 30 workers, it will take them 4 hours. Draw a graph that shows workers on the *x*-axis and time on the *y*-axis. Use the graph to estimate how long it would take if she hired 50 workers, and how long it would take if she hired 6 workers.

If you were Ms. Pomme, how many workers would you hire? Why?

5. JEANNE'S ORIGAMI BOOK

Jeanne wrote a booklet showing people how to do origami folds. She then photocopied it (each one cost her $1.45 to copy) and sold the copies for $2.00 each. She also bought a small ad, costing $24, to advertise the book. Not including any consideration for her labor, how many books would she need to sell before her endeavor turns profitable?

6. CHRISTMAS TREE LOT

Jocelyn owns a store and wants to sell Christmas trees in her parking lot. She wants to fence in three sides of a rectangular area with 200 feet of fencing and use the wall of her store as the fourth side. What is the maximum area she can fence in?

7. BOX

Cut same-sized squares out of the corners of an 8.5-by-11-inch piece of paper. Fold the paper up to form an open-topped box. What is the maximum volume thus obtained?

8. JAWS

The movie *Jaws* was a big hit and grossed $130 million. The sequel didn't do quite as well, and neither did *Jaws III* or *Jaws IV*. Using the information shown below, draw a graph and predict how much money *Jaws V* might have grossed if the producers had filmed it.

Movie	Jaws	Jaws II	Jaws III	Jaws IV	Jaws V
Gross (in millions)	$130	$50	$26	$12	?

9

MORE PHONE CALLS

Shown below is a list of several phone calls made during the day, the evening, and the night. Each time period has different first-minute charges and subsequent-minute charges. Determine the first- and subsequent-minute charges for each time period.

Time (in minutes)	5	7	8	9	10	11	13	18
Cost	$1.74	$1.86	$2.12	$1.66	$3.39	$2.90	$4.38	$3.28

10. **BIG PROBLEMS**

Allen and Jerry are trying out for the football squad and want to put on weight. Allen is eating and working out, and has found that he gains about 1 pound each week. At this point he weighs 180 pounds. Jerry, on the other hand, weighs 167 pounds and is eating, working out, and then eating more. He is gaining about 5 pounds every 3 weeks. How long will it take for Jerry and Allen to weigh the same?

11. **SAILING**

Diane was sailing. She had been timing herself and charting the average reported wind speed to determine what kind of times to expect if she were sailing a race. On five previous trips, she had recorded the following times and wind speeds:

Wind speed	20 kn	8 kn	12 kn	23 kn	11 kn
Time	45 min	112.5 min	75 min	39 min, 8 sec	81 min, 6 sec

Today the weather report predicts an average wind speed of 17 kn. What time should she expect to have on the course?

Problem Set A-2

Make a scale drawing for each problem.

12. YOUR BEDROOM

Make a scale drawing of your bedroom. Choose a scale that allows you to fit your drawing nicely onto a piece of paper. Include all your furniture. Label all the interesting parts of your diagram with their actual measurements.

13. TELEPHONE POLE

You wish to measure the height of a telephone pole. Standing 40 feet away from the pole, you measure the angle between the ground and the top of the pole to be 35°. How tall is the pole?

14. STADIUM POLE

You want to measure the height of a stadium light pole. However, it is on the other side of a fence and you don't want to test the trespassing laws. Instead, you stand at point A and measure the angle to the top of the pole and find it to be 40°. You then walk 50 feet from point A in a direction directly away from the pole and measure the angle to the top again. This time it measures 28°. How tall is the pole?

15. HOW WIDE IS THE RIVER?

Mai Khanh wants to measure the width of a river. She stretches a 100-yard string parallel to the river along the ground. (The river is completely straight for these 100 yards.) Directly across the river from one end of the string is a tree on the riverbank. From the other end of the string, she sights to the tree and finds that the angle between the string and the line of sight to the tree is 35°. What is the approximate width of the river?

16. FRISBEE ON THE ROOF

Lisa is standing on the ground, looking up at Judy in the second-story window. Ed is on the roof retrieving a Frisbee. From where Lisa is standing, the angle of elevation to Judy is 22° and the angle of elevation to Ed is 40°. Judy is 12 feet above the ground. How far is Lisa standing from the building, and how high off the ground is Ed?

17. KITE STRING

It's Lisa's turn to go on the roof after the kite—it got stuck on the chimney. The string is caught on the chimney about 25 feet off the ground. Ed can sight Lisa at about a 15° angle from the ground. How long is the kite string from Ed to where Lisa is?

Problem Set A-3

Draw a tree diagram for each problem.

18. SIXTEEN-TEAM TOURNAMENT

Draw a tournament diagram for a tournament with 16 teams, each one seeded from 1 to 16.

19. FOURTEEN-TEAM TOURNAMENT

Draw a tournament diagram for a tournament with 14 teams, each one seeded from 1 to 14. Show the needed byes in the first round.

20. ORDERING PIZZA

How many pizzas made from the following ingredients can be ordered? Choose one of each item.

Crust: thick, thin, or medium

Meat: sausage, pepperoni, hamburger, Canadian bacon

Veggies: olives, onions, mushrooms

21. INTERVIEW ORDER

In how many ways can four basketball players be interviewed after a big game?

22. BAG OF MARBLES

A bag contains three blue marbles, two red marbles, and five white marbles.

a. What is the probability that if you select one marble, it will be white? Not red?

b. Now suppose you were going to draw two marbles out of the bag (without replacing either of them). What is the probability that both marbles are white? That one marble is red and the other is blue?

c. Now suppose that you are going to draw one marble out of the bag. If it is white, you will put it back into the bag along with two extra white marbles. If the marble you draw out of the bag isn't white, you will just put it back into the bag but you won't add any additional marbles. Then you will draw a second marble. What is the probability that the second marble you draw is red?

23. BUSY SIGNAL

On any given evening, many high school students are on the phone, especially the students taking algebra. Of all the algebra students in one high school, 60% are 9th graders and 40% are 10th graders. On a given evening, 80% of these 9th graders are on the phone and only 50% of these 10th graders are on the phone. If an algebra student is not on the phone, then what is the probability that the student is a 10th grader?

24. LAWN MOWER

Jay has a business mowing lawns for the people in his neighborhood. He charges $13 for his basic lawn job. One neighbor offers to make him a deal: He will put two $10 bills and eight $5 bills in a bag and let Jay draw out two bills. Is it in Jay's favor to accept? Why?

25. FOUR ACES

The four aces from a deck of playing cards are lying face down on a table. We turn over one card at a time until a red ace is found or until two black aces are found. What is the probability of finding a red ace?

26. X-RAY

An X-ray will reveal with probability .8 the presence of a certain lung condition in all affected patients. If the X-ray is negative (fails to show the condition), then a second X-ray is taken. If the results of the two X-rays are independent, what fraction of affected patients will be diagnosed by this technique?

27. WORLD SERIES

Suppose the Red Sox and the Cubs are playing in the World Series (seven games). So far the Cubs have won two games and the Red Sox have won one. If the odds for either team to win any game are even and the series ends when one team wins four games, what is the probability that the Cubs will win the series?

SONS AND DAUGHTERS

A woman has three sons (Adam, Barry, and Cosmo) and six grandchildren. Adam has two sons, Barry has one son and one daughter, and Cosmo has two daughters. While talking to you over the telephone, the woman states that one of her sons has left his children in her care for the day. In a few minutes you hear a boy's voice in the background. What is the probability that the children at her house are Adam's?

29. **DISEASE**

Suppose that the presence of a certain disease can be detected by a laboratory blood test with probability .94. If a person has the disease, the probability is .94 that the test will reveal it. But this test also gives a false positive in 1% of the healthy people tested. That is, if a healthy person takes the test, it will imply (falsely) that he or she has the disease, and this will happen with probability .01. Suppose that 1000 persons have been tested, of whom only 5 have the disease. If 1 of the 1000 is selected at random, find the probability that he is healthy, given that the test is positive (the test says that he has the disease).

Problem Set B

1. **SODA JERK**

As a clerk at a soda counter, Larry had to take orders, get the right-flavored soda in the right-sized cup, and get the drink to the right customer. On his first day on the job, he didn't fill a single order correctly. He did, however, get the flavor right on 13 orders and drink size right on 12 orders. He also managed to get 9 drinks to customers who'd actually ordered drinks, but the size, the flavor, or both were wrong. In defending himself to his manager he said, "At least there were 14 drink orders where only one thing was wrong, and only once did I give a wrong-flavored soda in a wrong-sized cup to a customer who had not ordered a drink." What is the minimum number of orders that Larry got wrong? What is the highest possible percentage of drinks that were salvageable (the right flavor was in the right cup; it just needed to be given to the right customer)?

2. LICENSE PLATES

License plates are issued systematically. In a state where the license plates contain three letters followed by three numbers, the following sequence of license plates could be issued: CMP998, CMP999, CMQ000, CMQ001, and so on. The most recent license plate issued in this state is AZY987, which has no repeated letters or digits. How many license plates must be issued after this one before a license plate will again have no repeated letters or digits?

3. KAYAKING

Darlene and Boris both live on the lake. To get to Boris's house by land, Darlene has to take Mountain View Road 2 miles south and then take Lakeshore Drive 3 miles east. Boris called Darlene and suggested they go watch a soccer game at the end of School Road. To get to the end of School Road, Boris simply needs to kayak due north across the lake. If Darlene kayaks directly from her house to the end of School Road, it turns out to be exactly the same distance that Boris has to go. How far is it from Boris's house to the end of School Road?

4. THE DIGITAL CLOCK AND THE MIRROR

As I look in the bathroom mirror while I'm shaving, I can see the reflection of the digital clock in my bedroom. Sometimes the time I see in the mirror (a reflection of the actual time) is the same as the actual time. How many times does this happen per day? (Ignore the colon because I can't see that anyway—the clock is too far away.)

5. THE LATTICE

Barbara and Archie are building a lattice out of wood. The lattice will be in the shape of a right triangle. The frame for the lattice measures 18 feet along the base and 12 feet high. They are going to put in vertical strips of 1-inch-wide wood every 9 inches, connecting the base to the hypotenuse. How many feet of 1-inch-wide wood will they put into the lattice?

Appendix

Converting Metric Measurements

Consider the basic unit of length in the metric system—meters. Now consider this question: How many centimeters are in a dekameter?

To answer the question, you must convert dekameters into centimeters. To convert from one metric measurement to another, you must first know the metric prefixes and what they represent. Metric prefixes are combined with the basic unit names of metric measurement (meter, liter, and gram) to indicate a multiple or submultiple of the unit measurement. Six common metric prefixes are kilo-, hecto-, deka-, deci-, centi-, and milli-. One way for you to remember these prefixes is to memorize a mnemonic, a device that helps you remember something. A mnemonic can be something like a rhyme, an acronym, or a sentence. To help you remember metric prefixes, use the sentence "Kind hearts don't use dirty crummy manners." Here's how this mnemonic sentence corresponds to the prefixes:

kind	hearts	don't	use	dirty	crummy	manners
kilo-	hecto-	deka-	unit	deci-	centi-	milli-

So, now that you've memorized the mnemonic to remember this chart of prefixes, what do the prefixes mean?

kilo-	hecto-	deka-	unit	deci-	centi-	milli-
1000	100	10	1	0.1	0.01	0.001

Note that each prefix represents a multiple of 10 that is 10 times as large as the one to its right. The word "unit" in the middle refers to the basic unit of measure in the metric system (meter for length, liter for volume, or gram for mass). Each prefix in the chart is combined with the basic unit name to indicate a new measure. For example, 1 kilometer equals 1000 meters, 1 centigram equals 0.01 grams, and 1 milliliter equals 0.001 liters.

As you move from one space to the next in the chart, you either multiply or divide by 10, depending on whether you're moving left or right. Let's return to the question asked earlier: How many centimeters are in a dekameter? In the chart, the deka- position is three places to the left of the centi- position, so multiply 10 times 10 times 10 (that's 1000). So there are 1000 centimeters in 1 dekameter. Sometimes it is easy to get this statement backwards and say that there are 1000 dekameters in 1 centimeter. To figure out the correct conversion, think about which unit is greater. Centimeters are very small, so it takes a whole lot of them to make up a dekameter.

You can also find the answer to the question by canceling units:

$$\frac{1\ \text{dekameter}}{1} \times \frac{10\ \text{meters}}{1\ \text{dekameter}} \times \frac{10\ \text{decimeters}}{1\ \text{meter}} \times \frac{10\ \text{centimeters}}{10\ \text{decimeters}}$$

Or you can try this:

$$\frac{1\ \text{dekameter}}{1} \times \frac{10\ \text{meters}}{1\ \text{dekameter}} \times \frac{100\ \text{centimeters}}{1\ \text{meter}}$$

Or perhaps this:

$$\frac{1\ \text{dekameter}}{1} \times \frac{10\ \text{meters}}{1\ \text{dekameter}} \times \frac{1\ \text{centimeter}}{0.01\ \text{meter}}$$

In all three cases, all the units cancel except centimeters and the arithmetic comes out to 1000. So the answer is 1000 centimeters.

Here are a couple of other common—and interesting—metric prefixes.

micro = 1 millionth (0.000001, or 1×10^{-6})

nano = 1 billionth (0.000000001, or 1×10^{-9})

Abbreviations of Units of Measure

Here are lists of commonly used abbreviations of measure, many of which appear in this book. Note that whether the units of measure are in singular or plural form, the abbreviations for the units are the same. For example, the abbreviation for both mile (singular) and miles (plural) is mi.

DISTANCE (ENGLISH)		TIME		VOLUME	
foot	ft	hour	hr	gallon	gal
mile	mi	minute	min	quart	qt
yard	yd	second	sec	fluid ounce	fl oz
inch	in.	day	dy	cubic foot	ft³
		year	yr		

METRIC UNITS		METRIC PREFIXES			
meter	m	kilo-	k	deci-	d
liter	L	hecto-	h	centi-	c
gram	g	deka-	dk	milli-	m

Abbreviations of metric measures—other than the basic units of meter, liter, and gram—are formed by adding the abbreviations of metric prefixes to the abbreviations of the metric units. For example, to abbreviate kilogram, you combine the abbreviation for kilo- (k) with the abbreviation for gram (g). The result is the abbreviation kg.

Common Conversions

Here are lists of common conversions from one measurement to another. Many of these conversions will come in handy as you work through the problems in Chapter 8.

DISTANCE (ENGLISH)	DISTANCE (METRIC)
12 inches = 1 foot	100 centimeters = 1 meter
3 feet = 1 yard	1000 millimeters = 1 meter
5280 feet = 1 mile	1 kilometer = 1000 meters

VOLUME (ENGLISH)

1 gallon = 4 quarts

1 quart = 4 cups

1 cup = 8 fluid ounces

TIME

1 day = 24 hours

1 hour = 60 minutes

1 minute = 60 seconds

1 week = 7 days

1 year = 365 days*

*Note that if you're converting four or more years to days, you must multiply the number of years by 365.25 days to account for leap years.

METRIC TO ENGLISH

Distance: 1 meter $\approx$ 3.281 feet

Volume: 3.79 liters $\approx$ 1 gallon

Adding, Subtracting, Multiplying, and Dividing Fractions

To add fractions, find the common denominator of the fractions, then add the numerators.

$$\frac{1}{6} + \frac{2}{3} = \frac{1}{6} + \frac{4}{6} = \frac{5}{6}$$

To subtract one fraction from another, find the common denominator of the fractions, then subtract the second numerator from the first numerator.

$$\frac{2}{3} - \frac{7}{12} = \frac{8}{12} - \frac{7}{12} = \frac{1}{12}$$

To multiply fractions, multiply the numerators together and multiply the denominators together.

$$\frac{3}{4} \times \frac{1}{2} = \frac{3}{8} \qquad \frac{1}{2} \times \frac{3}{5} \times \frac{3}{7} = \frac{9}{70}$$

To divide a fraction by a fraction, multiply the first fraction by the reciprocal of the second fraction.

$$\frac{5}{8} \div \frac{2}{3} = \frac{5}{8} \times \frac{3}{2} = \frac{15}{16}$$

Area

Triangle: $A = \dfrac{1}{2}bh$

where b is the base and h is the altitude to that base.

Square: $A = s^2$

where s is the side of the square.

Rectangle: $A = bh$

where b is the base and h is the height of the rectangle.

Parallelogram: $A = bh$

where b is the base of the parallelogram and h is the altitude to that base.

Trapezoid: $A = \dfrac{1}{2}h(a + b)$

where a and b are the parallel sides of the trapezoid and h is the altitude between them.

Circle: $A = \pi r^2$

where r is the radius of the circle.

Volume

Cube: $V = b^3$

where b is the edge of the cube.

Parallelepiped: $V = abc$

where a, b, and c are nonequal edges of the parallelepiped.

Cylinder: $V = Ah$

where A is the area of the base and h is the height of the cylinder.
When the base is a circle, $A = \pi r^2$ and $V = \pi r^2 h$.

Pyramid or Cone: $V = \dfrac{1}{3}Ah$

where A is the area of the base and h is the altitude to the base.

Sphere: $V = \dfrac{4}{3}\pi r^3$

where r is the radius of the sphere.

Similar Triangles

The corresponding sides of similar triangles share a common ratio.
So $\dfrac{a}{d} = \dfrac{b}{e} = \dfrac{c}{f}$.

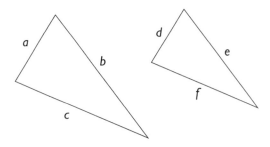

Pythagorean Theorem

If a and b are the legs of a right triangle and c is the hypotenuse,
then $a^2 + b^2 = c^2$.

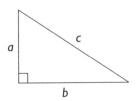

Glossary

Numbers in brackets refer to chapters in which the term is defined or significantly covered.

act it out A problem-solving strategy in which people play roles in the problem. [10]

adjunct list A list of connected information made in conjunction with a logic matrix. [4]

algebra A strategy for solving a problem using variables and equations.

area The measure of a bounded region in square units.

assumption An unfounded idea about a problem, which can be tested to be true or false. [4]

bouncing A substrategy through which information on one part of a matrix is aligned with different, connected information to produce a connection with previously unconnected information. See also **cross-correlating**. [4]

change the representation A strategy that combines changing focus with some other strategy, often a diagram. [16]

change your point of view A strategy for solving a problem by looking at it in a different or unexpected way. [16]

Changing Focus An overall theme to several problem-solving strategies, in which a shift in perspective is intrinsic to the strategy. [7, 16]

coefficient A number by which a variable is multiplied in an algebraic expression. [14]

complement Something added to complete a whole; either of two parts that complete each other. [16]

complementary angles Two angles whose sum is 90°.

complementary problem A problem that, taken with an original problem, completes a whole picture. For example, computing the number of days someone works in a week may be computed by subtracting from 7 the number of days not worked. [16]

compound unit A unit that is a combination of units multiplied or divided together. [8]

cross-correlating A substrategy through which information on one part of a matrix is aligned with different, connected information to produce a connection with previously unconnected information. See also **bouncing**. [4]

cryptarithmetic An arithmetic problem based on letters, usually with a clever combination of words, such as "SEND + MORE = MONEY." Each letter stands for a different digit, 0 through 9.

denominator The bottom number in a fraction; it divides the top number, or numerator. [9]

diagonal A line connecting two non-adjacent vertices in a polygon. [9]

diagram A pictorial representation used in solving a problem. [1]

disjoint A description applied to sets that have no elements in common. [12]

dogs Mythical creatures alternately credited with human-like intelligence or a wide range of erratic behavior. Reported sightings are frequent, though there is no proof that they exist.

easier related problems A problem-solving strategy in which the solver considers smaller, simpler versions of the problem to be solved, in order to develop a process for solving the original problem. [9]

eliminate possibilities A problem-solving strategy in which all elements or outcomes are listed and then as many elements or outcomes as possible are removed from consideration through logical deduction. [12]

exercise One of a number of repetitive tasks. [0]

expected value In probability, an estimation based on the average output of a function. [17]

exponential function A function in which a number is raised to the power of the input variable. If consecutive integers are used as input values in an exponential function, the output values form a geometric sequence. [14]

Family family An imaginary family consisting of a father, mother, two daughters, a son, and five dogs.

finite differences A strategy for finding an equation for a table of input/output values by subtracting pairs of outputs. [14]

function A relationship between sets in which, for each and every element of the input set, there is exactly one element of the output set. A function with a rule or equation is a predictable, consistent relationship between the elements of the input set and the elements of the output set. [5]

graph A picture clearly showing the relationship between variables. [17]

guess-and-check A strategy for solving a problem by making and refining estimations. [6]

heuristic Based on discovery, rather than taught. [0]

histogram A diagram used to show the frequency of data values, often used as a form of statistical analysis. [2]

indirect proof See **seeking contradictions**. [3]

intersecting In a Venn diagram, a set that has characteristics of two or more distinct sets. Also known as **overlapping**. [12]

isomorphism A one-to-one correspondence of mathematical sets. [16]

logic matrix A matrix used to organize information in which related information is entered in consecutive cells of a row or column. [4]

manipulative An object that can be moved or positioned. [8, 10]

matrix An organization of information in rows and columns, in which each and every element in any given row or column is related to the rest of the information in that same row or column. [4]

matrix logic A series of eliminations and deductions based on clues. The information used to solve the puzzle is organized in a chart. [4]

mixture problem A common application problem, solvable by algebra, in which two or more substances are mixed together to form a blend, the two substances differing in some characteristic such as tint, concentration, or economic value. [13]

model A physical representation of a problem that can be helpful in finding a solution. [10]

nomograph A graph with parallel scales on which you can join values on two scales with a straightedge in order to read a value on a third scale. [17]

one-n-o A fraction that equals one, used in converting units. [8]

one-to-one correspondence A linking of elements such that for each and every element of one set, there is exactly one element of another set, with no duplication in either set. [4]

Organizing Information An overall theme to several problem-solving strategies, in which the organization of information is intrinsic to the strategy. [7, 15]

pattern A coherent rule or characteristic shared by elements of a set. [5]

perimeter The total length of the boundary of a region.

physical representation A strategy for solving problems by using physical objects. [10]

pipeline A diagram used to represent unit conversions in which lines connect related units for which a conversion relationship is present. [8]

polygon A closed figure in a plane consisting of vertices and edges. **Triangles, quadrilaterals, pentagons, hexagons, heptagons,** and **octagons** are all polygons, with three, four, five, six, seven, and eight sides respectively. [9]

polynomial A sum of terms in which each term is the product of a coefficient and a power of the variable. For instance, $x^3 - 2x^2 + 3x - 1$ is a cubic polynomial. A **polynomial function** has values given by a polynomial. For a **linear function,** the greatest power of a variable is 1, for a **quadratic function** the greatest power is 2, and for a **cubic function** the greatest power is 3. [14]

position The location of a term within a sequence.

prism A shape that has polygon bases, and congruent parallelograms for sides. [9]

problem A task that may not have a clear path to the solution. [0]

proof by contradiction See **seeking contradictions**. [3]

quadratic equation An equation in which 2 is the highest power of any variable.

ratio A comparison of two numbers by division. [8]

reciprocal The multiplicative inverse of a fraction. A fraction and its reciprocal multiplied together equal one. [8]

region In Venn diagrams, a bounded area of the diagram containing elements that share a characteristic. [12]

scale drawing A drawing in which the relative proportions of lengths and areas are preserved. [17]

seeking contradictions A process for proving a conjecture that involves first making the opposite assumption, then examining the assumption for its validity by carrying it to its (contradictory) conclusion. Also known as **indirect proof** or **proof by contradiction**. [3]

sequence A set of numbers ordered by a consistent rule, or set of rules, that determine all the terms. [5]

set A collection of particular things. Each thing is an **element**, or **member**. A set is composed of one or more elements, except an **empty** set or "null set," which has zero elements. A **subset** is a set within a set. [12]

slope The ratio of the change in the dependent variable to the change in the independent variable, also expressed as the change in y over the change in x. For a line graph, slope measures steepness and the direction of slant. [17]

solution An answer to a problem and an explanation of how the answer was reached. [0]

Spatial Organization An overall theme to several problem-solving strategies in which the spatial layout of the problem and solution information is intrinsic to the strategy. [7, 17]

square number A number that is the square of a whole number. [5]

step function A function whose output is not continuous, but "steps" from one value to another. [17]

strategy A method for solving a problem. A **substrategy** is a smaller part of a strategy, used with other substrategies to solve the whole problem. [0]

subproblem A smaller problem that is part of the whole problem. [7]

substitution A substrategy where known, connected information is used to replace other connected information in sentences. Used frequently in matrix logic problems. [4]

supplementary angles Two angles whose sum is 180°.

system A procedure for performing a task or tasks in an organized, methodical way. [2]

systematic list A list generated by organizing elements. [2]

term A member of a sequence. The **nth term** is a generic description used to refer to any member of the sequence. [5]

transitive property A relation of numbers used in algebra, stating that if $a = b$ and $b = c$, then $a = c$. [4]

tree diagram A type of systematic list in which options are shown as branching diagrams. [2, 17]

triangular number A number that can be arranged as a triangle, of the form $n + (n - 1) + \ldots + 3 + 2 + 1$. For example, 10 is a triangular number, and this characteristic is used in the set-up of 10 bowling pins. Here, 1, 3, 6, and 10 are shown as triangular numbers. [5]

trigonometric function A function based on the ratio of the sides of a right triangle. [14]

unit analysis A method of organizing quantitative information that carefully keeps track of units during computation in order to produce the correct quantity (number and unit) in the answer. See **unit conversion**. [8]

unit conversion A method of changing units by **canceling**, or multiplying by a one-n-o with the original unit in the denominator, and a different unit in the numerator. [8]

universal set In a given problem, the set of all possible elements. [12]

variable An unknown quantity in a problem. For a function, the **independent variable** is the input and the **dependent variable** is the output. [17]

Venn diagram A diagram with bounded regions containing elements that share a characteristic. [12]

vertex A corner of a figure; a point. Plural: **vertices**. [9]

working backwards A strategy for solving a problem by reversing the steps of a process. [11]

y-intercept The value of the output when the input is zero. The point where a graph crosses the vertical axis. [17]

.
.   .   .   . .
.   . .   .
.   . .   .
1   3   6   10

Index of Problem Titles

General Index

Page numbers in **bold** denote glossary terms.

A

accounting, 43
acting it out, **301**–304
adjunct lists, **82**, 86
algebra, 385–408, **545**
    diagrams and, 385, 406–408
    equations, writing of, 385, 392, 393, 398
    exponent rules, 281–283
    expressions, 392, 397
    graphing and, 496–500
    guess-and-check and, 179, 182–184, 386, 388, 391–392, 393, 397–398, 401
    language of, 391–392
    mixture problems, 203, 397–398
    physical representations vs., 386
    quadratic formula and, 420
    slope-intercept form and, 420
    subproblems and, 203, 407–408
    as tool, 385–386, 408
    unit analysis and, 255
    working backwards compared to, 345
all, as term, 355

area, **545**. *See also* Area and Volume Formulas, **543**
assumptions, making of, **106**–108
averages, **285**–287

B

Barson, Alan, 485–486, 491
Bingham, John, 318
bouncing, **85**–87

C

calculators, using, 236
canceling. *See* unit conversion, **548**
change the representation, **482**–487
change your point of view, 471–477, **472**
Changing Focus, **193**, 268, 330, 455, 471–487
clues, 78–81, 82, 95–98
coefficients, **421**
combining clues, 96–98
common denominator, 276
common difference, 421–425

complementary problem, solving, 477–482, **478**

complement, defined, 478

compound units, **245**–256

computer programming, 42–43, 256–257

cone, 211

contradictions, seeking, **55**–60, 106–108

Cook, Marcy, 311

cooperative behaviors, 174

cross-correlating, **85**–87

cryptarithms, **57**, 58

cubic functions, 438–445. *See also* polynomial function, **547**

D

decimals, 254, 280–281

Dell Math Puzzles and Logic Problems, 75–76

denominator, **276**

dependent variable, 497. *See also* variable, **548**

diagonal, **296**

diagrams, **13**–23

    algebra and, 385, 406–408

    guess-and-check and, 169

    matrix logic and, 82–83

    occupational, 23

    physical representations compared to, 301

    pipelines, **239**–240

    systematic lists compared to, 33

    thoughts expressed by, 13–14, 18, 23

    tree. *See* tree diagrams

    Venn. *See* Venn diagrams

    working backwards and, 339, 341–342, 344

    See also scale drawings; graphs

dimensional analysis. *See* unit analysis

disjoint loops, **361**

Donohoe-Mather, Carolyn, 232

drug testing, 524–525

E

easier related problems (ERP), 268, 295–296, **546**

    conditions, changing, 283–285, 287–290, 296

    eliminate unnecessary information, 269–271, 296

    and equations, finding, 419–420

    guess-and-check compared to, 268

    list of methods using, 268, 295–296

    set of specific easier examples, 266–268, 271–275, 277–280, 296

    smaller or easier number replacement, 269–271, 280–283, 285–287

    specific easier examples, 276–277, 295

    subproblems compared to, 291–295

    variable replacement, 285–287, 295

    Venn diagrams and, 376

element, 356. *See also* set, **547**

eliminating possibilities, **50**, 60, 67–68

    matrices and, 76–78, 81

    seeking contradictions, **55**–60, 106–108

employment, cooperation and, 174

empty regions, **359**, 361

empty set. *See* set, **547**

English unit conversions, 238–245

equations, 392

    algebra and. *See* algebra

    coefficients, **421**

    cubic, 438–445

    ERP strategy and, 419–420

    exponential, **419**, 445–446

    finite differences and. *See* finite differences

    letters used in, 420

    linear, 420–422, 496–511

    quadratic, graphing, 511–512

    slope-intercept form, 420–422, 497–499

    valid, 392

    writing of, 385, 392, 393, 398

    See also functions; polynomial functions

ERP. *See* easier related problems

exercise, **5**

exponential functions, **419**, 445–446

exponent rules, 282–283

F

Fibonacci sequence, 138–140

finite differences, 415–417, **419**–420

    arithmetic mistakes in, 447

    common difference, 421–425

    cubic functions, 438–445

    data insufficient and, 446–447

    ERP strategy and, 419–420

functions applicable to, 419, 445
general charts in, 422, 425–426, 434, 441
key to strategy, 425–426, 434
limitations to strategy, 419, 445–447
linear functions, 420–422, 431–433
quadratic functions, 423–431, 434–438
working backwards and, 419
functions, **131**
cubic, 438–445. *See also* polynomial
functions
exponential, **419**, 445–446
finite differences and. *See* finite differences
linear, 420–422, 431–433. *See also*
polynomial functions
patterns of and rules for, 131–138
polynomial, **419**, 445
quadratic, 423–431, 434–438. *See also*
polynomial functions; quadratic
equations
trigonometric, **419**
See also equations

G

Games, 75–76
games of chance, 526–528
Gardner, Martin, 285
Gauss, Carl Friedrich, 265–268
gender, 105
graphs, **496**, 512
linear equations, 496–511
nomographs, **513**–514
quadratic equations, 511–512
slope, **497**–498, 501–502
step functions, **503**–504
variables, **512**, 513
y-intercept, **497**, 498–499, 501–502
See also scale drawings; diagrams
guess-and-check, **159**–160, 184–185
algebra and, 179, 182–184, 386, 388,
391–392, 393, 397–398, 401
arithmetic mistakes and, 164, 167, 184
bracketing, 168
charts for, 161–164, 185, 387
cooperation with others and, 174
diagrams and, 169
discarding approaches, 171, 184

easier related problems compared to, 268
language of, 391–392
subproblems and, 205–208
working backwards and, 174
wrong guesses, 164, 174, 184

H

heuristic, **5**
hexagon, 297. *See also* polygon, **547**
histograms, **43**
Holmes, Sherlock, 50
How to Solve It (Pólya), 5, 288

I

independent variable, 497. *See also* variable,
548
indirect proof. *See* seeking contradictions
intersecting loops, 357, **359**
isomorphism, **487**

L

landscaping, 514–515
Lee, David, 348
linear equations, 420–422, 496–511
linear functions, 420–422, 431–433. *See also*
polynomial function, **547**
logical arguments, 75
logical reasoning, 75–76
logic matrix, **546**
logic problems, 75–76
manipulatives and, 312–315, 316–317
matrices and. *See* matrix logic
one-to-one correspondence, **77**
Lucas, Edouard Anatole, 139

M

magic squares, 485–487
making an assumption, **106**–108
manipulatives, **227**
logic problems and, 312–315, 316–317
physical representation and, 301–302,
306–319
unit analysis using, 227–237
working backwards and, 339
matrices, other methods using, 453–454,
458–464

matrix logic, **76**–78, 82–84
   adjunct lists and, **82**, 86
   assumption, making of, **106**–108
   bouncing or cross-correlating, **85**–87
   clues and, 78–81, 82, 95–98
   connections, 76–77, 78, 82
   eliminating possibilities and, 76–78, 81
   labels of, 104–105, 110–111
   number needed, 82, 108–109
   one-to-one correspondence, **77**
   organization of, 82–84, 109–111
   subscripts in, 104
   thinking negatively, 81–82
   See also logic problems
maximum value, **512**
member, **356**. *See also* set, **547**
meteorology, 414
metric unit conversions, 238–243
Meyer, Carol, 213
Migliore, Ed, 458–461
Mission: Impossible, 471–472
mixture problems, **203**–208, 397–398
models, **308**–310, 315–319, 386
monetary units, 220–221
mpg, 222–223
mph, 223

N
NASA, 317–318
nautical mile, **516**
nomographs, **513**–514
*n*th term, 141–143. *See also* term, **548**
nutrition, 506–508

O
one-n-o, **232**–237
one-to-one correspondence, **77**
Organizing Information, **193**, 217, 386, 455
overlapping section, 358. *See also* intersecting, **546**

P
palindromes, 491
Patch Adams, 477
patterns, **121**–122, 127–128, 138
   complexity of, 128

finite differences and. *See* finite differences
functions. *See* functions
other information-organizing methods and, 455–457
sequences. *See* sequences
tables for, 127–128, 129–131, 149
pentagon. *See* polygon, **547**
per, as term, 223
percentage problems, 201, 203–208
physical representations, 301–302, 315–319
   acting it out, **301**–304
   algebra compared to, 386
   diagrams compared to, 301
   manipulatives and models, 301–302, 306–319
   types of problems solved by, 315–317
pipeline diagrams, **239**–240
point of view, changing, 471–477, **472**
Pólya, George (György), 5, 288
polygon, **296**
polynomial functions, 445, **491**
position, **547**
prism, **296**
probability, 521–528
problems
   defined, **5**
   introductions to, 98
problem solving
   alternative solutions, pursuing, 60
   defined, 5
   experimentation with strategies, 42
   heuristic strategies, **5**
   many correct approaches to, 6, 14–15, 31
   more than one answer, 54
   multiple strategies required in single, 64
   process and, 217
proof by contradiction. *See* seeking contradictions

Q
quadratic equations, 420, 511–512
quadratic functions, 423–431, 434–438. *See also* polynomial function, **547**
quadrilateral. *See* polygon, **547**

R

ratios, **218**–219, 237
   canceling units, 221, 223–227, 237
   compound units, 245–256
   manipulatives and, 227–237
   metric conversions, 238–245
   one-n-oes, 232–237
   per and, 223
   reciprocals, **225**, 232–233
   writing of, 218, 223, 243
reciprocals, **225**, 232–233
regions, 356–359, **357**
representation, changing, **482**–487
representation, physical. *See* physical
   representations
rounding numbers, 236

S

Sallee, Tom, 194, 213, 268, 295
SAT (Scholastic Aptitude Test), 3, 319
scale drawings, 513–518, **514**
   See also diagrams; graphs
science, unit analysis and, 245, 256–257
Scientific American, 284–285, 345
seeking contradictions, **55**–60, 106–108
sequences, **122**–128, 133
   Fibonacci, 138–140
   *n*th term, **141**–143
   square numbers, **125**–126
   terms of, **122**
   triangular numbers, **126**
sets, **356**
   isomorphism, **487**
   universal, **358**, 362
   Venn diagrams and, 356, 358
slope, **497**–498, 501–502
slope-intercept form, 420–422, 497–499
solution, **547**
solve the complementary problem, 477–482,
   478
some, as term, 355, 357, 359
space program, 317–318
Spatial Organization, **193**, 301, 495–528
square numbers, **125**–126
step functions, **503**–504
Stewart, Ian, 284–285, 345

strategy, **548**
subproblems, **193**–200, 203, 208
   algebra and, 203, 407–408
   easier related problems compared to,
      291–295
   guess-and-check and, 205–208
   mixture problems, 203–208
   percentage problems, 201, 203–208
   unit conversion and, 237, 240, 244
subscripts, 104
subset, 356. *See also* set, **547**
substitution, 95–**96**
substrategy. *See* strategy, **548**
supplementary angles, **548**
system, **29**
systematic lists, **29**–40, 42–44
   diagrams compared to, 33
   graphing and, 504–505
   histograms, **43**
   matrix categories and, 109
   tree diagrams, 41–42

T

table of values, 132–134
tax preparation, 182–183
telephone costs, 500–504
term, **122**
tic-tac-toe, 486–487
time, 254
tournament diagrams, 481–482, 518–529
traffic accidents, 515
transitive property, **85**
transportation field, 248–249, 252–253
tree diagrams, **41**, 518–528
   counting problems, 520
   probability, 521–528
   systematic lists and, 41–42
   tournament diagrams, 481–482, 518–529
triangular numbers, **126**
trigonometric functions, **419**
Tsugawa, Matt, **514**

U

unit analysis, 216–218, **217**, 234
   by calculator, 236
   choosing units, 243–245

Photo Credits

Chapter 0 © Tony Stone Images; Chapter 1 © Garry Gay/The Image Bank; Chapter 2 © Corbis/Catherine Karnow; Chapter 3 © Tony Stone Images; Chapter 4 © Corbis/Roger Ressmeyer; Chapter 5 © Corbis/Roger Ressmeyer; Chapter 6 © Corbis/Stephanie Maze; Chapter 7 © Corbis/Bob Krist; Chapter 8 © StockPhoto; Chapter 9 © *San Francisco Chronicle*; Chapter 10 © Corbis/Bob Krist; Chapter 11 © Corbis/Layne Kennedy; Chapter 12 © Key Curriculum Press; Chapter 13 © Corbis; Chapter 14 © Dwayne Newton/PhotoEdit; Chapter 15 © Santi Visalli/The Image Bank; Chapter 16 © Corbis/AFP; Chapter 17 © Tony Stone Images